CW01020670

PLANTS & US

How they shape human history and society

PLANTS & US

How they shape human history and society

John Akeroyd
with
Liz Cowley & Donough O'Brien
Designed by Tony Hannaford

Foreword by Sir Tim Smit

GB Publishing Org
www.gbpublishing.co.uk

First published 2021
Published by GB Publishing Org

ISBNs:
978-1-912576-75-3 (hardback)
978-1-912576-76-0 (paperback)
978-1-912576-77-7 (eBook)
978-1-912576-78-4 (Kindle)

A catalogue record of the printed book is available from the British Library.

GB Publishing Org
www.gbpublishing.co.uk

Contents

Contents

Contents

SELECTED BIBLIOGRAPHY

AKEROYD, John (1999) *The Encyclopedia of Wild Flowers*. Dempsey Parr.

ANTHONY, Leslie (2017) *The aliens among us*. Yale UP.

ATTENBOROUGH, David (1995) *The Private Life of Plants*. BBC Books.

BARKER, Juliet (2005) *Agincourt*. Little, Brown.

BROWN, Dee (2001) *Here that lonesome whistle blow*. Henry Holt.

BROWN, Dee (1970, 2001) *Bury my heart at Wounded Knee*. Henry Holt.

BRYSON, Bill (1998) *Made in America*. Black Swan.

BRAUDEL, Fernand (1993) *A History of Civilization*. Penguin.

BRIGHTMAN, Frank (1966) *The Oxford Book of Flowerless Plants*. Oxford UP.

CAMPBELL, Susan (2005) *A history of kitchen gardening*. Frances Lincoln.

CHAMOVITZ, Daniel (2012) *What a plant knows*. Scientific American.

CHURCHILL, Winston (1948, 2002, etc.) *The Second World War*. Pimlico.

COWLEY, Liz (2013) *Outside in my dressing gown*. Bene Factum.

COWLEY, Liz (2015) *Gardening in Slippers*. Gibson Square Books.

COWLEY, Liz (2019) *Green Fingers*. Gibson Square Books.

CROSBY, Alfred (1972, 2003) *The Columbian Exchange: Biological and Cultural Consequences of 1492*. Greenwood Publishing.

DALLMAN, Peter (1998) *Plant life in the world's Mediterranean climates*. Oxford UP.

DALRYMPLE, William (2019) *The Anarchy. The relentless rise of the East India Company*. Bloomsbury.

DEIGHTON, Len (1979) *Blitzkrieg*. Jonathan Cape.

DOBROW, Larry (1985) *When advertising tried harder*. Smith.

DAVIES, Norman (1997) *Europe. A History*. Pimlico.

DE ROUGEMONT, G.M. (1989) *A Field Guide to the Crops of Britain and Europe*. Collins.

EVANS, Julian (2014) *God's Trees. Trees, forests and wood in the Bible*. Day One.

FAGAN, Brian, ed. (2003) *The Seventy Great Mysteries of the Ancient World*. Thames & Hudson.

FELL, Derek (1997) *The Impressionist garden*. Frances Lincoln.

GREEN, Edmund P. & SHORT, Frederick T. (2003) *World Atlas of Seagrasses*. UNEP & University of California Press.

GRIGSON, GEOFFREY (1955) *An Englishman's Flora*. Phoenix House.

GUTSTEIN, Linda (1988) *History of the Jews in America*. Book Sales.

HARVEY, Robert (1998) *Clive*. Hodder & Stoughton.

HERODOTUS, transl. WATERFIELD, Robin (1998) *The Histories*. Oxford UP.

HEUVELMAMANS, *Bernard In the wake of the Sea Serpents*

HOBHOUSE, Henry (2005) *Seeds of Change. Six plants that changed mankind*. Pan.

HOBHOUSE, Penelope & EDWARDS, Ambra (2002, 2019) *The story of gardening*. Pavilion.

HOLMES, Richard (2001) *The Oxford Companion of Military History*. Oxford UP.

HYAMS, Edward & MACQUINTY, William (1985) *Great Botanical Gardens of the World*. Bloomsbury.

JOHNSON, Hugh (1973) *The International Book of Trees*. Mitchell Beazley.

KEAGAN, John (1994) *A History of Warfare*. Pimlico.

KENEALLY, Thomas (1998) *The Great*

Shame. Chatto & Windus.

KENNEDY Frances H. (1998) *The Civil War Battlefield Guide*. Mariner Books.

LAMB, Christian(2004) *From the ends of the Earth*. Bene Factum Publishing.

LEWINGTON, Anna (2003) *Plants for people*. Transworld.

LORD, Tony (1994) *Best Borders*. Frances Lincoln.

LORD, Tony (1995) *Gardening at Sissinghurst*. Frances Lincoln.

MABERLEY, David (2017) *Maberley's Plant-book*. Cambridge UP.

MABEY, Richard (1996) *Flora Britannica*. Sinclair-Stevenson.

MACKAY, Richard (2008) *The Atlas of Endangered Species*. Earthscan.

MILTON, Giles (1999) *Nathaniel's Nutmeg*. Macmillan.

MOXHAM, Ray (2001) *The Great Hedge of India*. Constable.

HUXLEY, Anthony, BRENAN, J.P.M. & MOON, Brenda (2000) *A vision of Eden. The life and work of Marianne North*. Royal Botanic Gardens, Kew.

O'BRIEN, Donough (2006) *Banana Skins*. Bene Factum.

O'BRIEN, Donough (2003) *Fame by Chance*. Bene Factum.

O'BRIEN, Donough (2013) *WHO?* Bene Factum.

O'CALLAGHAN, Sean (2000) *To Hell or Barbados*. Brandon.

PAKENHAM, Thomas (2015) *Meetings with remarkable trees*. Orion.

PAVORD, Anna (1999) *The Tulip*. Bloomsbury.

PHILLIPS, R. & RIX, Martyn (2002) *The Botanical Garden. Vol. 1 Trees and Shrubs, Vol. 2 Perennials and Annuals*. Macmillan.

PRANCE, Ghillean & NESBITT, Mark (2005) *The Cultural History of Plants*. Routledge.

RACKHAM, Oliver (1986) *The History of the Countryside*. Dent.

ROBERTS, J.M. (2014) *The Penguin History of the World* (6th ed, rev. WESTAD, O.A.). Penguin.

ROBINSON, William (1880, 2009) *The Wild Garden*. Timber Press.

SACKVILLE-WEST, Vita (1968) *V. Sackville-West's Garden Book*. Michael Joseph.

SCOTT-JAMES, Anne (1974) *Sissinghurst. The Making of a Garden*. Michael Joseph.

SHELDRAKE, Merlin (2020) *Entangled life*. Vintage.

STEARN, William T. (1992) *Stearn's Dictionary of Plant Names for Gardeners*. Cassell.

STEARN, William T. & RIX, Martyn (1987) *Redouté's Fairest Flowers*. Herbert Press & Natural History Museum

SWAHN, J.O. (1990) *The lore of spices*. Crescent Books.

SYKES, Sydney *The Country Diary Book of Decorating: English Country Style. Michael Joseph*

TALALAJ, Stanislav, TALALAJ, Daniela & TALALAJ, Janusz (1992) *The strangest plants in the world*. Robert Hale.

TANKARD, Judith B. (2011) *Gertrude Jekyll and the country house garden*. Aurum Press.

TAYLOR, Patrick (2006) *The Oxford Companion to the garden*. Oxford UP.

THOREAU, Henry David (1854) *Walden*.

Dent (Everyman ed.).

TOMASI, Lucia & HIRSCHAUER, Gretchen (2002) *The flowering of Florence.* Botanical Art for the Medici. National Gallery of Art, Washington.

VAN WYK, Ben-Erik & WINK, Michael (2005) *Medicinal Plants of the World*. Briza, Pretoria.

VAUGHAN, John & GEISSLER, Catherine (1997) *The New Oxford Book of Food Plants.* Oxford UP.

VICKERY, Roy (2010) Garlands, *Conkers and Mother-die. British and Irish plant-lore.* Continuum.

WARD, Geoffrey C., BURNS, R. & BURNS, K. (1990) *The Civil War. An illustrated history.* Alfred A. Knopf.

WILLES, Margaret (2015) A *Shakespearean Botanical*. Bodleian Library.

WILLIAMS, Richard L. (1976) *The Loggers.* Time-Life.

WOHLLEBEN, Peter (2016) *The hidden life of trees.* Greystone Books.

ZOHARY, Daniel & HOPF, M. (2000) *Domestication of Plants in the Old World*. Oxford UP.

ZAMOYSKI, Adam (2005) 1812: *Napoleon's fatal march on Moscow.* HarperCollins.

ACKNOWLEDGEMENTS AND THANKS

We would like to thank all those who have kindly contributed their knowledge, material, expertise and encouragement:

Royal Botanic Gardens, Kew
Dr Mark Watson: Royal Botanic Garden Edinburgh
Dr Peter Wyse Jackson: Missouri Botanic Gardens
Sir Tim Smit, The Eden Project, Cornwall
Dr Jo Elworthy, The Eden Project, Cornwall
The Duchess of Northumberland, Alnwick Castle
The Poison Garden, Alnwick
Major-General Sir Robert Corbett
Neil Dixon, wood industry specialist
Timothy ffytche, surgeon
Ray Palin, aircraft historian
Sydney Sykes, art specialist
Marianne Koenig
John Wynne-Williams
The National Trust
Thrive Charity
American Horticultural Therapy Association
Asthma UK and British Lung Foundation Partnership
Nigel Dickie: The Kraft Heinz Company
Historic Royal Palace, Hampton Court
Camila Hurra, Flora and Fauna International
Deere and Company
Unilever
Guinness
Regimental Headquarters, Irish Guards
Alisdair Moore, Lorna Tremayne, James Stephens, The Lost Gardens of Heligan, Cornwall
Sanderson Morris & Co
Murrough O'Brien

Sally-Jane Coode DL, Cornwall
Kathrine Reippurt Nielsen, CarlsbergMarstons
Mukesh Prajapati
Rupert Lendrum, Secretary, Bucks Club
Stowe School
Jeanne Hollande, Palace of Versailles
Kiki McDonough
Amy Harvey, Royal Albert
Patrick Scott
Mark Fleming, Fiskars
Veronique Foureur, Moet et Chandon
Antoine Puech, AgLogic
Anna Colina Segala, Dendra Systems
Chris and Marty Spring
United States Marine Corps, Annette Amerman, Captain Samuel Stephenson
The People's Mosquito Charity, Stewart Charman
Carmen Ouari
Nilo Athilla
Martin Hernandez Mirabel
The Hon Brian Alexander
Earl Alexander of Tunis
Danny Litani
Monica Van der Eb
Petra Guemmer
Giverny.org
Levi Strauss & Co
New York Historical Society
Royal Military Academy, Sandhurst
Joanna Lumley
David McDonough
Monika Cooke
Colin Anderson
Gordon Burns
Alexander Coode
Bryan Coode
Barry Dinan
Prue Fox
The late Dick Laurie
The late Sir William McAlpine
Alan Ogden
Sue Paice
Peter Paice
Katy Young
Roger Crudge, Fyffes PLC
Andrew Radice
Don Faulkner
Laura Chirila
Amanda Patten
Botanical Society of the British Isles
Henry Williamson Society
Heather Ewbank
Janet Weiner
WWF
Dendra Systems
Dr. Tean Mitchell
Dr. Jamie Compton

PICTURE CREDITS

Picture credits have been acknowledged below. Every effort has been made to acknowledge all sources. If any picture has, in error, not been credited, please contact the publisher.

Cover and book design: Tony Hannaford

AgLogic, 115,116
American Horticultural Therapy Association, 36
Bacardi, 190
La Bambouseraie, Anduze, 314
Brooklyn Botanical Garden, 304
Buck's Club, 202
Rhoda and Robert Burns, 129
Cavalry and Guards Club, 20
The Coca-Cola Company, 279
Continental Tyres, 16
Deere and Company, 53
Dendra Systems, 278
The Eden Project, 300, 301, 302, 303
Royal Botanical Garden, Edinburgh, 293
John Fowler, 55
Glasnevin Botanical Garden, 311
Richard Grenville, 92
Michael Grimsdale, 96
Tony Hannaford, 318, 319, 320, 321,324
Irish Guards, 29, 157
Peter Wyse Jackson, Missouri Botanical Garden, 304, 305
Royal Botanical Gardens, Kew, 289
Kirstenbosch Botanic Garden, 309
Kraft Heinz, 181
The Lost Gardens of Heligan, 297, 298, 299
Kiki McDonough, 271
Ben Mehadin, 149
Moët et Chandon, 227
Robbie Murphy, 150
Noah's Ark Foundation, 339, 341
Irina Nescu, xv
New York Botanical Garden, 306
Donough O'Brien, 81, 91, 156, 288
Murrough O'Brien, 331
Amanda Patton, 370
Graeme Peacock, 75
Thomas Ryan, RHA, 103
Stowe School, 286
Thrive Charity, 35
Palace of Versailles, 284
The Watercress Line, 203

FOREWORD

Everything we eat or use is either grown or mined. You cannot get away from it. You can write lots of books about ecology and joined-up 'systems thinking', and how science was originally natural philosophy, with holism not merely an alternative worldview. But the heartbeat for gaining and ordering knowledge is forgotten in an epidemic of specialism, blinding all but the few to the majesty of Nature's networks and systems that create circular economy and ecology but also ensure there is no 'away' – that mythical country which humans have persuaded themselves exists. Everything returns to the soil to be reborn as something else. Even that which is mined does so but over a longer period.

The beauty of the informed generalist is that they can explore relationships. How extraordinary it is that there is a green Kingdom of Plants that eats sunlight and transforms the energy into food for the rest of us. Such a monstrously 'cool' idea that we have never really found an easy way of explaining how it works nor yet, until recently, started to understand the undreamed-of future of living machines and engines made of photosynthesising materials. It is also true that the phytoplankton in the seas has the potential to lock up more carbon than anything else in our climate change armoury – if only the oceans were clean enough.

My introductory words are meant more to shock than anything else. Today, 'clean meat' (vegetable meat substitutes) companies are the fastest growing stocks in Silicon Valley. Globally, futurists are saying that within 15 years Big Agriculture as we know it will be over. Cell-tech (cellulose technology) too is set for a fermentation revolution, growing proteins in sealed systems, undercutting food prices by 70%.

Why is this interesting? Well, plants are at the heart of all this technology which supporters say will bring cheap food for all, an extraordinary aspiration. And many scientists and writers are revisiting the concept of healthy and balanced diets in a growing understanding that plants have a lot more to offer than previously suspected.

In parallel, research is hinting at far closer relationships between our own human invisible bacterial world and the mycorrhizal (fungus-plant) relationships that connect plants in a 'Wood Wide Web'. This microcosmic, sophisticated underworld speaks to the networks referenced above. I believe that young people will experience the unravelling of some of these mysteries of interconnection – echoing the ideas of astronaut Edgar Mitchell and astronomer Carl Sagan, that we are all stardust, in so many ways the same but made visible, differently. This may, in a secular age, inspire a new spiritual revival, a 'green enlightenment' based on the notion that our human arrogance, which assumes us to be the end point of evolution, will give way to an understanding that we are a part of an indivisible system – which could change almost everything we know about the world, and how to live within its limits. The natural world has selected us for a moment on trial but could just as easily find us wanting! The Octopus and Squid are waiting in the deep, biding their time...

I write this in order to emphasise that Plants are the foundation of all life on Earth (barring extremophiles that 'eat their light' from magma vents in oceanic depths!) and I believe that we're only now starting to realise how these marvellous living organisms have the most extraordinary tales to tell.

Plants & Us gathers together many of these plant stories, past and present, with a look as well towards the future. Enjoy this book and let it encourage you to dream in ways you've never thought of before.

Sir Tim Smit
The Eden Project
Cornwall

Plants & Us

AUTHORS' NOTE

Not a day goes by – even an hour – when our lives aren't in some way affected by plants, even if we rarely think about them consciously, or do so and just take them for granted. We wake up in beds made of wood, under cotton duvet covers and in cotton pyjamas or night-dresses, and go to the kitchen to make tea or coffee, perhaps sweetened with sugar. Then we bath or shower with plant-scented soaps and shampoos before putting on cotton clothes and having a breakfast of toast (wheat or rye flour) and marmalade (oranges and sugar), fruit or a bowl of muesli (mixed grains and dried fruits), cereal (corn or rice) or porridge (oats).

Now it's time to get the children to school by bicycle, car or bus, all running on rubber tyres; meanwhile buying a newspaper but probably resisting the sweet counter – quoting sugar, obesity and tooth decay. The children will write or paint on paper and use wooden pencils and rubber erasers.

Soon we're sitting in offices, probably on wooden chairs, and at wooden desks, and breaking off for tea or coffee; later perhaps having a sandwich lunch (more flour) or a salad. After work, we might go to the pub for a glass of wine (grapes), beer (barley, hops) or cider (apples), or after a tough day, a stiff gin and tonic (juniper, potatoes and quinine) with a packet of potato crisps or peanuts.

Then, perhaps pausing to buy a bunch of flowers, or top-up on fruit and vegetables, we walk home through tree-lined streets, parks or commons. We water our house, patio and garden plants, and maybe mow the lawn. Later, supper probably includes vegetables, pulses, herbs and spices, washed down with wine and perhaps concluded with more coffee, tea or herbal infusions.

We'll watch TV and the latest news about plants – global warming, bush fires in Australia, Portugal or California, de-forestation in the Amazon and, perhaps with more pleasure, a gardening programme or an exploration of some exotic desert, forest, steppe or mountainside with David Attenborough, where the animals live intimately in amongst plant life.

From dawn to dusk our lives are completelyinterwoven with plants and their products and influences. Food, drink, health, enjoyment, appearance, clothes, furniture, jobs, hobbies – this book can only attempt to draw attention to some of the wealth, variety and consequences, intended and unintended, of the extraordinary contributions of plant life to human history and existence. Plants and us; we are inextricably entwined.

Why are plants so important?

Plants are integral to our lives, but much more than that, they make our very existence possible. Most people like plants, at least those about them, such as the trees in the park and the shrubs and flowers in their gardens or which decorate their homes and offices. Yet their real value is frequently unappreciated and it can reasonably be said that they are the poor sisters of animals with regard to how people regard them. Even as the conservation movement expanded from the 1960s, plants were for a long time overlooked by both the general public and the conservation establishment. Animals make great TV stars and, not only do plants compare badly with birds and small furry mammals in their emotional appeal, but also the Plant Kingdom at first sight lacks 'big cuddlies' – the bears, elephants, lions, tigers,

Plants and Us

leopards and other cats, and the much-loved Giant Panda.

This is unfortunate because plants are absolutely central to life on Earth. They derive their energy and ability to survive, grow and reproduce from the harvest of sunlight; hence they are the primary source of all the energy in the food chains that enable animals and humans to exist and survive. They absorb and fix carbon dioxide in the presence of sunlight and the green plant pigment chlorophyll, using the sun's energy to split water molecules and convert carbon into sugars and other plant foods, while releasing oxygen, on which life depends.

Then there is vegetation – the complex communities that plants form - which is the structural basis of most of the ecological systems which animals and humans inhabit. Animals eat plants and live and nest among them. Plants maintain the physical and also chemical integrity of these complex natural and modified 'ecosystems' by providing a range of vital ecological 'goods and services'. En masse they trap the water vapour of mist, fog and clouds, they moderate wind, rain and water run-off, their roots consolidate unstable slopes, gravel, help mud and blown sand and their dead remains build up soils.

Plants yield food, medicines, timber, fibres and the host of other everyday products that sustain and enhance human life. These products and the trade in them, together with that in various crops and ornamental plants, have been the basis of human civilizations and remain a major portion of the world economy. Therefore, plants are central to everyday life, reflected in the way that botany and gardening have always closely linked the worlds of the sciences and the arts. Plants are also for pleasure: they feed, cure and clothe us and moreover, uplift us, and inspire painting, architecture, product design, fashion and other creative endeavours. Steeped in myth and legend, plants symbolize, illuminate and denote the rituals of birth, courtship, marriage and death.

Therefore, we all need to do whatever we can to nurture, protect and in many cases actively work to save them. Their conservation is an urgent task that requires constant vigilance. Estimates vary as to the rate of loss of global and regional plant diversity, but each year several species, varieties or old crop cultivars – each one with potential that may not have yet been fully assessed – disappear without any chance of ever being replaced. Extinction is forever.

Fortunately, recent years have seen a growing public awareness of plants. The opening in 1999 of the Eden Project in Cornwall was a significant milestone, alongside the increased showcasing of plants in both TV gardening and cookery programmes and in newspaper and magazine articles. And there is also progressive awareness of climate change and other environmental crises, as we see with Britain hosting the Climate Change Conference in Glasgow in November 2021 and the welcome change of heart about climate in the United States. A major new initiative is the roadmap for the future proposed in HRH The Prince of Wales's 'Terra Carta' – analogous to Magna Carta – recovery plan for Nature, People & Planet, which seeks to integrate conservation with industry to put 'the fundamental rights and value of Nature' and its diversity centre stage as the engine of sustainable growth and innovation. Another project and one which echoes the original Eden concept, Noah's Ark in southern Africa will utilize cutting edge technology to create covered GeoDomes within an inspirational nature park that will display global ecosystems and biodiversity on a huge scale.

This book is neither a botany textbook nor a plant identification guide (identities can readily be checked online these days), and it does not pretend to be comprehensive. It takes a broad sideways look at plant life, why it matters and how it has affected so much of human existence, past and present. We have concentrated on the Flowering Plants, the most successful and dominant group of plants on Earth, but we have further included some so-called 'lower plants' such as ferns, mosses and seaweeds. These plants are often neglected but equally important and, before the Flowering Plants had evolved, were once themselves dominant life forms. We have also taken the liberty of including some fungi, including the microscopic species that produce penicillin. Fungi are no longer regarded as plants, with which they are often intimately associated, and in fact lie closer to animals, although by convention were included in traditional botany courses.

The book arose partly from one of us, John Akeroyd, working as a guide and lecturer with tour groups in the British Isles, Europe and the Mediterranean region, often with participants keen to know, thankfully, more than just the names of the plants we found. It was during such a botanical tour in southern France that this book was conceived, over some rosé in a convivial café, with old friends and co-writers Liz Cowley (poet and author) and Donough O'Brien (historical writer).

Every plant has a story to tell, and, in particular, crops and other economic plants – about their origins and links to human history, migration, trade and culture. Indeed, to understand plants one perhaps needs to look not just at botany - but geography, history and humanity as well.

We hope our book does that in a surprising and interesting way.

Dr John Akeroyd,
Liz Cowley,
Donough O'Brien

PLANTS AS HEROES

THE ROSE, ULTIMATE SYMBOL OF LOVE

Of all our flowers and plants, there is no doubt that the rose is probably the best known. Is this because it has the strongest possible association with love and romance? The rose, as a wild flower, probably existed 35 million years before any humans appeared, but people began to appreciate their beauty very early – and all over the world. The Chinese began cultivating them 5,000 years ago, and probably for romantic reasons. Roses ever since have been universally loved, surely the most popular flower in the world, and not surprisingly. They are so elegant and pretty, come in a wonderful variety of colours (there are 7,500 variations), many have superb fragrance, they are found all over the world and are easy to grow and maintain.

The red rose, in particular, became a symbol of love. The contrast between the beautiful flowers and the cruel sharp thorns so well represents both joy and pain. The Greek goddess Aphrodite is said to have wounded herself on the rose's thorn and stained the flower red. The Romans took to roses, filling their baths and rooms with the petals. In Islam, the rose has pride of place, as it does in Hindu society. In Christianity, the rose became associated with the Virgin Mary and created the rosary.

In England, the rose is the national flower and roses were the symbols of the fifteenth century civil war, the 'Wars of the Roses', with the white rose of York and red rose of Lancaster, while the Tudor Rose used a rose that combined both colours to promote unity. In 1986, the United States adopted the rose as its floral emblem and five U.S. states have roses as their state flower – Iowa, North Dakota, Georgia, New York and Oklahoma, while Portland and Pasadena are both nicknamed the 'City of Roses'.

All over the world, too, the red rose also became the symbol of Socialism – from the Paris Commune of 1871 to today's British Labour party.

But it is the rose's links with romantic love that are truly universal. What woman the world over doesn't love being given a bunch of roses because of their association with adoration? And, with red roses, their association with red-hot passion?

For women, or, for that matter, anyone in a loving relationship, there's nothing like the symbolic bouquet of, preferably, red roses to make a real statement, and, no other flowers that do quite the same.

Nor is that ever likely to change. Nothing says it as roses do!

The *unofficial* English Rose

Although Robbie Burns and other poets have long loved garden roses, the smaller more delicate wild roses of woods, heaths and hedgerows have inspired them as well. These native roses colour the countryside for just a brief period, mostly in the month of June. Rupert Brooke wrote in 'The Old Vicarage, Grantchester', his famous poem of nostalgia for England, of the flowers in the vicarage garden and of the wild roses in the nearby countryside:

'Unkempt about those hedges blows
An English unofficial rose'

Pink- or white-flowered **Dog-rose** (*Rosa canina*) is the commonest of the several species of wild rose and probably ought to be the true Rose of England. But another wild rose, **Eglantine** or **Sweet Briar** (*Rosa rubiginosa*), with its pink flowers and apple-scented shoots, was especially beloved by Shakespeare, Wordsworth and several others.

PLANE TREES AND POLLUTED CITIES

London is now only the world's 26th largest city. But in the 17th century it was about to overtake Beijing and Constantinople to become the biggest in the world – and certainly on the way to being the most polluted. So it was not surprising that a new pollution-resistant Plane Tree, destined to become be the most famous of all street trees, fitted the bill exactly.

In his Vauxhall garden, botanist John Tradescant the Younger grew two trees, **American Sycamore** (*Platanus occidentalis*) and **Oriental Plane** (*Platanus orientalis*), which crossed, by accident or design, to create the **London Plane** (*Platanus acerifolia*). This robust tree grows to 30 metres tall, with a straight trunk, broad, deeply cut and maple-like leaves, and stalked, tight-hanging balls of tiny one-seeded fruits. But its most important feature is the thin greyish-green bark that peels and flakes into a camouflage-like pattern of grey, pale green and cream patches. Hardy, fast-growing, tolerant of pollution, and casting a welcome shade, it was widely planted in parks and streets like the Mall in London, leading to Buckingham Palace (above)–not only in London, but also in Paris, Berlin and other European cities and in the south of France – notably along the banks of the Canal du Midi.

Its secret defence against urban life is its flaky bark, which gradually falls off and so doesn't accumulate toxic pollutants. The large, shiny leaves too, act like a green filter

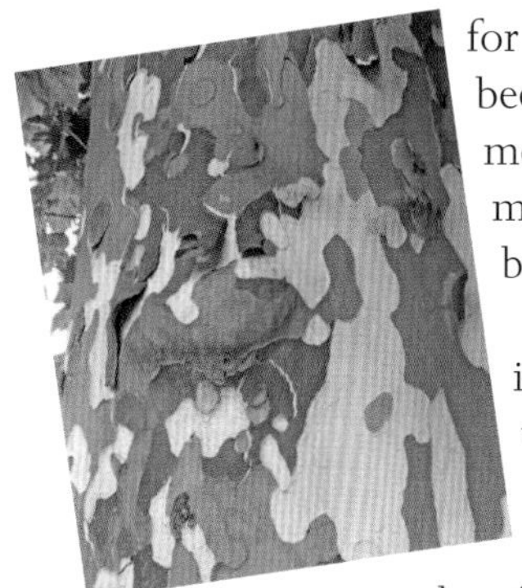

for the polluted air. It's become one of Europe's most iconic trees and made a huge contribution to urban life.

The Oriental Plane is every bit as valuable, with a massive, often gnarled and knobby trunk, thicker and less flaky bark, and more deeply cut leaves. It's native beside springs, in ravines and by mountain torrents in the eastern Mediterranean region, and also planted from Spain to India for shade and ornament. Oriental Plane trees are a feature of wayside springs, village squares, cafés and places where locals meet to talk, eat, drink and dance under their spreading branches. They can achieve immense size and age. One, on the Greek island of Kos with a girth of 60 metres, is said to be the tree under which Hippocrates, the 'Father of Medicine', taught in the 4th century BC.

Gardeners have long admired this great tree. Others, too: Greek historian Herodotus tells of how Xerxes, King of Persia (486–465 BC), so admired the planes of Lydia, now in Turkey, that he commanded that one be decorated with golden ornaments and guarded by his élite guard. Handel used this story in his opera *Xerxes* – the Persian King himself addressing the tree with an aria more familiar today as the orchestral piece 'Handel's Largo'. But today all is not well for this species.

Sadly, both Plane Trees are now under severe threat in Europe. During World War II a fungal disease arrived with munition boxes used by American soldiers in Italy made from the unseasoned infected wood of American Sycamore. Subsequent spread of the disease has greatly damaged stands of London Plane (including the famous ones along the Canal du Midi) and, even more worryingly, has affected the native populations of Oriental Plane in Greece. American Sycamore, native to stream-sides and moist ravines in east and central North America from NE Mexico to Ontario, is one of the region's largest trees, up to 50 metres tall and with a stout trunk that hollows out in older specimens. It, too, has its fungal problems, and a fungal canker disease apparently introduced with Oriental Planes has ironically led to many urban trees being replaced by the more resistant London Plane.

City pollution is a major issue, with traffic bans and tree planting, as in Paris and Barcelona. Trees that help this problem will become ever more important and it's vital that they survive.

In 1792 the Buttonwood Agreement, said to have been signed under a Sycamore (also known as Buttonwood) in Wall Street, laid foundations for the New York Stock Exchange. A weekly 'Buttonwood' column still appears in *The Economist* magazine.

In World War II, the German camouflage clothing *Platanenmuster* (plane tree pattern), based on the peeling bark of London Plane, was the first mottled military camouflage pattern, said to reduce gunshot casualties by 15%, and is now copied by armies worldwide.

MANGROVES AND COASTAL PROTECTION

In December 2004, a huge earthquake under the sea off Sumatra sent a massive tsunami or 'tidal wave' racing across the Indian Ocean, devastating the coasts of countries in South-east Asia and causing damage as far away as East Africa. Over 270,000 people lost their lives and many more their homes. Some areas suffered less than others – but why? Following the disaster, scientists concluded that extensive areas of natural and semi-natural habitat and vegetation had helped to limit casualties and the destruction of infrastructure and livelihoods in coastal urban, fishing and farming communities. And the most important of these habitats were the region's mangrove forests.

Trees can grow in most habitats except the hottest deserts and coldest alpine and tundra regions. And in the wet Tropics, some forests even thrive on tidal salt marshes along coasts and in estuaries. But only the best adapted trees and shrubs can survive, because at high tide the forests are semi-immersed in salt water and the muddy, peaty soils contain little or no oxygen. These adaptable trees are the mangroves, mostly found in South-east Asia.

In order to survive, mangroves have evolved different and ingenious strategies. **Red Mangrove** (*Rhizophora mangle*) has roots acting as filters to exclude most salt. Their numerous prop-roots, containing air spaces and pores in the bark to allow gas exchange, descend from the branches into the mud. **Grey Mangrove** (*Avicennia marina*), and **Black Mangrove** (*A. germinans*) excrete salt through special glands in their leaves. They have aerial roots that grow up out of the mud and are exposed at low tide to allow gas exchange through pores in the bark. The tangled thickets of mangrove roots, branches and decaying vegetation hold sediment and organic material, which accumulate and gradually extend the coastline out to sea. The large seeds germinate while on the tree and fall off to grow nearby, or be dispersed in the seawater as 'ready-to-go' plantlets.

Unfortunately, these valuable mangroves have been cleared at an alarming rate in recent decades. All too often they are replaced by rice paddies and other crops

or, especially in Thailand and Indonesia, extensive shellfish farms, which have caused at least a third of all mangrove losses. These feed an insatiable global demand for large tiger prawns (Americans eat four pounds of prawns per head every year). This destruction continues despite mangroves being, for local people, a significant ecological and economic resource – provided that they are managed sustainably. The hard, dark wood yields charcoal and local building material, and the bark is used for tanning. The flooded forests also support crabs, shellfish and other sea creatures, and are the spawning grounds of fish.

Perhaps, most importantly, mangrove swamps protect coasts against high winds, large waves, erosion and storm surges and, as was seen in 2004, they appear to reduce the force of the tsunamis that are an ever-present danger generated by the earthquakes and volcanoes of the Pacific rim 'Ring of Fire'. They build up soil in response to rising sea levels, and the trees and peaty soils accumulate large stores of carbon that might otherwise contribute to climate change. They also filter and purify water, removing excess sediment and nutrients that contribute to damage to coral reefs. Mangroves are indeed plant heroes.

Since the 2004 disaster, governments in South-east Asia have belatedly come to recognize the enormous value of mangroves as both a protection against the power of the sea – and as a major resource.

However, despite some efforts at mangrove restoration and curbing of excessive prawn farming, these unusual wetlands remain one of Earth's most threatened ecosystems.

The Sunderbans Forest

This 10,000 square kilometre (3,860 square miles) area on the borders of India and Bangladesh in the delta confluence of the Ganges, Brahmaputra and Meghna rivers in the Bay of Bengal, is a network of channels, mudflats and islands dominated by mangrove forest. One of the largest stands of mangrove forest in the world and a UNESCO World Heritage site, the Sunderbans supports rich plant and animal diversity, and a human population who earn their living from farming, fishing and harvesting forest products, including honey. It is, too, the last stronghold of the Bengal tiger, some 200 of which still survive.

CITRUS FRUITS AND SCURVY

How many Americans know why they call people from Britain 'Limeys'? And why it was connected to curing something very nasty?

Scurvy is indeed a hideous disease. It starts silently with fatigue, poor appetite and weight loss. Then bruises appear on the skin and the gums begin to bleed. Soon the joints become painful and swollen as their cavities fill with blood, haemorrhages turn the whites of the eyes red, the teeth fall out and the breath becomes foul. Anaemia, fever, incontinence and paralysis follow. Death comes slowly, but dignity goes long before. And all this through lack of a simple chemical in the diet - ascorbic acid or Vitamin C.

Vitamin C is essential for collagen production and iron absorption in the body. Many animals are able to synthesize it, but humans cannot, and must obtain it from outside sources like citrus fruits, tomatoes, peppers, spinach and broccoli.

Scurvy emerged as a major maritime problem with the advent of long voyages of exploration. Before the end of the fifteenth century most sea trading was in small vessels sailing close to land. But global commerce led to journeys lasting weeks or months – with the difficulties of preserving fresh food. The disease became a major cause of death, for example with Vasco da Gama losing half his crew on his way to India in 1491 and Magellan 80% on his circumnavigation in 1521. Scurvy had become '*the plague of the sea, the spoyle of mariners*'.

In 1739 James Lind, a young Scottish physician, joined the Navy as a surgeon's mate. After service in the Mediterranean and the West Indies, he was promoted to surgeon of HMS *Salisbury* in the Channel Fleet in 1747. During his years aboard ship he had observed the effects of scurvy on crews, especially Admiral George Anson's catastrophic circumnavigation in 1740 in which a shocking 1,400 out of 1,900 men died. Lind, already aware that eating citrus fruits might have an effect on scurvy, wished to prove that and on HMS *Salisbury* he set up one of medicine's first clinical trials.

Lind selected twelve sailors suffering from scurvy, and divided them into six groups of two. They received the same basic daily diet, but to one group he added a quart of cider, to another twenty-five drops of sulphuric acid, and group three had six spoonfuls of vinegar, group four half a pint of sea water, group five two oranges and group six a mixture of garlic, mustard and horseradish, mercifully combined with barley water. It was Group five that responded. Within days one sailor was fit for duty and another had almost recovered.

Lind retired from the Navy, returning to marry and practise medicine in Edinburgh. In 1754 he published *A Treatise of the Scurvy* and three years later *On the Most Effectual Means of*

Preserving the Health of Seamen. In both books he carried out a systematic review of what had been written on the topic by others – again not something that medical writers had done before, and in both he recommended giving sailors citrus fruits on long voyages.

Amazingly, it took forty years for his advice about this to be taken seriously by the Navy. However, eventually the message got through. More and more captains took citrus fruits with them on long voyages, and when in 1793 an East India fleet – well-supplied with lemon juice – reached Madras scurvy-free after nineteen weeks, the Lords of the Admiralty conceded. In 1795 they introduced lemon juice to all fleets and scurvy vanished from the Royal Navy. The battle against an enemy, which, in Lind's words, had '*caused more deaths in the British fleets than French and Spanish arms combined*', was finally won.

So that American nickname 'Limey' is actually half rude – but half admiring.

SOAPWORT AND ITS GENTLENESS

However did our ancestors keep their clothes clean? Certainly with difficulty and by laborious washing in rivers and streams – if they were lucky enough to live near them. But there was one plant frequently found nearby that came to their rescue – **Soapwort** (*Saponaria officinalis*), also called Wild Sweet William, Crowsoap, Soapweed or Bouncing Bett. This patch-forming, slightly sprawling perennial, with leaves in opposite pairs and clusters of showy pink or white flowers, proved to be a gentle detergent that really did work – and is still used today to clean fabrics, and especially ancient and delicate tapestries. As Richard Mabey notes in his *Flora Britannica*, '*Simply rubbing a leaf between the fingers will produce a slight, slippery froth.*'

Boiling Soapwort's leafy shoots and roots releases 'saponins', natural plant soaps which in water create a lathery liquid that can dissolve fat or grease in about ten minutes. Then, when the liquid is strained, it is ready for use – to clean both plant fibre textiles and woollen fabrics.

And Soapwort's cleaning effect has been going on for a long time. It is likely that Stone Age (12,000 BC) people grabbed its leaves to scrub off dirt as they washed in streams. Then the Ancient Egyptians, Greeks and Romans used it to remove the grease in newly shorn wool. Indeed, its scientific name Saponaria comes from '*sapo*' – the Latin word for soap. A tribute to its soapy success is the patches that survive on riverbanks and roadsides close to villages and small rural communities all across Europe, from Ireland to the Balkans and beyond.

Thankfully, this useful plant is very widespread, a native of cooler climates in Europe and western Asia, and introduced in the USA and elsewhere. It also remains a classic cottage garden plant, appreciated for its prolific scented, often 'double' flowers – it is in the carnation family or Caryophyllaceae – if a bit inclined to spread. It is appreciated too as a gentler detergent than conventional soaps, especially for those with dry or delicate skin.

Its mildness has been of special value for museum conservators faced with cleaning unique and precious fabrics. It is even thought that Soapwort may have been used to clean the famous 'Shroud of Turin', purported to have held the body of Christ.

Soapwort root is also useful in food and drink as an emulsifier, especially when added to the crushed oily seeds of **Sesame** (*Sesamum orientale*) to make the tahini paste used in preparing hummus and the sweet 'tahini halva' of the Middle East. And it has been used to give some beers a better 'head'. Another use of Soapwort is in herbal medicine to alleviate bronchitis, and chesty colds and minor skin ailments.

But for much of history its greatest contribution was enabling women – for it was, alas, mainly women who were left with large families (and no contraception)to wash clothes until the invention of washing machines, and forced to lug heavy loads down to the river and far heavier ones back.

SPHAGNUM AND PEAT

From carbon storage to bog burials

How many of us ever think about moss – except when clearing it from garden steps with some irritation? Or using it for compost for growing plants? Yet the moss family has huge influence, in particular bog mosses – to be found wherever water flows or collects on heaths, moors and mountains. These small and feathery green, red, yellow or orange plants, which don't produce roots and conventional stems nor flowers and seeds, form huge spongy carpets under permanently wet conditions. Importantly, the dead moss tissue not only resists decay, but also does not decompose in the waterlogged and thus airless conditions, so that over years, centuries and often millennia it accumulates to form deposits of peat. The moss leaves, arranged on whorls of small branches, have cells of two types: small living cells and larger dead ones able to store many times their own weight of water – both when the plants are living and are dead.

The first huge influence they have is environmental. The mosses themselves create the huge bogs in which they live and cause them to spread on to drier ground during prolonged wet periods. They can also affect the acidity of the water by replacing the calcium and magnesium ions in their cells by the hydrogen ions that make the bog more acidic. It is these bogs that have long provided the peat for horticulture. But much more important for all of us, peat bogs store vast quantities of carbon in the form of dead plant material, of which the bulk is moss. Loss of bogs and the release of this carbon in any quantity greatly adds to the levels of greenhouse gases causing global warming and climate change. British TV viewers were recently startled to see pine trees being cut down but in order to revive much more environmentally useful moss bogs.

Worldwide there are some 380 species of **Bog Moss** (*Sphagnum*), all difficult to distinguish without a microscope. They are concentrated in the bogs, forests and tundra of a great belt across the northern hemisphere, in Canada, northern Europe and Siberia, and in the southern Andes, New Zealand and Tasmania. Scientifically, the bog habitat of *Sphagnum* comprises many large, important and biodiversity-rich wetlands that are ecologically essential for maintaining and buffering the human race as well as the natural environment. Indeed, recent repeated flooding in northern England is now being partly mitigated by the restoration of moorland peat bogs in the Pennines.

Horticulture has long consumed immense quantities of peat, also known as 'sphagnum peat' or (in North America) 'sphagnum peat moss', in compost for growing plants and as a soil conditioner to increase the water-holding capacity of light or sandy soils. Campaigns in recent years against the over-use of what is effectively a non-renewable, or at best a slowly renewable, natural resource that is extracted from wetlands of great conservation value have gradually reduced the peat harvest. Peat has partly been replaced by other organic materials, notably coconut-shell fibre or coir, a largely waste product imported mostly from India and Sri Lanka. The USA obtains most of its horticultural peat from Canada, and the UK from Ireland and northern Britain.

Then there is the medical influence. Being both very absorbent and antiseptic, *Sphagnum* was employed during the First World War to dress the wounds of soldiers, augmenting the supply of bandages as a good alternative to cotton lint (page 30). Reports of its effectiveness go back at least as far as the Irish using it to staunch their wounds after the Battle of Clontarf in 1014, when Brian Boru overcame a Viking-Irish army – as did the defeated Scots after the Battle of Flodden in their failed invasion of England in 1513.

It is probably only visitors to Ireland who appreciate another influence – peat as a fuel. However, digging for peat for fuel was once widespread in Europe, and the lakes of the Norfolk Broads, today popular for sailing, are really flooded medieval peat diggings. In Ireland, where the bogs have long been a source of fuel and a stalwart of popular culture, the Peat Board (Bord na

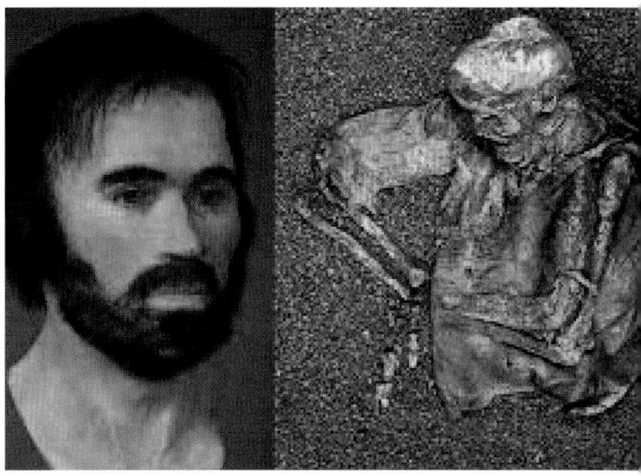

Móna) has developed intensive mechanized peat harvesting and processing. Peat is still burned in a few power stations, although this is rapidly being phased out from a peak in the 1960s when it generated some 40% of the nation's electricity. Less successful was the Irish experiment, during coal shortages, of peat-fired steam locomotives, including a rather advanced design by British engineer Oliver Bulleid called the 'Turf Burner'. On a smaller scale, one can still sit around a 'turf fire' in rural Ireland. Our own experience is that it yields too little heat, but one of that country's most evocative smells!

Finally, the preservative qualities of peat bogs give them a special place in the study of vegetation history and past climates, and in archaeology. Plant remains and pollen grains from cores drilled into bogs tell their own tale and allow the accurate reconstruction of past habitats and climates. More sensationally, bogs in Britain, Denmark, Ireland and elsewhere have yielded up well preserved human bodies – especially what appear to be ritualistic bog burials of important individuals from the Iron Age such as 'Grauballe Man' and 'Tollund Man' from Denmark and 'Lindow Man' – aka 'Pete Marsh' from Cheshire in England.

Compared with flowering plants, stately trees or even ferns, the humble mosses are frequently overlooked by most people. But they – and especially the great peat deposits the bog mosses produce – do form an indispensable element of the ecology of our planet.

HEMP OR CANNABIS - 'THE DEVIL'S WEED'

Some wild or cultivated plants have so many uses that one cannot perceive them simply as good or bad. Too often a bad reputation, as with that of some poisonous plants, detracts from valuable medicinal, industrial or other practical virtues. But one plant in particular has all too often suffered official disapproval and hostile public opinion.

Cannabis or **Hemp** (*Cannabis sativa*) may be seen as a villain but has long served people well. A fast-growing annual plant native to central and southern Asia, but now cosmopolitan, it yields a strong, versatile fibre and an edible oil, it provides human, farm animal and bird feed, and is a prized medicinal plant, though some of its variants can make you high. It is this last quality that has demonized what is one of the most valuable of all the plants that people have ever utilized or domesticated on a large scale. Hemp is one of the world's most ancient crops, probably cultivated since before 4,000 BC in China, which is today the largest global producer of the fibre crop.

This important plant, Hemp, has many

uses and applications, but it is its drug-rich variant usually known as cannabis that has attracted more publicity – and notoriety. It is no new intoxicant. Inquisitive Greek historian Herodotus recorded in *The Histories* in c. 480 BC how the Thracians grew cannabis (a Greek word) for its fibre, which he said made cloth as good as linen (page 252). Yet he also noted how the Scythians of the Eurasian steppes would ritually purify themselves after a family funeral. Inside a tent of felt blankets they would throw cannabis seeds on to red-hot stones and '*shriek with delight at the fumes*'. Today's addicts and Rastafarians, who regard cannabis smoking as a sacred rite, would certainly have approved.

During the 20th century the US Government became almost hysterical in its demonization of cannabis and spent huge sums of money fighting what was probably the least harmful element of the illegal drug trade. In retrospect, much of this irrational fear seems to have stemmed from one man, Harry Anslinger, the first Commissioner of the Federal Bureau of Narcotics, who served from 1930 to 1962. As soon as the disastrous 'Prohibition' of alcohol, of which he was an active proponent, ended in 1933 he began a crusade against marijuana, quoting one Victor Licata of Tampa, Florida, who murdered his parents and three siblings with an axe while allegedly high on cannabis. Similar scare stories were used against Absinthe (page 54), but again the real problem was mental illness.

The cinema sensationally harped on this concern – films like 'The Devil's Weed', 'Devil's Harvest' (subtitled for good measure '*A good girl until she lights a reefer*'), or the infamous, absurd and frequently-mocked 'Reefer Madness' of 1936. A constant theme, as in related posters and books, was of young women gone astray, either as weak vulnerable victims or just bad girls who encouraged others into a life of depravity. As late as the 1950s, Anslinger claimed that '*marijuana was a shortcut to the insane asylum*', even though experts by then regarded it as being of little threat and more a drug of beatnik subculture than mainstream recreation. He saw it as an epidemic, one threatening the very fabric of America. Jazz musicians were a particular target, partly because Anslinger was undoubtedly driven by racism. He used extreme language to denigrate black people and also steered a shift away from the word 'cannabis' to the Mexican marijuana as a slur on the Hispanic population.

The 1937 Marijuana Tax Act, drafted by none other than Anslinger, was directed at the drug and hemp itself – said by some to have been a conspiracy to protect both the wood pulp and the newly-created nylon industry. However, in wartime 1942 the American hemp farmers were asked to grow hemp for ropes and hawsers for the US Navy, an echo of Tudor England, when East Anglian farmers were compelled by law to grow hemp for the sails and cordage of the Royal Navy.

In the early 1960s, at about the same time that Anslinger retired, cannabis as a recreational drug did indeed take off in North America and Britain, and found its niche in the louche, colourful and subversive subculture of the hippies, especially among college students and other young people. President Richard Nixon, another enemy of cannabis, and no admirer of the students he notoriously labelled 'college bums', from 1971 took up the cudgels against cannabis with fervour. He failed miserably.

However, recently another factor has emerged in favour of this controversial substance: Cannabis is a plant medicine with considerable potential. It has also been used to reduce pain since antiquity and is mentioned, for example, in ancient Chinese texts and the Ebers Papyrus of ancient Egypt. It was used in medieval Islamic medicine. Indeed, the Qur'an does not forbid cannabis in the same way it does alcohol.

Doctors increasingly prescribe medical cannabis, in which the active principal cannabidiol (CBD) replaces the psychoactive D-9-trahydracannabinol (THC) of the recreational drug, for pain relief and muscle spasm, and it appears to be effective at alleviating the symptoms of multiple sclerosis.

The use of cannabis remains illegal in most countries of the world, and under US Federal law, although many American states have now decriminalized or legalized it. Uruguay legalized recreational use in 2015, Canada in 2018.

Concerns over possible association with several forms of mental illness and some physical ailments means that the legalization debate will continue for the foreseeable future.

That's surely a good thing.

Hemp or **Cannabis**: a useful and often ignored plant, except for drug use. Fast-growing and productive, it needs little water and is dense enough to suppress weeds. Surprisingly, it helps to create a great many products:

Fibre, stronger and more durable than cotton
Paper, cardboard and fibreboard
Ropes, string and garden twine
Sails ('canvas' derives from cannabis) and tarpaulin
Quality textiles
Car bodywork (mixed with fibreglass)
Plastic substitutes
Cosmetics and shampoos
Medical cannabis
Edible hempseed
Hempseed oil (edible, or for paint and varnishes, etc.)
Animal feed
Birdseed
Fishing bait
Biofuel

DATE PALM - LIFELINE FOR A DESERT PEOPLE

Many cultures venerate their food plants. But how many people have the close bond the Arabs share with the tree that has for so long provided food, shelter and shade amid the heat and harshness of the desert? The tall graceful **Date-palm** (*Phoenix dactylifera*), one of the most famous of all trees and prized since early Antiquity, is instantly recognizable with its stout, straight trunk up to 25 metres tall and topped by a crown of arched leaves up to six metres long, divided into narrow sharp-pointed segments. Male and female flowers are borne on separate trees, and in fruit, the fleshy oblong dates, orange ripening to dark or reddish-brown, hang in huge stalked clusters weighing 10 kilos or more.

The desert civilizations and cultures of the Middle East were built on date-palms and their fruit, a staple food and major economic commodity. The tree copes well with the hot dry climate, though it does needs irrigation or underground water. As the Arabs say, '*It must have its feet in running water and its head in the fire of the sky*'. Dates remain an important food and central sacred element in Arab and Berber culture and, more than any other religion, Islam has stressed the holiness of the date and the date palm. Indeed, the Qur'an mentions it more than any other fruit-bearing plant. The Prophet himself is said to have rightly praised its virtues: '*There is among the trees one which is blessed, as is the Muslim among men; it is the date palm.*' Rich in sugar, also fibre, vitamins, and minerals, dates make a perfect food at sunset to break the daily fast during Islam's festival of Ramadan. And in Muslim countries dates are always a symbol of welcome and hospitality.

Dates were probably first cultivated in the Persian Gulf region and Mesopotamia, modern Iraq, from at least 4,000 BC and later in Egypt. Genetic evidence suggests that North African dates, including the popular Medjool and Deglet Noor varieties, derive from crosses from around 1,000 BC between Middle Eastern cultivated trees and **Cretan Date Palm** (*Phoenix theophrasti*). This smaller tree, with little inedible dates, survives near the sea in Crete and SW Turkey – and many cafés in Crete are named *Finiki* or Palm (similar to the Latin *Phoenix*). From the 7th century Arab armies spread Date-palm as far as Persia, India, Morocco and southern Spain. Ideal provisions for desert nomads, as well as for the light cavalry that were the Arabs' greatest military strength, dates are energy-rich, keep well and are readily dried and transported.

Over 600 date cultivars exist, divided into three main classes – soft, semi-dry ('Christmas' and 'fancy' dates) and dry, the latter an Arab staple. The Date-palm remains an important crop from Morocco to the Punjab but is particularly important in the Maghreb region of North Africa, with Algeria and Tunisia producing large amounts for export. The most northerly date grove, one of the largest but no longer commercially harvested, is the Palmeral de Elche near Alicante in Spain – from where the Spanish first took dates to Mexico and California, the early origin of a now substantial New World crop.

Containing more than half their weight in sugar, dates are eaten in large quantities 'as they are' and in both sweet and savoury dishes. In Arab countries date juice replaces sugar in tea and coffee. The fruits are fermented into vinegar, the crushed seeds serve as animal feed, and roasted, have been used as a coffee substitute. Old trunks yield firewood and timber for construction of buildings and, with other woods, Arab dhows. The fronds provide roofing and fencing, and their fibres are woven into bags, baskets, mats and ropes. As an ornamental plant, the date-palm embellishes the skyline, adding an exotic feel to Mediterranean landscapes.

Long before Islam, in ancient Greek mythology the twin gods Apollo and Artemis were said to have been born in the shade of a palm tree, and there is an ancient tradition in the Mediterranean region of planting them at pagan shrines and near churches. A vestige of this old sacred association is the use of palm fronds in churches on Palm Sunday, the week before Easter, symbolising the cut branches cast before Christ as he entered Jerusalem mounted on a donkey (St Matthew 21: 1-11).

But, above all, Date-palm belongs to the heritage of Islam and the Arabs. In 2019, based on a submission by fourteen Arab countries, UNESCO added their date-palm culture to the listings of the Intangible Cultural Heritage of Humanity.

DANDELIONS AND THEIR RUBBERY FUTURE

Regarded as a weed, **Dandelions** (*Taraxacum officinale*) have been rather overlooked as a useful plant. However they have several potential uses – not least as a substitute for rubber.

Rubber, one of the most widely employed of all materials, comes from the natural milky sap or latex present in specialized plant cells. Normally it is trees that are cultivated as a rubber crop, especially the **Rubber Tree** (*Hevea brasiliensis*) the main source of the world's rubber supplies since the 19th century. However, scientists are now hopeful that a smaller, perennial plant that also yields latex might provide rubber in the future – a close relative of the familiar dandelion. This hardy, resilient weed has the huge advantage that it can be grown as a fast-growing field crop, maturing in months and giving two harvests a year, rather than a plantation crop of trees that can take ten years before producing a sufficient yield of latex.

In dandelions, the latex is extracted from their long, sturdy brown taproots, traditional enemies of gardeners everywhere! Dandelions form a group of closely related species and microspecies. All of them produce latex, the white sticky substance oozing from a cut stem or root that stains your fingers brown, but the dandelion that has the best potential to make rubber is

Kazakh or Russian Dandelion (*Taraxacum koksaghyz*), which produces an extra-large amount of latex, 10–15% by dry weight. German parts manufacturer. Continental has already produced prototype tyres that perform just as well as those made from traditional rubber.

This innovative tyre project began when a German professor was inspired by the sight of a meadow of flowering dandelions and observed the latex in the stems. In fact dandelion rubber already had an illustrious history and had proved its worth – to the Red Army. Botanists discovered Russian Dandelion in 1931 in the mountainous Tien Shan region of eastern Kazakhstan (see Apple, page154) and the state soon began to experiment with extracting and using the rubber as part of a national programme of self-sufficiency. This source served the Soviet Union well in World War II when rubber was cut off as the plantations of South-East Asia fell to the Japanese. Always short of motorised transport, the Russians cultivated 200,000 hectares of dandelions, and in this period the USA too experimented successfully with dandelion rubber. However, by the 1950s, with the resumption of cheap rubber supplies and the arrival of synthetic rubber made from oil, dandelion rubber research and use languished.

But today researchers in Germany, the Netherlands and USA have rekindled interest in this potentially valuable product, working on raising latex yields, improving the processing techniques and the growth and performance of the dandelion plants. They are also exploring uses for the by-product, inulin, a starch-like food substance stored in the roots, used as a high fibre, low calorie sugar substitute with several health benefits, especially for the digestive system. Researchers are also looking into converting this substance into ethanol biofuel and plastic for bottles. Nevertheless, dandelion rubber may have a problem attracting support from companies and investors when conventional rubber prices are low (as with fracking when oil prices fall). For the environment, such substitutes for South-East Asian rubber may reduce plantation encroachment into the precious rainforests as the world demand for rubber increases.

Apart from their industrial potential, dandelions are rather overlooked as a food. They provide a healthy, if rather bitter salad, the flowers can be made into a syrup or a wine and the roots can be roasted, ground and used like chicory as a coffee substitute (chicory roots too contain inulin).

Furthermore, the flush of dandelion flowers in spring that can colour roadsides and grassy places gives emerging bees and bumblebees a rich and ready source of pollen and nectar. If dandelions don't give us a buzz, it certainly does them!

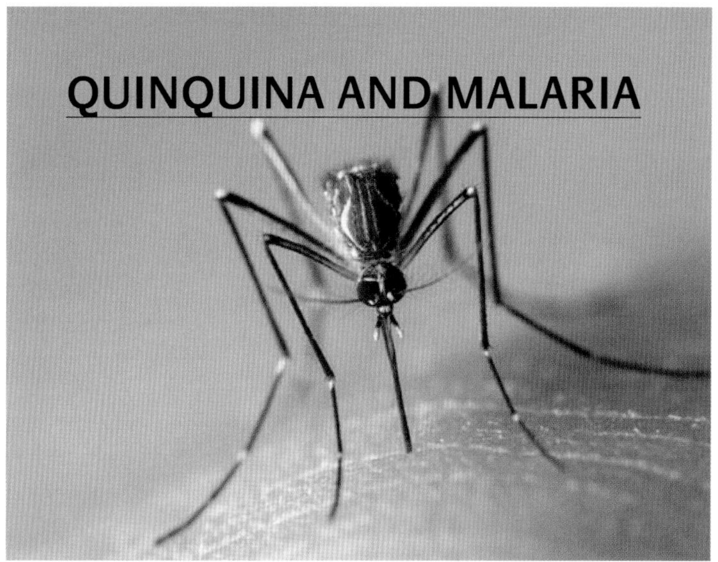

QUINQUINA AND MALARIA

Malaria has always been a worldwide and deadly scourge, its effect critical at pivotal moments. For instance, it destroyed successive invaders of Rome –Visigoths, Vandals, Huns and Ostrogoths. Even in the colder north, a Roman invasion of Scotland once lost half its 80,000 men. Expeditions, colonisation missions and engineering projects from many nations failed because of malarial fever, and for centuries whole armies were decimated.

The Spanish, in their vast colonies of South America, were all too familiar with the disease, although the way it was spread by mosquitoes was yet to be understood. But it was a Spanish aristocrat who, by chance, would help to save the world from this terrible affliction.

In 1638, Ana de Osorio, the Countess of Chinchón and the beautiful wife of the Spanish Viceroy of Peru, was close to death, desperately ill with malaria, and racked by its cold rigours and hot fevers as she lay in the Viceregal Palace in Lima.

The doctor suggested to the Count that they try using a local remedy, an extract from an Andean bark, quinquina. Miraculously, the Countess was saved.

In fact, Spanish Jesuit missionaries had discovered the healing power of quinquina four years earlier. But nobody paid attention. As so often, it required the dramatic saving of 'a celebrity' for the medical and botanical world to sit up and take any notice.

When the Countess returned to her estates at Chinchón near Madrid, she used the quinquina bark to protect her workers from malaria, turning the swamps into profitable rice paddies. The bark from the tree, which botanists had designated, but misspelled *Cinchona*, was brought back by her physician and sold in Seville. Called the 'Countess's bark', it was at first only available to the rich. However, the Jesuits became involved and it became something of a Catholic monopoly, so some Protestants stubbornly and sadly refused to take it. Indeed, Oliver Cromwell called it the 'power of the devil' and died prematurely after suffering from bouts of malaria all his life, a victim of his own religious prejudice.

Two centuries later, less-blinkered fellow countrymen soon grasped the need for quinine on an industrial scale. With their huge Empire mainly in hot climates, the British knew only too well the devastating effects of malaria, which killed or crippled both colonised and colonisers alike: '*Beware, beware the Bight of Benin. One comes out, where fifty went in*'.

An enthusiastic amateur botanist, Clements Markham, persuaded the Indian Office and Kew Gardens to finance an expedition to find the original quinquina plants and reproduce them in India. The £10,000 voted proved to be a bargain for the British Empire. Between 1859 and 1862, Markham brought cinchona trees to India and large scale production began, aiming to protect British and Indians at a fraction of the cost of the original 'Countess's' bark or 'Jesuits' bark'.

Quinine became the world's main protection against malaria, breaking the cycle by killing the reservoir of parasites in humans before they could be re-transmitted by the mosquito.

The British ex-colonial habit of drinking 'gin and tonic' becomes logical if you use the old American version – 'gin and quinine water'.

While malaria still is a killer, the saving of one influential celebrity life in Peru helped to save tens of millions of lives in the centuries to come.

One of the best examples of mosquito control was over the Panama Canal. Ferdinand de Lesseps, the hero of the Suez Canal, had been ruined by Panama, with yellow fever and malaria killing 30,000 of his workers.

When the United States later stepped in, a decisive figure emerged. American medical officer, Colonel William Gorgas, fully understood that to prevent mosquitoes from spreading yellow fever and malaria, strict measures were required to cover all stagnant water with oil and insecticide to prevent the insects from reproducing. He also made it compulsory to put screens on all windows, not just to protect the inhabitants, but also to stop them being reservoirs of the diseases. And, of course, Gorgas made them all take 'quinine'.

Only then could construction start under an engineering team from the U.S. Military Academy at West Point. Thirteen years later, in August 1914, the first ship passed from one ocean to another. A tiny enemy was beaten and nearly 8,000 miles of sailing round South America was reduced to a mere ten hours.

MOSES AND HIS BASKET

In ancient times, if you wanted to carry anything remotely heavy or bulky, there were few choices. There were no boxes, waggons, wheelbarrows or paper bags – and of course no plastic ones! The answer, all over the world, was the straw basket, woven from any locally available plant. For thousands of years such baskets have been used to carry food and other essentials, and they are still widely sold in markets for just that purpose.

But there was one such basket that was to alter the history of the world.

The Israelites had been enslaved by the Egyptians, and the Pharoah Rameses II decided that they might become so dangerous that he ordered that all male babies be killed (a sinister precursor to the Holocaust when the Nazis decided to kill Jewish children along with their parents in case they grew up and sought revenge).

When young mother Yocheved could no longer hide her little baby son Moses any longer she resorted to placing him in a wicker basket, probably made of **Papyrus** (*Cyperus papyrus*) or **Common Reed** (*Phragmites communis*) and waterproofed with pitch. She left it to be discovered among the 'bulrushes' bordering the Nile river. Luckily, the infant was indeed found – and by no less than one of the Pharoah's daughters, who adopted the child.

Years later, Moses becomes leader of the Israelites and asks the Pharoah if his people could leave. On his refusal, Egypt suffers ten devastating plagues, so Moses is at last allowed to take his people out. The Pharoah's plan was to massacre them 'out of town' (again like the Nazis having their death camps away from prying eyes). However, they escaped because the Red Sea engulfed the vengeful, pursuing Egyptian army.

But for the actions of a frightened young mother, and the successful water-proofing of the basket, we would never have heard of Moses or his Ten Commandments. For that matter, the Jews might well have remained a small, enslaved tribe in Egypt and we would probably never have heard of them either. Thus, no Israel, no Jesus and no Christianity.

Never has a plant, made into a small wicker basket, had such a huge political and religious influence. Yet that's something we never (or rarely)think about.

CAPTAIN SCOTT, MARIE STOPES AND THE FOSSIL PLANTS

The 1911 journey of Captain Robert Falcon Scott to the South Pole, sadly ending in his death and that of four companions, is a classic British story of both heroism and tragic failure. Their sacrifice was a morale booster in World War I and after, and every schoolchild used to know the immortal words of Captain Lawrence Oates (pictured) as he left the tent in the blizzard: 'I'm just going outside and may be some time.'

However, it's easily forgotten that the ill-fated group dragging sledges across the ice was part of a scientific expedition which yielded much information about a then almost unknown region. Found with the dead men were thirty-five pounds of rocks containing plant fossils. Why were they there? And might this extra weight have even contributed to preventing the group, sick and weak on their terrible return journey, from reaching a food and fuel depot just eleven miles from where the last three men perished?

One of the expedition's scientific tasks was to collect and bring back these rock specimens. It was hoped that they would show how Antarctica was not only once a land of forests but was also part of a southern super-continent comprising the now detached land masses of India, South America, Africa and Australasia. Known to scientists as Gondwanaland, it broke up by continental drift as Earth's continents assumed their present layout. A key fossil plant linking these regions is the 'Seed Fern' (*Glossopteris indica*), a tree with tongue- or spear-shaped leaves and somewhat similar to Monkey-puzzles and other primitive coniferous trees.

Scott's diary records how his group collected the rocks with fossil layers of 'beech-like leaves' from outcrops of Permian sandstone and coal seams. This lost a very precious day on the weary return journey after finding that the Norwegian explorer Roald Amundsen had beaten them by 35 days to the South Pole – his expedition simply focused on that objective rather than science. Scott clearly regarded the rocks in their baggage as important, despite the dire state of his party, who had jettisoned much other baggage. A man of honour and duty, he wanted to complete this part of the mission.

When the rescue expedition finally returned to England, the specimens passed to Professor Seward at Cambridge University, who published a paper on them in 1914, confirming the Glossopteris-Gondwanaland hypothesis. It was one of the major scientific outcomes of the expedition and a valuable contribution to the modern theory of continental drift.

However, the scientist who had first suggested this fossil quest must have been most unhappy her news had been pre-empted by Seward. In 1904 Scott had met and charmed Dr Marie Stopes, a brilliant young palaeobotanist, Britain's youngest Doctor of Science and the first woman on the academic staff of Manchester University, then determinedly carving out a career in the male-dominated world of natural science. For all manner of reasons, Scott had to turn her down to join an all-male expedition, but she persuaded him to let her give him a quick course in fossil plants and it seems he then promised to seek out the rock specimens she needed.

Because of her other fame, most people have ignored or forgotten Marie Stopes's distinguished botanical career. During World War I she applied her specialized knowledge to work for the British Government on the constitution of coal, but by then she was off on another tack. On the basis of a fleeting and unsatisfactory marriage to the Canadian botanist and geneticist Professor Reginald Ruggles Gates, in 1918, she published the famous sex guide *Married Love*, an immediate best-seller. Thus motivated, she established the career for which most people know her, as an indefatigable proponent of marriage, sexuality and, above all, contraception for women, especially among the poor. One of the contraceptives she endorsed was simple and botanical – a sponge soaked in olive oil, known to the ancient Greeks and Romans as a spermicide. Unsurprisingly she clashed with both the Church and the medical establishment! Today there are more than 450 Marie Stopes Clinics worldwide.

So it was that two remarkable figures of the early 20th century, totally different in background and interests, but each fired by a sense of duty and iron determination, are linked by, of all things, a group of obscure fossil plants familiar only to a select band of academic botanists.

A little-known reason why Scott failed was his love of dogs since childhood. Amundsen, and later the American Robert Peary, took teams of huskies and progressively shot them, feeding their meat to the surviving dogs. Scott thought this completely barbaric and made his party haul their 200lb sleds by human power, '*like dragging heavy bathtubs across the Sahara*'.
Love of animals may be commendable, but perhaps not in circumstances like polar exploration.

SWEET CHESTNUTS AND STARVATION

Most of us enjoy chestnuts in autumn and winter, as hot street food, roasted by the fire or preserved as *marrons glacés*, but quite unaware that they once saved the poor from starvation over large areas of Europe. These starch-rich nuts replaced the cereal crops in wooded and mountainous districts of southern Europe, and chestnuts and chestnut flour were formerly staples of the Mediterranean mountains, notably in the Cévennes region of south-western France, and in Portugal, Corsica and Tuscany. Frequently abundant, they're the fruits of **Sweet Chestnut** (*Castanea sativa*), a large tree up to 30 metres tall, with a broad crown and a distinctive deeply and spirally fissured brownish-grey bark. The hedgehog-like, soft-spiny fruit cases split on falling to the ground, revealing 1–3 shiny brown egg-shaped nuts up to 3.5 centimetres long.

The Cévennes, especially, owe a huge debt to the Chestnut, which forms extensive woods and terraced plantations in the valleys that lead up into the mountains. The nuts have long enabled people to survive in this remote rugged countryside of poor soils, and have often staved off hunger, as in 1709 when the region immediately to the north endured famine but the Cévennes suffered no food shortage. Along with the silk industry and mining, chestnuts enabled the region's population to increase greatly during the 19th century. The nuts provided food, a surplus to sell elsewhere and work opportunity for casual labour, including farm workers from the Causses plateaux that were snow-bound in winter.

This most useful tree, native only to Italy and the Balkans to the Caucasus, forms distinctive stands in woodlands and on terraced plantations in the Mediterranean region, from 300 to 800 metres in the hills and lower mountains, on lime-poor, well-drained soils. From Roman times it has spread far and wide, planted for its fruits and timber. Chestnut trees are also a major feature of parts of southern England like Surrey and Kent, but are not native – originally probably introduced by the

The Hundred Horse Chestnut
The world's largest Chestnut tree, in the commune of Sant'Alfio on the eastern slope of Mount Etna in Sicily, is thought to be as much as 4,000 years old. Today it consists of a group of large trunks arising from a shared rootstock, but in 1780 its trunk's circumference was measured as 58 metres (190 feet). Reputedly, in the late 15th century Joanna of Aragon, Queen of Naples, and her retinue of one hundred knights and staff were able to shelter under the spreading branches of this great tree during a severe thunderstorm. Just 8 km (5 miles) from Etna's crater, the tree has remarkably avoided destruction, even perhaps well-fertilised by millennia of eruptions. An astonishing survivor.

Romans. In England and elsewhere the trees have often been grown as coppices, regularly cut back to the ground in order to encourage numerous stems to sprout that can be used as smaller items of timber. For it's not just the nuts that are valuable. The hard, durable wood, despite a tendency to split, withstands outdoor use well, weathering to an attractive silvery-grey, and provides fences, palings, stakes, poles and boards, while the bark is still used to tan leather.

Medically, an infusion of the leaves treats coughs and ailments of the skin or scalp, and the mysterious 'Bach flower remedy' against despair is a tincture of chestnut. Beers, aperitifs and liqueurs are made from the nuts, which characterise a range of savoury and sweet regional dishes. They also remain an important natural resource for fattening free-range pigs, as in the mountains of Corsica.

PAPYRUS, PAPER AND RECORDING THE WORD

There is no doubt that **Papyrus** (*Cyperus papyrus*) is a very useful plant. It was, and still is, both a food and the material for mats, ropes, sandals, baskets, fences, roofs and even boats. (Many of us remember Thor Heyerdahl's *Kon-Tiki* expedition and his later *Ra II* trans-Atlantic voyage in Papyrus boats). But the influence of this giant sedge, growing by the side of rivers like the Nile, is that it was the material on to which mankind could first record the written word, changing the world forever.

Papyrus was being used in Egypt 3,000 years before Christ was born, able to record historic events, with documents such as the Ebers papyrus. The stems of the plants were sliced into long strips, laid next to each other and pressed to make large sheets called papyri rolls, then impregnated with juices that made them resist fungal and insect attack. This meant that they could survive for hundreds of years, especially in the dry climate of Egypt, giving us an insight into many aspects of ancient history.

Confusingly, some ancient scholars called the food derived from the plant 'papyros' and other materials 'biblos'. From that we have the modern words 'bibliography' and 'bible', while papyrus gave us the name for 'paper'.

Papyrus was also used by the Romans for correspondence and legal documents – graded into six qualities – from the finest white 'Augustan' down to coarse material for wrapping paper. Gradually, however, papyrus was replaced by parchment and vellum and the last recorded date of its use was for a Papal Decree of 1057.

By then, too, a Chinese invention from the Han Dynasty called paper was beginning to make its mark. This was made of mulberry wood, fishnets, rags and hemp as its base materials and it became a widespread writing medium by the 3rd century AD. Some three hundred years later in China, it was being used as toilet paper and for teabags and the Song Dynasty (960-1279 AD) became the first government to create printed money. Soon the Islamic world took to paper-making in a big way, while in Europe parchment and papyrus held their own. But the later European invention of moveable type and bulk printing propelled paper-making into the huge industry it has become today. In 1807, the Fourdrinier brothers' machines started production of huge long rolls. Then in 1844 machines begin making paper from wood pulp rather than pulped rags.

The move to wood as the base material for paper has led to whole forests being devoted to trees destined for wood pulp for printing. In the forests of the Northern Hemisphere, in Scandinavia, America and Canada, this presents little problem, but in virgin tropical rainforest countries it is a very different matter, with the Indonesian island of Sumatra being the worst culprit for huge deforestation, leading to international protests and boycotts of the resulting products.

SEMI-DWARF WHEAT AND NORMAN BORLAUG

Norman Borlaug was one of the greatest life-savers of all time. Yet this remarkable man, creator of the 'Green Revolution', and credited for preventing one billion deaths through starvation, is still remarkably little known. In 1970 he was awarded the Nobel Peace Prize for increasing the world's food supply, especially in Mexico, India and Pakistan.

Borlaug was born in Iowa in 1914, and experienced the horrors of the 'Dust Bowl', (page 247), when so many crops failed, and no longer held the soil in place. At university he became fascinated by plants and their diseases. In 1944 he went to Mexico and, backed by the Rockefeller Foundation, developed a new kind of wheat with a stout, short stalk. This high-yield, disease-resistant, low pesticide 'semi-dwarf wheat' underpinned the 'Green Revolution' which saw Mexico increase its output of wheat by six times. The world now relies on such semi-dwarf wheats.

With populations rocketing, Borlaug decided that the only solution was high-yield crops, sustained by inorganic fertilizers and

irrigation. By 1963, in spite of huge U.S. food shipments, India and Pakistan faced famine. Borlaug imported 35 truckloads of seeds to plant the non-traditional crop of wheat, only for war to break out between the two countries. Some of Borlaug's planting had to be done under shellfire, but yields jumped by 70%. Paul Ehrlich had written in *The Population Bomb* in 1968, that '*India cannot possibly feed 200 million people by 1980*'. Borlaug proved him hopelessly wrong. By 1974 India had 600 million people (now 1.4 billion), yet was self-sufficient, as was Pakistan.

When he was presented with his Nobel Peace Prize in 1970, Borlaug stressed that the 'Population Monster' had not gone away and turned his attention to Africa. Suddenly he was blocked by an environmental movement, which equated providing food with encouraging population growth, and he became enraged at the environmental lobbyists. But with the support of former President Jimmy Carter, himself a farmer, soon many countries in Africa also saw their yields leap. They certainly needed to, because Uganda, for instance, will soon have the very same population as Russia.

Before he died, at last recognized as a great man, Norman Borlaug realized the need for a radical next step. Population growth was the critical factor, since there was a limited amount of arable land, water tables were falling and salt-contaminated soils were increasing, climate change was causing droughts and floods, and fertilizer, herbicides and fuel for tractors were getting too expensive.

He felt that breeding Genetically Modified Organisms (GMOs) was the next way to increase food production and that GMOs were not inherently dangerous, but were vital for future food production. Herbicide resistance, to allow spraying against weeds, and defence against insects could be built into the crop plants themselves. Indeed, it can be argued that if GM had been around in 1845, the potato blight, *Phytophora infestans*, might not have starved a million people to death in Ireland (page102), nor would Phylloxera have wiped out Europe's vines (page 114).

The evidence in favour of the use of GMOs is conflicting and has raised strong opposition, especially in Europe. The very title 'Genetically modified' seems to evince creepy connotations ('Frankenstein food'). However, the fact is that the cat is out of the bag, with GM plant varieties now being grown in 29 countries by 16.7 million farmers on 395 million acres – an area the size of Europe. Above all, China has readily embraced GM crops for fibre (cotton), feed (maize) and food (rice and soya), and the rest of Asia may well follow.

Microsoft tycoon Bill Gates, who has donated millions to help agricultural research and GM, told the 2009 World Food Prize Symposium, '*We have the tools. We know what needs to be done. We can be the generation that sees Dr Borlaug's dream fulfilled – a world free of hunger*'.

But this apparently easy solution has to be set against the considerable, often unpredictable dangers that will inevitably arise from the cultivation of GM crops: damage to animal species higher up the food chain (including ourselves), the creation of resistant 'super weeds', and crossing with the irreplaceable wild crop relatives and ancient cultivars needed by plant breeders. The debate still rages.

HEALTH AND PLANTS - WHAT ELSE TO TURN TO?

Plants & Us

1.poppy 2. henbane 3. mandrake 4. nutmeg 5. pepper 6.clove 7. pomegranate 8. castor 9. aloe 10. sienna 11. fig 12. willow 13. garlic 14. juniper 15. corianader 16. elecampane 17. flax 18. quinquina 19. kelp 20.wych hazel 21. pine 22. blue gum 23. opium poppy 24. meadowsweet 25. evening primrose 26. licorice 27. camphor 28. crocus 29. rhubarb 30. senna 31. white psyillium 32. cascara 33. periwinkle 34. coca 35. snakeroot 36. curare 37. foxglove

For thousands, perhaps hundreds of thousands of years, people have turned to plants to relieve their ailments – and for good reasons. Where else were they to look for cures and alleviation of pain? Indeed, plants provided the only form of medical solutions available until the last couple of hundred years.

The oldest written evidence of the use of plants for obtaining medicines, curatives and drugs dates from around 5,000 years ago on a Sumerian clay slab. It suggested twelve recipes for healing and listed 250 plants, including **Poppy**, **Henbane** and **Mandrake** – interestingly, all of them capable of alleviating pain.

The Chinese Emperor Shen Nung, reputedly the inventor of tea drinking, wrote a treatise on medicinal plants in 2,500 BC, listing 365 drugs which could be made from from them, many still used today. The scholars of ancient India, too, cited a large number of medicinal plants, and those such as **Nutmeg**, **Pepper** and **Clove** remain familiar to us. Moreover, in ancient Egypt, the **Ebers Papyrus** (written in 1,550 BC, listed no less than 800 prescriptions derived from 700 plants, including **Pomegranate** (Page 31) and **Castor oil** (Page 27) as well as **Aloe**, **Sienna**, **Garlic**, **Onion**, **Fig**, **Willow**, **Coriander** and **Juniper**.

Homer's Iliad and Odyssey refer to 63 plants used in Minoan, Mycenaean and Egyptian or Assyrian society, and one of them, **Elecampane** (*Inula helenium*) is actually named after Helen of Troy. Plants from the genus *Artemisia* are all related to the Greek word '*artemis*', meaning 'safe and sound'. The historian Herodotus and the famous philosopher Pythagoras also wrote about medicinal plants, as did Hippocrates of Kos (from whom we get the traditional 'Hippocratic Oath'), while Theophrastus (371–287 BC), a colleague of Aristotle and often called 'The Father of Botany', effectively founded botanical science with his two surviving books classifying 500 plants, many of them with medicinal uses.

Travelling with Emperor Nero's Roman army in the 1st century, Pedanios Dioscorides studied plants wherever he went and wrote *De Materia Medica*, referring to 944 drugs derived from 657 plants. Pliny the Elder (23–79 AD), who was able to travel to Germany and Spain, went even further and looked at over 1,000 medicinal plants in his book *Historia Naturalis*. Later, Claudius Galen, physician to three Roman Emperors, also added several more uses of plant therapy.

After the collapse of the Roman Empire, it fell to Christian monasteries to provide therapies and cures from plants, all of which the monks grew and made use of within their walls. Charlemagne (742–814 AD), the Holy Roman Emperor, who founded the Salerno medical school, ordered that medical plants be grown on state lands throughout his Empire. He especially recommended **Sage** (*Salvia officinalis*), called the 'salvation plant' from the old Latin word '*salvare*' or cure. Interestingly, Catholic monasteries are still compelled to grow it, and few modern gardeners don't have it in their herb beds, though for culinary reasons.

During the Middle Ages, the Arabs introduced yet more plants for medical use, benefitting from their trade with India and elsewhere. Andalusian botanist and pharmacologist Ibn al-Baitar (1197–1248) travelled widely in the Islamic countries of the Mediterranean and described over 1,000 plants of medicinal value, and many European writers were influenced by such Islamic studies.

From 1492, expanding European exploration became an important source of medicinal plants, linked as it was to the needs of the spice trade. Vasco da Gama, Albuquerque and other adventurers travelling to India, and the Spanish and Portuguese opening up of the Americas, all brought new and useful plants, the Portuguese in particular taking plants such as chilli peppers from the Americas to Africa, and thence to India. Tropical medicines like the **Quinquina** bark (*Cinchona*), which helped to eliminate the terrible scourge of malaria caused by mosquito bites (page 17), would eventually transform the treatment of that devastating worldwide illness.

18.

The early 19th century was a turning point, with the extraction and use of the newly discovered compounds such as plant alkaloids and glycosides, the beginnings of laboratory synthesis of plant drugs and the rise of the modern pharmaceutical industry. But many pure plant-based medicines are still being dispensed.

Here are some of the most influential medical uses of plants.

DRESSING THE WOUNDS

The most obvious outward signs that something is wrong with our bodies are exposed, open, bleeding wounds – anything from an accidental cut finger to a really serious gash or wounds in battle. **Cotton** is perfect for absorbing blood from a wound, often supplemented by various antiseptic dressings derived from pine or eucalyptus. **Sphagnum Moss** (page 9), with twice the absorption of cotton, was used to dress wounds, especially in the two World Wars. Bandages, too, are made from cotton, while 'lint' bandages are named after *linteus* or linen, referring to it being made from fibres of **Flax** (*Linum usitassimum*). Dressings from cloth impregnated with charcoal or alginates from **Seaweeds** (page 118) actively help wounds to heal. But, of course, it's no good covering up a wound without stopping infection.

KEEPING OUT THE GERMS

It took a long time for the 'modern' medical profession to understand germs and realise how bodies could be infected, or re-infected. In the 1860s James Simpson and then Joseph Lister, were appalled by death rates from post-operative infection which they noted were no less than a horrifying 50% in surgeries, but only 11% at home. Lister decided to follow Pasteur's theory that unseen bacteria were doing the killing in hospitals – which had no sterilization or disinfectant, and with some surgeons wearing their filthy, blood-encrusted aprons for months as a 'badge of honour'. In 1865, Lister decided to wash the wound of a post-surgery patient with cotton soaked in carbolic acid, a derivative of **Coal Tar**, derived from ancient plants. His patient, and then several others, recovered and his amputation mortality rate immediately dropped from 50% to 15% (page33).

Plants & Us

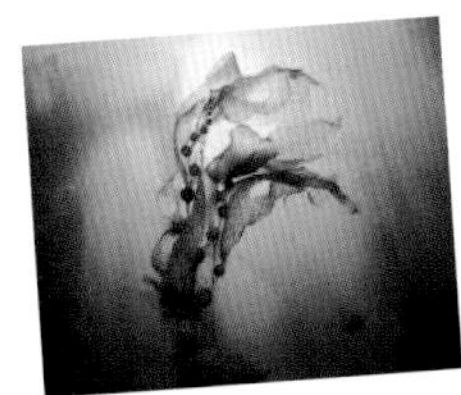

The next great innovation was the first antibiotic, derived from the mould Penicillin, famously discovered by chance by Alexander Fleming, but developed by Howard Florey and Boris Chain (page 40).

But long before such modern breakthroughs, over thousands of years our ancestors had learned to use plants to both offset or fight infection. Seaweeds like **Kelp** (*Laminaria*) yielded antiseptic iodine. **Wych Hazel** (*Hamamelis virginiana*) prevented inflammation and controlled bleeding, especially when combined with **Pine** (*Pinus*) oil. Pine Tar was found to protect the hooves of farm animals. **Tasmanian Blue Gum** (*Eucalytus globulus*) provides both oils and pastilles to counter throat infections, also treated with **Liquorice** (*Glycyrrhiza glabra*), **Ipecacuanha** (*Cephaelis ipecacuanha*) and **Camphor** (*Cinnamomum camphora*).

20.

22.

Nowadays we associate **Garlic** (*Allium sativum*) with food and cooking. But for centuries the chemical allicin, both antiseptic and anti-inflammatory and the origin of the garlic smell, has been used to counter colds, flu, chest congestion, and tonsil and sinus problems, whooping cough and bronchitis. Other *Allium* species – onions, leeks and chives have also traditionally been used to fight infection.

26.

27.

STOPPING IT HURTING

In the struggle to alleviate pain, **White Willow** (*Salix alba*) has a long history. Infusions of the bark were being used as far back as the time of Christ to treat toothache, earache and headache, as well as the pain from gout and rheumatism. By 1827, its active ingredient salicin was isolated, and it was then found that **Meadowsweet** (*Filipendula ulmaria*) naturally produced the related salicylic acid. When this was combined with acetic acid, it gave us the benefit of Aspirin, now the most popular pain-killer in the world.

24.

23.

The latex of the **Opium Poppy** (*Papaver somniferum*) yields the greatest natural pain-killer, Morphine, and its rather weaker cousin, Codeine (page 51). Morphine was isolated in 1804 and was widely used in the American Civil War, leading to widespread addiction among veterans. A by-product was heroin, incredibly sold in America until 1917 across the counter as a cough suppressant, before the danger of addiction was recognized.

25.

Millions of people suffer from permanent pain, notably arthritis, and that has been helped by the oil of **Evening Primrose** (*Oenothera biennis*) which has been found to counter many ailments. The sudden and very painful form

28.

29.

30.

31.

32.

of arthritis, gout, has also been alleviated by **Autumn Crocus** (*Colchicum autumnale*).

One of our rather routine and common needs is for laxatives. 5,000 years ago, the Chinese turned to **Rhubarb** (*Rheum palmatum* and hybrids), **Senna** (*Cassia senna*) and **Castor Oi**l (*Ricinus communis*). Still in use, these have been joined by **White Psyllium** (*Plantago ovata*), a plantain originally from SE Asia, and **Cascara Buckthorn** (*Rhamnus purshiana*), a small tree from western North America.

ELIMINATING THE AGONY

34.

The fear and horror of being operated on when awake was not really erased until the discovery in the 1850s of anaesthetic gases like ether or chloroform, and then more recently, chemical anaesthetics.

But plants did much to change this. The **Coca bush** (*Erythroxylum coca*) has given us the social drug cocaine and all sorts of problems. (page 67). But cocaine's ability to deaden nerve endings has proved a vital local anaesthetic for dental, ear, nose and throat surgery and especially for eye operations.

36.

In the right quantities, curare from the tropical **Curare** obtained from the *Chondrodendron tomentosum* vine, otherwise known as a deadly paralyzing poison in Central and South America (page 76), has found its place as an important muscle relaxant during surgery, for which many of us have reason to be grateful.

37.

AVOIDING THE HOSPITAL

33.

Of course, the best thing for all of us is to try never to go near a hospital. And many plants continue to help us with that aim. In spite of being dangerous in large quantities, **Grecian Foxglove** (*Digitalis lanata*) slows the heartbeat and **Rosy Periwinkle** (*Catharanthus roseus*) from Madagascar has proved to be a vital anti-cancer drug. Its alkaloid, vinblastine, is used against many cancers, vastly reducing the threat of Hodgkin's disease and also achieving a remarkable 90% remission rate for children with leukaemia. **Snake Root**(*Rauvolfia serpentina*) and **African Snake Root** (*Rauvolfia vomitoria*), are now recognized to reduce another potential killer, high blood pressure.

35.

Plants, either on their own, or refined into similar chemicals, alkaloids and glycosides, have never lost their importance in medicine, and with many plants not yet even discovered, let alone researched – they will continue to do so. There is little doubt that future generations, researching plants, will look back and bemoan our ignorance.

Meanwhile, are you taking any medicine? There's a strong chance you have plants to thank for it!

CASTOR OIL - ITS USES AND MISUSES

H*ere, your Castor* **Oil!** – words dreaded by post-war children whose parents thought their digestions needed a nudge. They were referring to the unpalatable, yet safe and efficient laxative, the most famous product of the Castor Oil Plant, one of 7,000 Spurges family species, which include rubber and cassava trees. The Latin name of the **Castor Oil Plant** (*Ricinus communis*) has, ironically, a sinister ring, considering it was used in one of the most infamous and public Communist assassinations. The active component that makes castor oil work as a laxative is ricinoleic acid, a fatty acid that binds to muscle cell receptors on the wall of the large intestine. However, much-maligned castor oil has many important industrial applications, but in unscrupulous hands has served more sinister purposes.

The Castor Oil plant is a semi-evergreen shrub up to five metres tall, with stalked, deeply cut, green, purplish or bronze leaves. The large untidy greenish clusters of flowers give rise to egg-shaped, spiny red fruits that split when ripe. The seeds, each looking like a beetle or tick, are up to 15 mm long and marbled grey and brown. An impressive sight when growing in groups, the plant is a weed of roadsides, waste ground, dry water-courses and rubbish tips in countries with a tropical or Mediterranean climate.

One of the most ancient of crops, it originally came from tropical Africa. The Castor Oil plant was native to the tropical south of Egypt, from where the ancient Egyptians introduced it into cultivation in c.4,000 BC. Ancient Greek historian Herodotus described the Egyptians growing the plants on the banks of water-courses and lakes in the Nile Delta. The oil was used as a lamp fuel, but one of the oldest surviving medical texts, a papyrus of 1,552 BC from Thebes (modern Luxor) in Egypt, describes the plant's numerous medicinal uses, including its role as a laxative.

Today over two million tons of Castor Oil are produced annually, mostly in India, China and Mozambique. Extracted by crushing the seeds, the oil not only provides the well-known laxative, but is also used in soaps, cosmetics, perfumes, paints, dyes, inks, waxes and varnishes. In addition, it goes into animal feeds, food preservatives, additives and flavourings, and is added to a number of medicinal drugs. During World War I, it was a high-quality lubricant in rotary engines of Allied aircraft, allowing them to perform better than equivalent German ones, and it's still used as a model aircraft engine lubricant.

However, the seed pulp also contains deadly poisons, notably ricin. Colourless and odourless, it's even more poisonous than cyanide. In 1978, Bulgarian Communist agents infamously employed ricin, injected in a tiny pellet via the hollow, pointed tip of an umbrella, to assassinate dissident writer Giorgi Markov at a London bus stop. More recently, Islamic extremist terrorists have been arrested in London in possession of ricin, but thankfully it's not an easy or effective chemical weapon, as it needs to

enter the bloodstream.

Nor is Mother's favourite medicine itself without its dark side. A 'dose of castor oil' may be a silly joke in Britain and elsewhere, but in Italy 'usare l'olio di ricino' has a distinctly sinister connotation. Mussolini's Fascist Blackshirts would administer both a beating and a force-fed dose of castor oil to political dissidents in order to humiliate them by unleashing the consequences of too much laxative – so in Italy the very mention of castor oil in a political context still conveys a sharp satirical message.

HENBANE AND TOOTHACHE

Anyone who has suffered from painful or persistent toothache will know why **Henbane** (*Hyoscyamus niger*) was such a popular plant from the Middle Ages when its apparently miraculous ability to relieve dental pain was utilized. A plant that is not so much unattractive as sinister in appearance (plus offputtingly malodorous), and poisonous if not handled carefully, it was considered an absolute blessing for anyone with persistent dental pain, avoiding or at least delaying the need for extraction.

Curiously, teeth were in many ways in better condition in the Middle Ages than today, almost entirely due to the fact that sugar was so rare and expensive (page 48). Most people used natural sweeteners as in fruits and honey and had a diet high in vegetables and cereals – almost what a dentist would recommend now. But that did not remove the need for Henbane, which was grown nearly everywhere where humans lived. You can see it even today persisting around old ruins. Although it may have long remained revered, nowadays its pain relieving properties are largely forgotten.

But the plant was not called 'Henbane' for nothing. Bane in Old English means 'death' and the seeds were said to poison

hens and many other animals. And there was another sinister connection. The alkaloid hyoscine, derived from this plant, was what Doctor Crippen, a homeopath who knew all about plant poisons, used in London in 1910 to kill his wife Cora. All of Henbane's parts are highly toxic, especially its leaves, and even smelling the fresh ones is known to cause giddiness and stupor. An overdose (as poor Cora was given) would lead to a dry mouth, dilated pupils, blurred vision and drowsiness, followed by hallucinations, convulsions and finally death. In small doses, these effects on the central nervous system had made Henbane both a painkiller and hallucinogen since Antiquity.

Crippen tried to escape with his mistress back to his native America on the SS *Montrose*, but was famously caught out when the suspicious ship's captain ordered that a wireless message be sent to London – the first one ever used to catch a criminal – and the pair were arrested by Detective Chief Inspector Walter Dew, who had crossed the Atlantic in a faster ship and boarded from the pilot's boat as the *Montrose* arrived in Canada.

It is not surprising that there is a waxwork of Crippen in Madame Tussaud's Chamber of Horrors in London.

Henbane is maybe not well known outside the world of botanists, but 'Dr Crippen' is a byword for a notorious and wicked murderer.

COAL TAR AND INFECTION

In the middle of the 19th century, far too often the surgeon's report ended, 'operation successful, but the patient died'. In hospitals and on the operating table the potential cure was often much more dangerous than the problem. Indeed, surgery itself was a terrible ordeal before anaesthetics (page 30). What is more, the after-effects of surgery could, and did, kill patients in huge numbers. British surgeon James Simpson was appalled that the mortality rate in British hospitals was over 40% and in France 60%, protesting that: '*a man laid on an operating theatre in one of our surgical hospitals is exposed to more chance of death than was an English soldier at Waterloo*'.

Simpson also noticed that while surgery in British hospitals was killing 40%, the figure was only 11% for surgery at home. Pioneers like Ignaz Semmelweis in Austria and Louis Pasteur in France were drawing the same conclusion – hospitals themselves were inadvertently to blame. Surgeons would arrive from the morgue or other operations without washing their hands 'to save time', and also dressed in contaminated clothes. A surgeon's frock coat was his insignia of office, acquiring a crust of dirt and dried blood of which its owner was fiercely proud! Patients were lucky if surgical instruments had even been washed in soapy water.

There were many theories about the mysterious but devastating death rate after surgery. In 1839, the chemist Justin von Liebig had asserted that sepsis was a kind of combustion caused by exposing moist body tissue to oxygen. It was therefore considered that the best prevention was to keep air away from wounds with plasters, cotton or resins.

Other ideas were frustratingly more vague. Perhaps 'miasma' or bad air was responsible for 'hospital disease'? Could opening the windows cure the problem, as Florence Nightingale had urged? Louis Pasteur came closer to the truth in 1865 - considering the presence of tiny organisms in the air. He suggested three ways to avoid

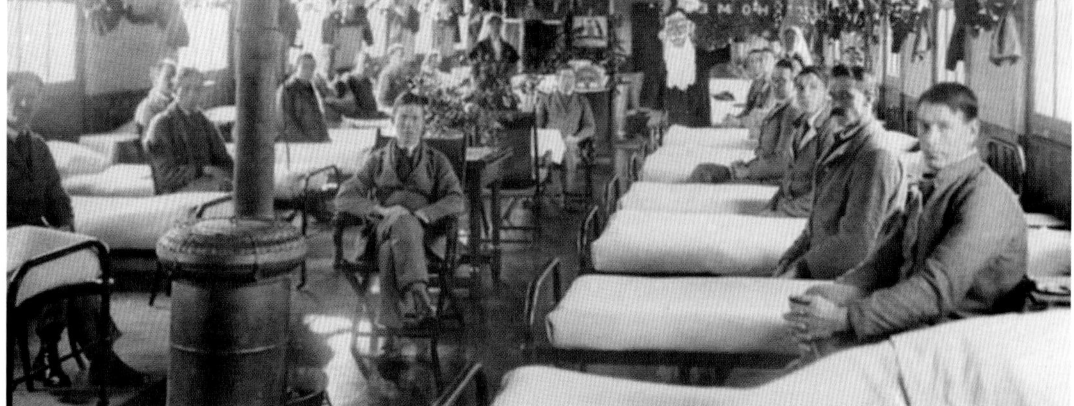

their ill effects; filtration, exposure to heat and exposure to chemical solutions. Only the last was appropriate for direct application to human tissue.

Joseph Lister, faced by a 50% death rate post surgery in his brand new Glasgow hospital, read Pasteur's paper with great interest and decided to experiment himself. He was well-placed to follow up such theories. The son of a prominent physicist, he was fluent in French and German, then the languages of medical research, and in the previous year he had heard that 'carbolic acid', the German innovation derived from **Coal Tar** (page 33), a product of fossil plants, was being used to treat sewage in Carlisle.

In 1865, a patient with a compound fracture of the thigh was admitted. Instead of virtually dooming him by amputation or allowing the usual infection to develop on the broken skin, Lister treated the wound with cotton soaked in carbolic acid. The man soon left fully recovered, as did a young boy a few weeks later. Lister then published the results in *The Lancet*. Amputation mortality rates in his ward now dropped dramatically from the usual 50% to 15%.

He also made surgeons wear clean gloves and wash their hands before and after operations with 5% carbolic acid solutions. Instruments were also washed in the same solution, and assistants sprayed it in the operating theatre.

At the outbreak of the Franco-Prussian war, Lister, an intensely religious man, tried to warn both sides of the dangers of sepsis to the wounded, and ways to avoid it. He even helpfully produced a pamphlet for the French. Either it did not reach them or they ignored it, because losses were horrendous. Indeed, the mortality rate after amputations performed by French military surgeons was a horrifying 75% or more, even after minor amputations, such as fingers and toes.

By contrast, the Prussians *did* listen and their losses were far lower. Lister later made a triumphant tour of leading surgical centres in Germany where he was duly feted for his life-saving advice.

However, as with so many medical innovations and improvements, there was real opposition to his methods. The British medical fraternity took years to accept them. While foreign hospitals benefited, London still regarded him – like William Jenner, who had eliminated smallpox – as a 'provincial'. And this was even after he had saved Queen Victoria's life when she was threatened by an abscess.

On visiting America, only New York and Boston received him with enthusiasm. The trouble was that surgeons wanted to wait for clear proof that antisepsis was a major advance. Lister knew that before his work would be generally accepted he must first convince London.

PLANTS AND THERAPY

Most of us would readily agree that visiting a beautiful garden can be uplifting and therapeutic, particularly if we have no outside space at home. But it was a very long time before our public gardens were obliged to make their facilities more accessible and enjoyable for the disabled.

Anyone who has ever been confined to a wheelchair or had to push one over an uneven ground, a rocky path or even damp grass will immediately recognise the importance of this and regret that changes were not made sooner.

In fact, it was not until the late 20th century in England that The Disabled Persons Act at last obliged all public gardens to provide proper facilities for the disabled and adapt their layouts to their needs. Kew Gardens, for example, offers free parking for the disabled, free wheelchairs at all entrances and an enlarged map for those with failing sight.

Thankfully, public gardens all over the world have now been adapted for disabled visitors, even when not legally obliged to do so. Others have gone further. In Chenai, India, there is an inspiring 'touch and smell' garden specially designed for blind children. In the United States, there is the American Horticultural Therapy Association which uses plants and gardens to help all kinds of mental and physical conditions, as does a similar organisation in Australia.

Another heartening example of helping disadvantaged people to enjoy the benefits of gardens is the work of the British Horticultural therapy charity called Thrive. This was established more than 40 years ago to bridge the worlds of health and horticulture and today is the UK leader in social and therapeutic horticulture. Hundreds of people attend its therapeutic gardening programmes which are run at Thrive centres in Berkshire, Birmingham and London, and also online. In social and therapeutic horticulture (STH), plants and gardens are used to develop wellbeing, with 'client gardeners' working with Thrive's trained therapists to pursue physical and mental health goals. The non-threatening and restorative environment of a garden is a place where social skills and connections can be made too, while gardening activities can promote learning and the acquisition of new skills. The sheer range of gardening tasks and their ability to be adapted means therapeutic horticulture is very flexible and can meet many needs. Children can enjoy gardening-themed programmes leading to horticultural qualifications now offered for those with special educational needs and all kinds of disabilities.

People who attend have a wide range of conditions, from learning disabilities and autism to sight loss and multiple sclerosis, and also those with mental health issues, who are looking to enter or return to employment.

In the United States, The American Horticultural Therapy Association (AHTA) has played a similar role since 1973 and is the leading voice devoted to promoting the profession of Horticultural Therapy. A long-recognized rehabilitation method, this integrates the growing and caring for plants with human health services.

Scientific-based research has shown that horticultural therapy can provide physical, cognitive, social, and psychological benefits, first realized while treating WWII veterans. Since then, horticultural therapy has been embraced by a wide variety of US medical, vocational, and rehabilitation programmes. Each year the AHTA hosts an international conference for its members, where the latest developments in the field are presented.

Highly trained horticultural therapy practitioners provide services to clients with a wide range of physical, cognitive and sensory disabilities and of all ages. Specifically-chosen horticulture activities assist participants to achieve therapeutic goals. For example, horticultural therapists can help a garden-based group with social contact or can facilitate a pruning activity to restore a range of motion and physical wellness.

Activities take place both outdoors and indoors, in settings ranging from hospital gardens to nursing home activity rooms, as well as in farm fields and greenhouses. For instance, many people have probably enjoyed exploring the plants in a sensory garden with flowers chosen for their scents, not knowing it was created by a horticultural therapist for their work with the visually impaired.

In both Britain and America, great progress has been made to use plants to help those whose impaired abilities have made them feel isolated and vulnerable. Connection with growing things clearly has major benefits.

FROM WILDFLOWER MEADOWS TO HOMEOPATHY

Since ancient times doctors have relied on medicines derived from plants. Some of these still have a role in modern medicine, while others are widely employed by the public as herbal medicines. Recent years have seen a rise in interest in 'Alternative' or 'Complementary' Medicine, including knowledge of plant medicine from India, China and elsewhere. And in Europe, as well as traditional herbal medicine, for over 200 years orthodox medicine has been complemented by another system, one that is largely plant-based – Homeopathy.

The story begins in 1777 when two men called Samuel met in Vienna. Samuel Hahnemann (1755–1843) (above) from Germany had started his medical training in Leipzig and was a scientific scholar and linguist. Samuel von Brukenthal (1721–1803) had just been appointed Governor of Transylvania in what was then Hungary. Austrian Empress Maria Theresa's own physician encouraged and helped Hahnemann and introduced him to Brukenthal, who, clearly impressed, invited the younger man to his palace in Hermannstadt (now Sibiu, Romania) in Transylvania to be his librarian and physician. Hahnemann stayed for two years before returning to Germany. Alongside his official duties, he was able to practise medicine in the city and is said to have learned much from a Transylvanian treatise on herbal cures. The wildflower meadows of Transylvania are even today a riot of floral variety and colour, including many medicinal plants like wild sages and scabious, and a plant-healing tradition going back to the region's ancient Dacian inhabitants.

Back in Germany, Hahnemann finished his medical studies. Increasingly unhappy with conventional medicine, he earned a living by translating medical textbooks while continuing his reading and research. He had read about cinchona bark, which contains the malarial remedy quinine (page17), and gave himself doses that resulted in mild intermittent fever, a symptom of malaria, a malady he knew from the marshy lands around Hermannstadt. He deduced that a remedy which can produce symptoms of illness in a healthy person will cure the same symptoms in a sick one. He thus proposed – as had Hippocrates in ancient Greece – that '*Similia similibus curenter*' or '*Let likes be cured by likes*', was the very guiding principle of all homoeopathy (Greek: *homoios*, similar).

Revolutionary by 18th century standards, Hahnemann wanted to give patients - not to mention his own eleven children - gentler treatment than the purgatives, leeches, bleeding, opium and toxins like lead or mercury that were then

Plants & Us

the mainstay of European medicine. He combined homeopathic remedies with exercise, fresh air and healthy food, in a regime we would now call holistic medicine. The process of preparing the remedies – from plants but also from animals, minerals and microbes – remains essentially the same today. The material is repeatedly diluted and vigorously shaken, a process known as 'potentization', in water, sugar solution or alcohol. Extreme dilutions may contain just a few molecules or even none of the original substance – preventing any toxicity or side effects but an anomaly frequently employed as a principal argument against the whole practice, in that the end product may be so diluted as to be indistinguishable from the diluent. However, some homeopathic remedies, from plants such as **Calendula** or **Pot Marigold** (*Calendula officinalis*) and **Arnica** (*Arnica montana*), contain pharmacologically active doses as in conventional herbal medicine.

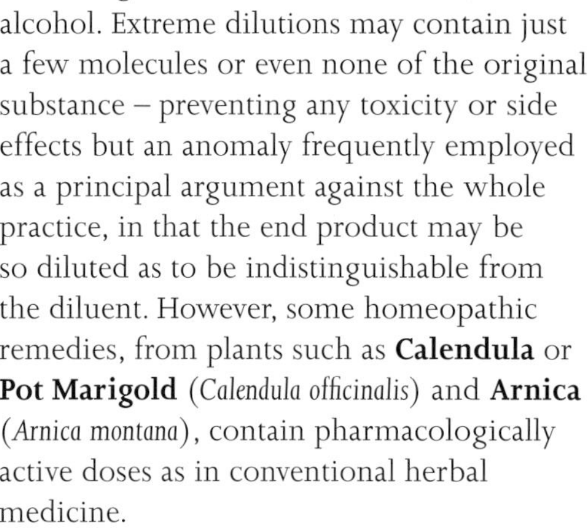

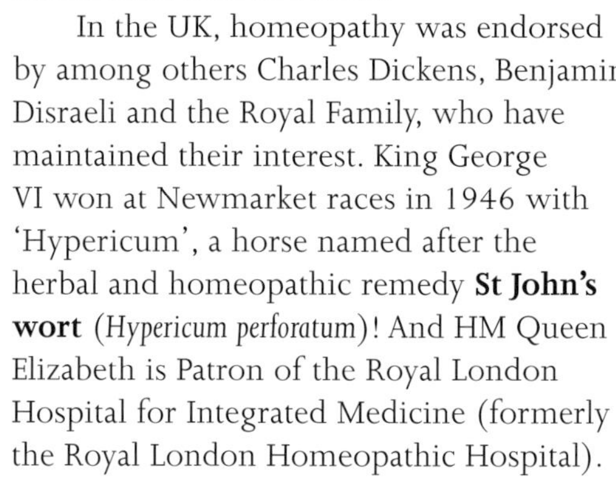

In 1796 Hahnemann summarised his ideas in a paper which he would expand into a book, *Organon of Rational Healing* (1810). He revived his medical practice, attracted numerous patients and even briefly and unsuccessfully became a professor. But, opposed and harried by the pharmacists (he made his own remedies, not theirs!) and the German medical establishment, he had to move around the country, eventually leaving in 1835 for Paris, where he died a rich celebrity.

By then homeopathy had spread across Europe and in 1825 one of Hahnemann's students took it to the USA, where it was favoured by many eminent people, not least oil magnate John D. Rockefeller (below), influential *New York Tribune* Editor Horace Greeley (he of 'Go West young man') and writers such as Louisa May Alcott, Henry Longfellow and Mark Twain. The latter drily observed, '*The introduction of homeopathy forced the old school doctor to stir around and learn something of a rational nature about his business.*'

In the UK, homeopathy was endorsed by among others Charles Dickens, Benjamin Disraeli and the Royal Family, who have maintained their interest. King George VI won at Newmarket races in 1946 with 'Hypericum', a horse named after the herbal and homeopathic remedy **St John's wort** (*Hypericum perforatum*)! And HM Queen Elizabeth is Patron of the Royal London Hospital for Integrated Medicine (formerly the Royal London Homeopathic Hospital).

Homeopathy remains a significant element of complementary medicine, despite much determined opposition from the medical establishment, especially in America. In the UK some 1,000 doctors practise homeopathy (as do some vets); in France and Germany it is 10,000. The US market in self-administered homeopathic remedies is worth $3 billion a year.

This curious 'pseudo-science' remains controversial, but clearly works for some, as well as nicely illustrating how plants interact with people and their lives. We are clearly inter-dependent.

PLANTS AND CONTRACEPTION

Most people probably think of contraception as a modern development and immediately associate it with the arrival of 'The Pill'.

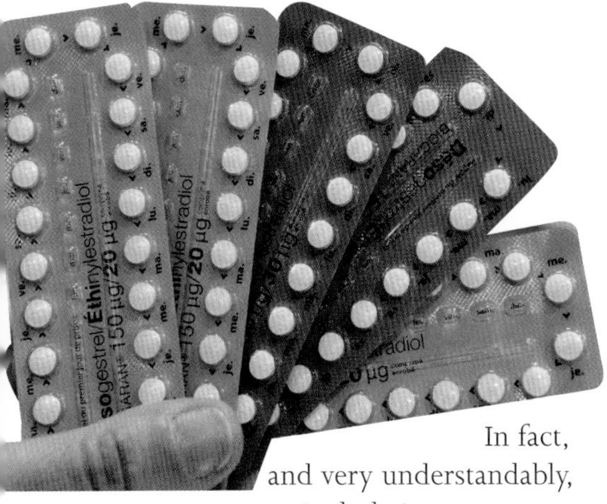

In fact, and very understandably, particularly in poorer regions, the practice goes back to antiquity.

In ancient Mesopotamia and Egypt, plants played their role with the vagina blocked with acacia leaves, honey and lint. More bizarre methods included blocking the cervix with pessary rings made of crocodile dung. (Contraception may have been achieved with men running a mile!) The frantic desire for a contraceptive plant in Greece led to the complete extinction of the rare giant fennel called **Silphium**, which only grew in one tiny part of today's Libya. Other plants used were **Queen Anne's Lace** (*Daucus carota*), **Willow**, **Date palm**, **Pomegranate**, **Artemisia**, **Myrrh and Rue**. Aristotle recommended **Cedar oil**, but that only worked by gumming things up a bit! Most Roman techniques were ineffective.

In early Islamic times, we find mention of pessaries made of **cabbages** and once again of dung – this time of elephants. (It's amazing that men and women wanted to get together at all!) In Asia, potions of **Palm** leaf were tried, and pessaries of the seeds of the **Palasa** tree. In Catholic Europe, contraception was regarded as immoral and illegal, although women used **Lily** root and **Rue** inserted in the vagina. The Catholic Church in its 'Witch-Bull' edict of 1485 even labelled any women helping either with abortion or contraception as witches, with the Inquisition authorized to hunt them down.

In the modern western world,

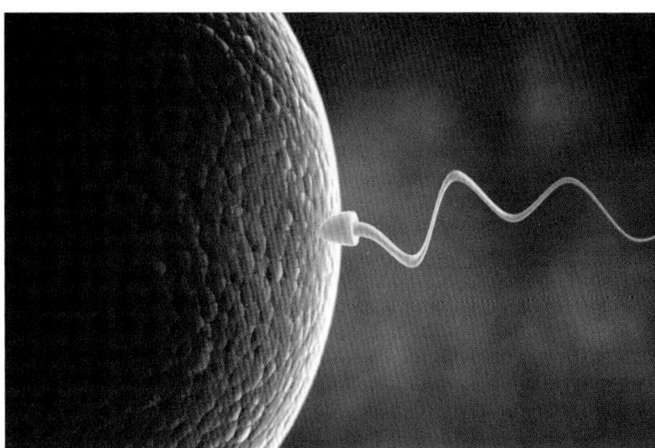

contraception began to rely on the 'mechanical' means of preventing the sperm reaching the egg – the condom and the cervical cap. But they did not always work. In many parts of the world, plants continue to play a role. **Acacia**, **Pine**, **Pomegranate**, **Date palm**, **Willow**, **Queen Anne's Lace**, **Blue Cohosh**, **Pennyroyal**, **Neem**, **Stoneseed**, **Ginger**, **Apricot** kernels and **Juniper** berries

are all still used. Indeed, there may be no less than 4,000 plants containing anti-fertility compounds. But there would be one plant that became the real heroine for women who did not want to conceive. It is now impossible for young people to imagine the agony of millions of unmarried women thinking they might be pregnant. Public shame was instilled, dangerous abortions were carried out, together with forced adoptions, doomed 'shotgun marriages', and the shame of being a single mother with a 'bastard' child.

The plant that rescued them was a **Mexican wild yam,** or **Barbasco** (*Dioscorea mexicana*), a climbing forest vine with an enormous tuber, heart-shaped leaves and small greenish flowers. It was from a natural

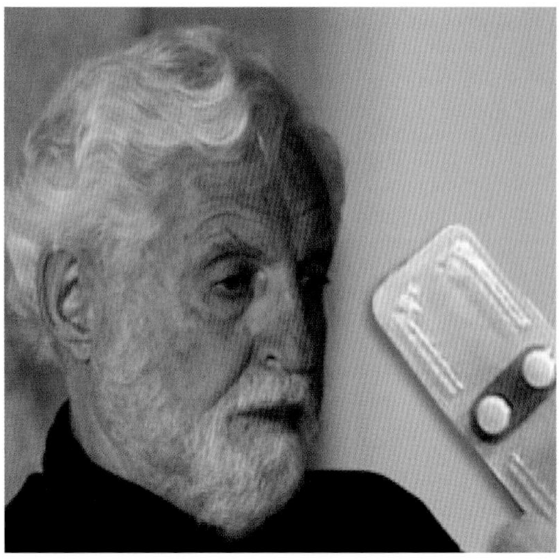

plant oestrogen, diosgenin, in the tuber that the chemist Dr Carl Djerassi (above), supported by the American birth control pioneer Margaret Sanger, synthesized norethindrone. This mimics how hormones work in a woman's body, tricks it into thinking it is already pregnant and stops the release of new eggs. Thus was born 'The Pill', which swept the world. Britain's National Health Service prescribed it in 1961, just in time for, and no doubt promoting, the 'swinging sixties'.

While Carl Djerassi was honoured all over the world, and men and women are eternally grateful, there are two downsides to this apparent miracle. First, oestrogen in the 'pill' goes through to water supplies and reduces male fertility. Secondly, birth-rates in developed countries are falling far too far. This may mean ageing populations, shrinking cities, pension crises, healthcare problems and weakened economies.

It would be a great pity if a problem solved after millennia leads to even more in the future.

A MOULD AND BLOOD POISONING

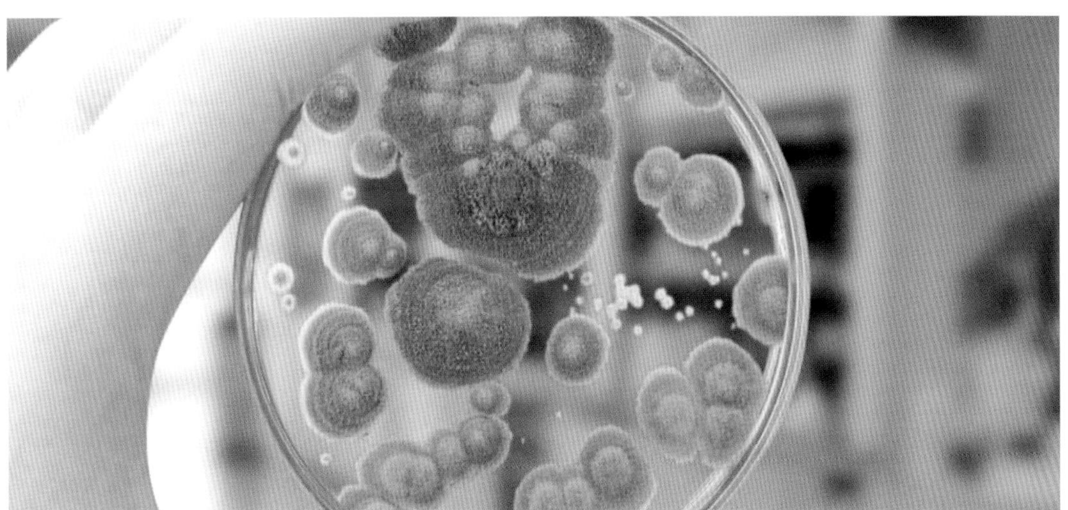

It could be argued that moulds are not plants – just as mosses and fungi, like truffles, might not be regarded strictly as plants. But we think one mould, called penicillin is so important to human society that we might bend the definition.

Today we take antibiotics largely for granted. They havc made our lives infinitely less dangerous and much of the expansion of our whole giant pharmaceutical industry stems from one discovery, the 'wonder drug', penicillin. It is a sobering thought that many of us might not even be here but for its existence, because our parents or grandparents could easily have died from something as trivial as a cut finger, which, if it became infected, could lead to sometimes fatal septicaemia, or 'blood poisoning'.

Most of us know the name of the man who discovered penicillin – because of a legendary event. Professor Alexander Fleming was later to say, '*When I woke up just after dawn on September 28, 1928, I certainly didn't plan to revolutionise all medicine by discovering the world's first antibiotic, or bacteria killer. But I suppose that was exactly what I did*'.

Fleming, a brilliant but somewhat untidy scientist, returned from holiday to discover that one of his petri dishes containing *Staphylococci* had been left open and was contaminated by a blue-grey mould, *Penicillium notatum*, and that it had destroyed the nearest bacteria. He experimented with his 'mould juice', eventually calling it 'Penicillin'. However, while finding that it could affect the bacteria causing scarlet fever, pneumonia, meningitis, diphtheria and gonorrhoea, Fleming realised that cultivating penicillin would be very difficult, and felt it might not last long enough in the human body to work. Thus, he gave up on it and moved on to other projects. Later, when famous, he was modest about 'the Fleming Myth' and went on to praise the two men who were then to transform his laboratory curiosity into a practical drug.

These two worked at Oxford University – Howard Florey and Ernst Chain. Raised in Adelaide, Florey was later described by his Prime Minister as '*the most important man born in Australia*'. Ernst Chain was

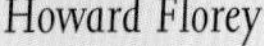
Howard Florey

Alexander Fleming

Ernst Chain

one of those Germans who fortuitously escaped Hitler's anti-Jewish persecution and would join England's war effort. With war looming, Florey and Chain managed to isolate penicillin and produce it in small quantities, at first using a bizarre array of culture vessels, including chamber pots, baths and milk churns, soon succeeding in protecting mice against dreaded *streptococci*. They then managed to save the life of a small child. However, treating a policeman who, while gardening, had been scratched by a rose thorn, after great improvement to his huge abscesses and swollen face, they ran out of the precious penicillin and he relapsed and died. Sadly, with tiny quantities to work with, only children could be treated.

They realized that to protect against the impending masses of war wounds, penicillin would now have to be produced in huge quantities. The overstretched British chemical companies could play a part, but they would have to turn to the still-peaceful United States. Florey arrived in October 1941 for meetings with the drug companies Merck, Squibb, Lilly and Pfizer. However, they were unresponsive. But then everything suddenly changed. His second meetings in that December were galvanized overnight by the Japanese attack on Pearl Harbor eight days before. Now, faced by war, there was real urgency for the drug, but it was not going to be easy to produce enough of it. As one American put it, '*the mould is as temperamental as an opera singer, the extraction is murder, the purification invites disaster and the assay is unsatisfactory*'.

However, moulds discovered on a rotting cantaloupe melon doubled the yield, then corn steep liquid improved this by nearly twenty times. By 1943, 21 billion units of penicillin were mass-produced, jumping to 1,663 billion the next year – just in time for D-Day. By 1945, when Fleming, Florey and Chain were awarded the Nobel Prize for their penicillin efforts, there was at last enough for civilian use.

Penicillin, with its derivatives, has proved to be one of the most important drugs ever created, estimated to have saved hundreds of millions, although because of resistant organisms, it is not used much now. While we all owe an immense debt to that chance discovery by Fleming, it was the dedicated work by the far less well-known Florey and Chain that really made it possible. Their names should be more familiar.

PLANTS AS VILLAINS

THE RYE OF SALEM AND ERGOT

How many of us haven't heard of 'The Witches of Salem', one of the most vicious examples of murderous panic in American history?

In 1792, in the small village of Salem, Massachusetts, two young girls started to behave most strangely. Abigail Williams and Elizabeth Parris were suffering fits, arching their bodies, thrashing violently and screaming out nonsense. As their condition became more inexplicable, the town was murmuring that supernatural powers were at work. It seemed to this very religious community that somebody or something was affecting them – probably witches working for the Devil.

The first accusations soon came, and the finger was pointed at Sarah Good and Sarah Osborne, two old women, and Tituba, a Caribbean slave. But the problem did not go away; more young girls were beginning to be afflicted. It was assumed that there must be others around who were in league with Satan, and more witches would have to be found. Trials duly began. Courts were established to hunt down the witches lurking within Salem and have them hanged. Whereas the first few people to be accused had been dubious figures in the village, some of the most respectable, church-loving pillars of the community were found guilty and imprisoned. Yet all the while the girls' fits continued. There were now eight of them afflicted, and every day they suffered further attacks, twisting their bodies about and appearing to see the most horrifying visions. Without any provable evidence, the respectable inhabitants of the village continued to find themselves accused, imprisoned and condemned.

Salem was soon to become a terrible place, with hangings on what was becoming known as 'Gallows Hill'. Almost a hundred and fifty languished in prison. Five had died while incarcerated, and twenty had been put to death. It seemed anyone could be accused of witchcraft. But relief from the witch-hunt was coming. The Massachusetts Governor, Sir William Phips, stepped in and officially ended the trials. The imprisoned were released, and the excommunications on the executed were rescinded.

What explanation, other than the supernatural, can be provided for Salem? Perhaps there was rivalry between Salem Village and Salem Town? Over the years, while the Village had held on to its strict Puritan values of sharing and community, those in and around Salem Town had become increasingly capitalist and prosperous. But could the atrocities of Salem really have been a simple case of local rivalry?

However, there is a more scientific conclusion – that the attacks were biochemical rather than paranormal. A fungus on cereals, called **Ergot** (*Claviceps purpurea*), produced an LSD-like chemical which may well have been responsible. Throughout history, bread made from **Rye** (*Secale cereal*) when tainted with ergot has created horrifying afflictions with all the symptoms of the Salem girls – hallucinations, muscle spasms, nausea and skin sensations. It was called ergotism or 'Saint Anthony's Fire'.

Undoubtedly the religious fanatics of Salem were unaware of the mysterious ergotism outbreaks in medieval Europe. In the 10th century, in southern France 40,000 people had died in agony, many losing limbs to gangrene. Victims complained of being 'consumed by fire' and ergotism became associated with St Anthony (251– 356), an early Christian 'desert father' said to have had hallucinations of the Devil, monsters and earthly temptation. Only when people fled to convents, churches and hospitals might the symptoms subside – less to do with religion than diet, because religious communities often used wheat, a cereal of better soils and one less prone to ergot, for their bread – not rye. Ergotism even altered history. In 1772, Catherine the Great of Russia had to abandon a strategic advance against the Turks because the army, with 20,000 sick, was crippled by an outbreak.

The warm damp summer that Salem experienced in 1691 would have provided perfect conditions for the fungus to thrive. Indeed, research has tracked such identical weather conditions to similar outbreaks of witch-hunts in Europe over the centuries. The last major outbreak of ergotism was as recent as 1951 in the village of Pont-St-Esprit in southern France, traced to a batch of contaminated rye bread.

So did ergotism result in the tragic deaths of twenty-five innocent people by poisoning the minds of the Salem girls?

Perhaps the most significant lesson to be learned from Salem is that, no matter how dangerous the powers of chemistry or the supernatural, suspicion, distrust and panic can be far more destructive. Arthur Miller's 'The Crucible' play about the Salem incident didn't just explore an historical incident, but was also an allegory of 'McCarthyism', when in the 1950s the US government fanatically persecuted Communists, real or imagined, in the entertainment industry, the army and the civil service.

JUNIPER, GIN AND DEPRAVITY

Imagine being so desperate for gin that you were prepared to kill your infant daughter to obtain it. The dreadful case of Judith Dufour in 18th century London illustrates how terrible were the events of the 'Gin Craze'.

Judith's little daughter had been taken into care and given a set of new clothes. Her mother turned up one Sunday to take her out for the day. Indeed she did take her out, only to strangle her, leave her in a ditch and sell the clothes for about a shilling to buy gin. While the story was an appalling shock to the public of Georgian England, such horrors were not unique. People were literally selling the 'shirts off their backs' to get a gin fix, and doing much worse.

How did this come about? The government was partly to blame, having taxed and restricted French brandy. Gin production was encouraged, and the farmers of East Anglia had flooded the market with surplus barley. The price dropped, and gin became preferable to beer, the previous choice of both men and women. But gin was now only too affordable by the poor – especially in crowded, licentious London. Soon the Magistrates were reporting that gin was '*the principal cause of all the vice and debauchery committed among the inferior sort of people*'.

Things grew worse and fifteen years later in 1736, they noted, '*Your Committee observes the strong inclination of the inferior sort of people to these destructive liquors*'. Gin was twice as strong than it is now, and people drank it by the pint! Indeed, one young visitor, for a bet, drank three pints in one session and fell down dead. A poet summed up the dire situation:

'Gin, cursed Fiend, with Fury fraught.

Makes human Race a Prey
It enters by a deadly Draught
And steals our Life away.'

In 1751, famous painter William Hogarth produced his powerful engravings, 'Beer Street' – full of wholesome, happy, productive citizens – and 'Gin Lane', full of despair, decay and madness, with a drunken, half-naked, prostitute mother dropping her infant into a gin cellar stairwell. So graphic was this, that recently the *BBC News Magazine* has called it the '*most potent anti-drug poster ever conceived*'. And we still use the phrase 'mother's ruin'.

The government tried to stop the destructive craze by taxing gin, but illegal gin sellers soon found ways around this. There was even a 'Puss-and-Mew' machine in a secluded alley window, where the buyer fed coins into a painted cat's mouth and the hidden gin-seller would pour gin down a lead pipe. No witnesses, no charges. After the 1750s, the Gin Craze mostly and thankfully died out, due to legislation, bad harvests and big increases in grain prices. A 19th century revival of the drink's popularity lent us the scornful expression 'gin palace' for a flashy pub, hotel or (as in 'floating') private yacht.

But what exactly is gin? The Dutch and Flemish distilled malted **Barley** (*Hordeum vulgare*) and mixed it with various herbs or 'botanicals' for flavouring, the most important being the berry-like cones of **Juniper** (*Juniperus communis*), a small coniferous shrub or tree of heaths and mountains. The drink 'Jenever', Dutch for juniper, gave gin its name, and when soldiers drank it before a battle, they gained 'Dutch courage'. The active ingredient, oil of Juniper, is also an effective diuretic.

Gradually gin went back to being a respectable drink. Indeed, it became the symbolic drink of the British Empire, with the juniper masking the rather bitter flavour in 'tonic water' of quinine, the essential ingredient in defeating malaria in the tropics (page 17). Between the World Wars, gin also became the base of many of the newly fashionable and curiously named cocktails (see panel). People still talk about going to 'cocktail parties', but how often do you ever see any cocktails being mixed, apart from in specialist bars?

Recently, gin has enjoyed a real revival, with 200 tons of wild-collected juniper berries imported each year into the UK from eastern Europe and Italy. Many excellent new brands have joined the market, often with innovative botanicals like pink grapefruit or rhubarb. Gin, as a result, now has a new young following.

Americans have always argued about how to make the best Dry Martini.
This gave rise to the (apocryphal) story of American Special Forces being briefed on occasions of extreme danger.
At the end of the course they were given a parcel, 'not to be opened except in extreme crisis'.
One young officer couldn't wait, and, in his room, opened the parcel. It contained a glass, a half bottle of gin and a tiny bottle of vermouth. When he opened the sealed envelope, he read:
'You are in great danger, hopelessly lost. There is no-one in sight to guide or help you. Mix yourself a Dry Martini – and within two minutes some sonofabitch will appear from nowhere and tell you how to make it properly.'

SUGAR CANE AND SLAVERY

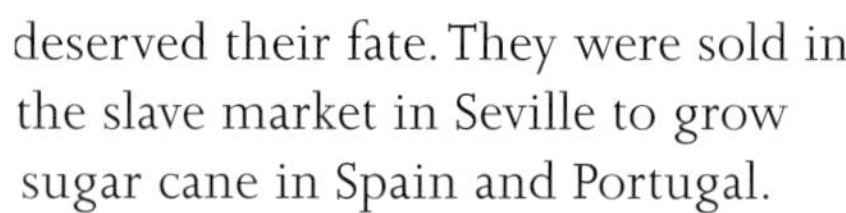

There are several reasons why **Sugar Cane** (*Saccharum officinarum*) should be considered a villain. Modern reasons would include childhood obesity, diabetes and tooth decay, but an older and more serious one was about sugar cane production's dependence on the evils of slavery.

For most of history, sugar – or the refined white sugar we know today – did not exist in Europe, and for centuries it would be too rare and expensive for most people. This huge perennial reed-like grass (in the grass family, Poaceae) is native to parts of South-East Asia and may have first been domesticated in New Guinea. From there it spread through tropical Asia, where it was improved by crossing it with related species, and during the first millennium BC became an important crop in India; whence sugar and sugar cane spread across Asia and, from the 7th century AD via the Arab conquests, into the Middle East, Egypt and western Mediterranean.

Honey, then, was Europe's great sweetener. The first sugar reached England in 1319 and, by gradually replacing honey, helped beer to replace mead as the national drink. But sugar cane still had to be grown far away in a warm climate.

Prince Henry the Navigator of Portugal (1394–1460) had set up the first sugar cane pulping and melting plant in recently discovered Madeira in 1432. Eleven years later he was persuaded to allow African slaves to be captured and bought to southern Europe. The moral excuse was that they were just 'ignorant children of Ham' who deserved their fate. They were sold in the slave market in Seville to grow sugar cane in Spain and Portugal.

Turkish westward expansion in the 16th century wrecked much of the Mediterranean sugar industry just when Europe was becoming addicted to sugar and Spain was colonizing the Americas. The Spanish worked out that the obvious solution was to take strong slaves used to hot climates direct from Africa to Spain's fertile new colonies in the West Indies like Cuba to grow sugar. The slave trade was born.

But it was the British, with their naval and mercantile superiority, who soon came to dominate this appalling practice. Protected from rivals by the Royal Navy, ships would begin the 'triangular trade' by leaving cities like Bristol and Liverpool laden with firearms, salt, iron bars and cloth. In West Africa, slaves captured by other Africans, terrified and bewildered, would be herded on to ships for the dreaded 'Middle Passage' (see ship plan above). The women and children might be allowed to move around a little, but the men would be chained below decks like sardines, not allowed to move for five filthy, horrible weeks. In the West Indies the surviving slaves (an average of 15% having died) would be auctioned off and the ships converted back to carry sugar and rum to England. Hundreds of ships were involved and tens of thousands of slaves.

For the slaves, actually producing the sugar was terrible work, from the physical effort cutting the tough canes to the searing 140 degree heat in the sugar houses.

But the sugar trade grew and grew, especially with the new European craze for drinking sweetened tea, coffee and cocoa. British colonies like Barbados, Antigua and then Jamaica were filled with slaves and dotted all over with sugar mills.

But things were changing. First, in 1807, William Wilberforce and his allies, after five attempts in the teeth of the sugar and slave interests, finally succeeded in outlawing the British slave trade by a large majority in Parliament. Meanwhile a rival to sugar cane had emerged. Back in 1747 Andreas Marggraf of the Berlin Academy had extracted sugar from the taproot of **Sea Beet** (*Beta vulgaris*). Now, encouraged by Napoleon, by crossing it with related cultivated beets, within a few years he created the Sugar Beet industry. Suddenly sugar could be grown in Europe without a single slave. Above all, the French never again wished to be dependent on sugar by permission from the Royal Navy.

Under such political and economic pressures, the sugar cane trade from the West Indies steadily declined, and country by country the slave trade also disappeared. Eventually the islands of the whole Caribbean region, and their artificially imported populations, were left in poverty, only recently partly rescued by tourism. Other, larger countries now grow sugar cane, especially Brazil and India, while sugar beet provides most of Europe's sugar.

Over 400 years, perhaps 20 million Africans had been torn from their homes to satisfy the white man's sweet tooth, an addiction that uniquely killed in huge numbers not the consumers (although it did them much damage) but the producers.

Among plants, sugar cane was, and indeed remains, a true villain.

The Irish 'white slaves'

Oliver Cromwell (below)is still hated in Ireland, and for good reasons. In England, during the Civil War, he had already sent Royalist prisoners-of-war to Barbados as 'white slaves'. Then, subduing Ireland, he went further. He not only sent any military survivors of his devastation of Drogheda and Wexford to Barbados, but sold off for profit no less than 50,000 innocent civilians - Irish men, women and children - to work in the sugar fields, in what we would now, shamefully, call 'ethnic cleansing'.

Arriving from the long, horrific voyage, the survivors were washed down and de-loused to appear more saleable. In the slave market, the elderly, called the 'refuse', were sold off first. (Bear in mind some of them were Irish landowners, even aristocrats!). Then, the more valuable men and boys were sold.

The Irish girls were selected for the planters' sexual pleasure, until, worn-out, they were sold off to the brothel-keepers of Bridgetown. All were branded with red-hot irons. Most were flogged for the slightest misdemeanour, tied to the dreaded 'whipping posts'. Some were flogged, and literally to death.
As they worked in the sugar cane fields, the 'white slaves' were treated even more brutally than the black ones – not least because they were less valuable and also regarded as evil Catholic 'Papists' by the Protestant planters. It is one of the least-known footnotes and most shameful aspects of the sugar trade in British history. It is also a startling fact that, due to Oliver Cromwell, Ireland lost 41% of its population – more than twice the horrific human devastation that Hitler wreaked by his 1941 attack on the Soviet Union.
The Irish might have been pleased that Cromwell finally died of malaria due to his religious prejudices. (Page17)

THE POPPY AND OPIUM

In the summer of 1917 the Assistant Director of the Royal Botanic Gardens, Kew, who was working with the Imperial War Graves Commission, visited the cratered wasteland left by the Somme battlefield of the previous year. He noted how a carpet of cornfield wildflowers had grown to cover the churned up chalky ground, derived from buried seed that can survive dormant for decades in the soil. He was especially impressed by the massed red flowers of **Common Poppy** (*Papaver rhoeas*): '*... the sheet of colour as far as the eye could see was superb: a blaze of scarlet unbroken by tree or hedgerow.*'

Those resurrected wild poppies remain an enduring symbol. For the last century, on and around Remembrance Day on 11 November, large numbers of people in Britain have worn a red paper poppy to commemorate the fallen of World War I. Although seemingly so British a custom, the idea of wearing poppies arose in America, where Moina Belle Michael (1869-1944), a philanthropist and professor at the University of Georgia, was inspired by perhaps the War's most famous lines of poetry:

'In Flanders fields the poppies blow
Between the crosses, row on row ...'

These are the opening lines of a short 3-verse poem 'In Flanders Fields' written in 1915 by Lt Colonel John McCrae, a Canadian soldier and doctor in charge of No.3 General Hospital at Boulogne, who died of pneumonia in January 1918. Moina Michael's own father had fought on the Confederate side in the American Civil War. After the war, she sold red silk poppies to raise funds for disabled veterans, an idea soon adopted by the American Legion Auxiliary and others. She later became known as 'The Poppy Lady'. Her poppy project reached Britain in 1921, when Earl Haig's British Legion Appeal Fund (now the Royal British Legion) sold nine million of them, raising more than £100,000 to help veterans. The French adopted another cornfield wildflower, the blue-petalled cornflower as their emblem of remembrance.

Several species of poppy are widespread colonists of open, tilled or disturbed land. Fast-growing annual plants, they have toothed or much-divided leaves, flowers with four colourful flimsy petals, numerous blackish stamens and pepper pot-like capsules or seed pods that, on shaking, release the tiny seeds from a circle of pores around the apex. When cut, the stems, leaves and unripe seed pods exude a milky latex. When farmers slit or score the pods of **Opium Poppy** (*Papaver somniferum*), drops of latex congeal and are harvested to provide the raw material for opium and related drugs. Taller and more robust than the Common Poppy, the Opium Poppy has waxy bluish-green leaves, lilac, mauve or red petals with a purplish spot at the base and stout capsules up to two inches long.

Opium, probably first domesticated in the western Mediterranean region by 4,000 BC, remains one of the most important of all drug-producing plants. Perhaps originally cultivated for the oil-rich seeds – still widely used (poppy seed) in bread, pastries and other cookery, especially in eastern Europe – artefacts such as pipes and depictions of fertility goddesses from ancient Crete, Greece and Cyprus imply the ceremonial use of opium as a drug. Ancient writers describe its pain alleviation and sleep-inducing properties, and in classical Greece opium mixed with henbane (page 32) was a more humane means of execution, most famously that of Socrates in 399 BC. In the Middle Ages, Muslim physicians used opium as a sedative, from where it reached Europe during the Crusades. From the 16th century a solution of alcohol with 10% powdered opium, laudanum, provided a useful painkiller. By the early 19th century it was being widely used and abused by all classes and ages, even being administered to infants to help them sleep. In an age plagued by TB, cholera and typhoid, a remedy such as opium or laudanum that might alleviate coughing, diarrhea and pain was bound to be popular; quite apart from stimulating the Romantic imagination of writers including Thomas de Quincey ('*Confessions of an English Opium-eater*'), Francis Thompson and Samuel Taylor Coleridge, who based one of his greatest poems Xanadu ('*In Xanadu did Kubla Khan a stately pleasure-dome decree…*') on an opium-induced dream.

But in the 19th century opium would have a much greater impact on the world stage, as Britain fought two unequal wars against China. The first was in 1839-42 to impose the opium trade on China, which had attempted to suppress widespread addiction to the drug, and open up ports to trade. The eventual treaty extracted territorial concessions, most importantly Hong Kong. The second (in alliance with France) in 1856–60 forced China to legalize the opium trade, open up more ports and allow both freedom of travel for foreigners in the interior and residence for envoys in Peking (Beijing), as well as giving the Kowloon peninsula to Britain. These and later violations of Chinese sovereignty by the intervention of western nations not only deepened endemic distrust of foreigners but also weakened Chinese imperial rule, ultimately leading to revolution in 1911 when China became a republic. Less than forty years later, in 1949 the Communist took control, and the result is today's super-power. Hong Kong was only returned to

China in 1997.

Opium remains a problematic plant product but one vital to human existence. Two alkaloids derived from opium, morphine and the less powerful codeine, remain medicinal staples for easing pain. Morphine was first extracted from opium in 1804, the first isolation of an active ingredient from a medicinal plant. It was widely used as a painkiller in the American Civil War, leading to high levels of addiction among veterans, and has long proved its worth in subsequent conflicts. However, the downside of medicinal opiates is the derivative recreational drug heroin, or diamorphine, processed from morphine but more powerful. It is still used in the UK, USA and elsewhere as a painkiller but is much more likely to be abused. The global trade stems from huge quantities of opium grown and processed illegally in warmer climates, especially in the 'Golden Triangle' on the Myanmar-Thailand border and in the 'Golden Crescent' of Afghanistan and adjacent borders of Pakistan.

Opiates continue to play a central role in bohemian and artistic circles. During the mid 20th-century, heroin was used by jazz performers such as Ray Charles, Billie Holliday and Charlie Parker, and from the 60s has been associated with a host of rock stars including Ginger Baker, Eric Clapton, Kurt Cobain, Janis Joplin, Keith Richards, Sid Vicious and many others. It has relaxed, entertained, inspired and sometimes, sadly, even killed them. And the Opium Poppy plant itself remains a colourful stalwart of suburban and cottage gardens, seeding itself freely – an anarchic garden 'nomad' that fills gaps and colonizes vacant spaces. Few gardeners question its slightly dubious affinities.

Afghanistan and Opium

For the last twenty years Afghanistan has provided some 90% of the supply of the world's and almost all of Europe's illegal opium. Opium production rose in the period of instability following Russian occupation during the 1980s. Then, the Taliban more or less eliminated opium production in 2000–2001, not least through a brutal compliance regime that included beheading and other atrocities. Subsequently, following the invasion by the USA and NATO allies, a collapsed rural economy, wholesale corruption up to highest levels of government, and control of the opium trade by warlords and Taliban insurgents, made farmers dependent for their livelihoods upon growing fast-growing crops of illegal opium. Attempts by US and British troops, notably in Helmand province, to suppress the trade in both opium and locally refined heroin, merely fuelled anti-western sentiment and gained support for the Taliban in what became a war to control the opium trade. Ironically, at the same time there has been a global shortage of morphine and codeine for medicinal use. Perhaps US and British forces would have been better employed – and their sacrifice 'in blood and treasure' less wasted – in guarding the poppy fields against the enemy and providing a legal outlet for the opium, rather than seeking to destroy the crop and thus impoverish and alienate so many unfortunate farmers and their families.

PRAIRIE GRASS AND JOHN DEERE'S PLOW

When the farming pioneers of America 'went West' they found the vast land of opportunities that they sought. The plains of the prairie stretched as far as they could see. However, when they tried to tame this fertile land with cultivation, they found a real problem – the tall prairie grass, with roots that go down several feet. Tallgrass prairie, punctuated by colourful wildflowers, asters, coneflowers and sunflowers, extended through the American Midwest and southern central Canada. This ecologically rich habitat was grazed by bison, deer and other animals, while the burrows of prairie dogs drained and aerated the deep virgin topsoil, bound together by the roots of the grasses.

But the farmers wanted to grow crops and the cast-iron plows they brought from the sandy soils of the east couldn't cut through these tough prairie grass roots. Worse, the rich soil then clung to the plows, so that the farmers had to stop and scrape it off every few yards. This was so frustrating that many settlers felt like heading back east. A young blacksmith, John Deere, had also come west. And, arriving in Grand Detour, Illinois, he found himself in great demand at once. But he paused from his heavy workload to consider his neighbours' plow problem, recalling how he had learned to polish needles in his father's tailor shop back in Vermont in order to push them through tough leather. Then, as a blacksmith, how he'd polished hay forks for the same effect.

So in 1837 he decided to try a plow with a highly polished mouldboard and share, which he sold to a local farmer – who was so pleased that he raved about it. More neighbours followed, and by 1841 he was making a hundred 'self-polishers' a year.

To expand, Deere moved to Moline on the Mississippi River to benefit from its transport links, but had insufficient high-quality steel. So he turned to England, then the steel-making centre of the world, and ordered special rolled steel. It had to come by steamship across the Atlantic, then up the Mississippi and Illinois rivers by packet boat and finally 40 miles by wagon. It proved worth the effort. By 1848 he was producing 1,000 plows a year – seven years later it was 10,000. He insisted on constantly reviewing quality. '*I will never put my name on a plow that does not have in it the best that is in me*'.

If you fly across America's Midwest, you look down on an endless sea of crops, with little towns with a grain elevator

every few miles. Thousands of big hopper cars sit in railroad yards ready for harvest time. It really is America's, if not the world's, bread-basket.

John Deere is now the largest maker of agricultural and forestry machinery in the world and in its founder's birthplace in Middlebury, Vermont, there's a monument that tells us why, with the words 'The plow that broke the plains'.

WORMWOOD AND ABSINTHE

One of the most famous paintings by French Impressionist painter Edward Dégas shows a sad-faced lady and a slightly louche fin-de-siècle gent at a bar table. She sits *distrait* in front of a small glass of pale green liquid, giving this 1876 painting its title – '*L'Absinthe*'. That notorious drink, otherwise known as '*La fée verte*' or green fairy, or even 'bottled madness', enthralled, stimulated and degraded the lively bohemian café society of late 19th-century Paris. Post-Impressionist artist Henri de Toulouse-Lautrec imbibed it enthusiastically and it may have inflamed Van Gogh's quarrel with Gauguin, which ended with his cutting off his own ear with a razor.

Absinthe is a strong liqueur flavoured and coloured green by the chlorophyll of a mix of anise, fennel, and **Wormwood** (*Artemisia absinthium*), a bushy aromatic plant in the daisy family with feathery leaves and clusters of tiny flowers. This plant contains a toxic chemical called thujone, which can induce hallucinations, but the main problem may have been cheap imitations (absinthe attracted poorer drinkers after Phylloxera (page114) devastated the French vineyards). Absinthe provided the proverbial 'strong drink', one that was easily available, and became nothing less than a craze among rich and poor. By 1910 the French were consuming annually an astonishing 36 million litres (9.5 million gallons). The closely related **Roman Wormwoo**d (*Artemisia pontica*) still flavours more respectable drinks like vermouth and hence James Bond's martinis without doing too much damage, unless one has one too many.

Absinthe originated in the late 18th century in the Swiss canton of Neuchâtel. From 1805 Henri-Louis Pernod fils

manufactured it in France. It was then popularised in the mid-19th century by French soldiers serving in North Africa, as a rough and ready defence against malaria, and they brought the habit back to France. It would become a favourite tipple of a Who's Who not only of artists but also writers of a certain disposition, including Edgar Alan Poe, Arthur Rimbaud, Marcel Proust and Oscar Wilde. Ernest Hemingway invented the cocktail 'Death in the Afternoon', a measure of absinthe topped up with iced champagne, adding "*Drink three to five of these slowly*"!

Absinthe long continued to be a soldier's drink. But five months after the start of World War I, in January 1915 a nervy French government banned this popular drink over concern at what they feared to be rampant alcoholism (often termed 'absinthism'), having been taken aback by the poor physical condition of army recruits, 20% of whom were unfit for service. In the years following the ban, a restructured Pernod-Ricard moved over to the pastis drinks we know today, harmlessly flavoured with fennel, anise and other 'botanicals', Pernod with Anise and (plus licorice) Ricard with Pastis.

Absinthe had long been demonised, and not just by a burgeoning temperance movement, with several other countries introducing a ban – notably Switzerland in 1905 after an intoxicated farmer murdered his family. The USA banned absinthe in 1912, a prohibition which remained until 2007, and the French ban of 1915 was not lifted until 2011.

It was never banned in the UK, although not that popular even if recent years have seen a small revival.

We British are perhaps not nature's greatest bohemians!

KNOT WELCOME!

Of all the plants we don't want in our gardens, **Japanese Knotweed** (*Reynoutria japonica*), now seen generally as the most pernicious weed in Britain, should be at the top of our list. Woe betide homeowners trying to sell with this plant running rampant in their gardens and becoming virtually ineradicable. It can knock 20% off the value of a house.

However, it is not surprising that after it arrived in Britain from Japan in 1850 this species was initially so popular, with its fast-growing thickets up to six feet, its heart-shaped leaves, attractive cream flowers in autumn and phenomenal power to propagate. In 1951 the *RHS Dictionary of Gardening* described it as a '*noble perennial best grown as an isolated specimen*', but conveniently overlooking the huge, deep and far-reaching root system. Indeed, by the 1970s it was common throughout Britain, rapidly overpowering other plants, and almost impossible to eradicate in gardens until it was too late, despite the efforts of many local

councils to warn homeowners of the risks of introducing such an aggressive species. It also grows in profusion on river banks, along railway lines and over substantial areas of Swansea in Wales! Recent research suggests that the powers of Japanese Knotweed may have been exaggerated; it is perhaps no more aggressive than some other weeds and it cannot grow through concrete and masonry unless in bad disrepair. The main problem is one of public perception and, more to the point, the views of property surveyors and mortgage lenders.

On the plus side, the young shoots are edible if a bit sour and can be cooked like asparagus, rhubarb or spinach, and it has been used in herbal medicine, but these little-known benefits pale into insignificance compared with the havoc the plant can wreak in our gardens. The three authors of this book have a great friend whose garden was once over-run by Japanese Knotweed. Incredibly he managed to sell his house, presumably to buyers unaware of this pernicious and fast propagating species. More serious, it cost no less than £70 million to remove the weed from London's 2012 Olympic site!

NETTLES AND THEIR STING

Most of us, after we've been stung by a **Stinging Nettle** (*Urtica dioica*), would call the plant a definite villain. It has, after all, given us the verb 'to nettle' or create irritation, and many English villages like Nettlebed and Nettlecombe are named because of its long-term nuisance to the locals. It is a plant that more often than not grows in crowds.

Or perhaps it was because of this plant villain's hidden virtues, for it also deserves to be called a hero – since in past times it would have been a valuable food during the spring 'hunger gap' before cultivated crops were ready. Persisting in abundance near long-lost Roman-British villages and deserted Scottish crofts, the presence of nettles is a reminder of how useful they once were, as during times of crisis like the Irish Potato Famine and the Second World War they proved a valuable subsistence food.

Nettles are also said to soothe the pain of arthritis and other joint ailments, although the method of deliberately stinging yourself must be only quite fun! The stem fibres once made clothing – the nettle family is related to the hemp family – and during the latter stages of World War 1, due to a cotton shortage, the Germans tried nettles for making military uniforms. The British government in World War II collected large amounts, but in order to extract dye for camouflage netting.

Nettle soup remains an excellent spring food, provided you collect the shoots before they get tough. It is best as well to wear gloves for picking, though the plant has also given us the phrase for taking a tough decision, 'to grasp the nettle' – gripping it so quickly and tightly that the stinging hairs don't pierce the skin.

Dock leaves to the rescue

How many young children today would recognise the vigorous leafy patches of **Broad-leaved Dock** (*Rumex obtusifolious*), now that fewer of them go out exploring – or know about its wonderful ability to soothe nettle stings? Older people will remember with affection this common wayside weed, its tall reddish-brown stems a feature of autumn walks, perhaps particularly women when they were young girls, because so few wore trousers or long knee socks in those days which at least gave some protection from stinging nettles.

FAMILIAR PLANTS AND UNFAMILIAR DANGERS

Like many people, one of the authors of this book, Liz Cowley, had no idea years ago that the seeds of **Laburnum** (*Laburnum anagyroides*) were the most common cause of plant poisoning of children. As an infant, her daughter used to sleep in her pram under the shade of a Laburnum tree in the garden, and toddle round it when she could walk. One day a horrified medical visitor pointed out that the little girl might eat the pea-like seeds, contained in pods smaller than, but similar to, those of garden peas. They contain cytosine, a poisonous alkaloid with similar effects to ingested nicotine.

However, despite the risks, laburnum remains ever popular in gardens, with its glorious drooping sprays in May giving it the name 'golden rain'. But it's not the only dangerous plant.

If asked, most people would be able to cite **Deadly Nightshade** (*Atropa belladonna*), with its the sinister, shiny-black, cherry-like fruits, as poisonous, but not many other plants. Luckily it is rarely grown in gardens, but lurks in the wild on woodland edges. However, there are a huge number of related garden favourites we should know about that can poison us, or at the very least cause serious irritation, such as **Chilean**

Nightshade (*Solanum crispum* 'Glasnevin'), **Angel's Tears** (*Brugmansia*), **Tobacco Plant** (*Nicotiana*) and even potato tubers that have been exposed to the light, which are green and poisonous and should always be avoided.

Consider, too, the berries of familiar, often much-loved woody plants – **Holly, Mistletoe, Ivy and Yew**. If eaten, all of them can cause nausea, vomiting, stomach cramps and even seizures. And the small clustered grape-like black berries of the less familiar **Pokeweed** (*Phytolacca*) can kill, as can any part of the ever-popular pink-or white-flowered patio shrub **Oleander** (*Nerium oleander*), which featured in frescoes in Pompeii and is today ubiquitous along boulevards and highways in the Mediterranean region.

In the UK, the Royal Horticultural Society and the Horticultural Trades Association have issued a startling list of no less than 260 garden and house plants that can be dangerous – by contact or by being eaten. Some, moreover, are very familiar and popular:

Amaryllis, **Arum**, **Asparagus Fern**, **Lesser Celandine**, **Comfrey**, **Lily-of-the-Valley**, **Foxglove**, **Euphorbia**, **Bluebell**, **Morning Glory**, **Lobelia**, **Lupin**, **Daffodil**, **Spanish Broom and Wisteria**. Other plants are a danger to pets, including members of the **Tulip** family. Lilies are particularly poisonous to cats, which can pick up the pollen on their fur and ingest it when they groom.

There are poisonous plants all over the world. Luckily most of them are in the wild rather than in gardens. But there are still plenty which are left to grow in our outside spaces and gardens and, if not identified and treated with respect, can be very risky friends to have around us. Particularly if we have young children about.

TREES, WOOD AND THE SCOURGE OF CHARCOAL

Most of us would only remember charcoal as the rather messy black stuff we used to sketch with in art classes at school. And it has certainly served art well, from cave paintings to the present. We had no idea of its other uses and certainly knew nothing of its possible threats to the environment.

Charcoal has been around for millennia. It is made from standard wood cut from trees and then burned slowly in a low oxygen environment, removing water and tar and giving off methane and hydrogen. The result is 'char', an almost pure carbon that provides a highly efficient source of heat. It is also light to transport, easily stored for long periods and burns at a very high temperature. You can still see it being used for its intense heat in any blacksmith's forge or indeed on barbecues, from family gatherings to Mediterranean restaurants. Wherever there are trees, you can make charcoal and it is a perfect fuel for basic cooking, heating and industry. However, it is a far from perfect utilization of wood resources.

The first problem arises from cutting down all those trees – in a word, deforestation. This was historically a problem in Europe, where hundreds of thousands of people were employed in charcoal production, and whole forests were cut down. In Finland and Scandinavia, pine forests were also sacrificed to the production of tar, with charcoal as a by-product. In Britain and elsewhere, tree cutting was managed better by coppicing, cutting trees and then letting them regrow in cycles, but laws still had to be passed to stop the country being totally denuded of trees for iron production. The inevitable shortages of charcoal led to the decision to switch from live trees and to go underground to dig for fossil fuels, creating the coal mining industry, with iron and later steel being produced using coke.

Sadly, deforestation is not a charcoal-fuelled disaster from the past. In much of South America it may be illegal, but it is still thriving, as it is in Asia – and in Africa an illegal charcoal trade is literally booming. Some 80% of African households now rely on charcoal, consuming 23 million tons a year. Indeed, charcoal use there has actually doubled in the last twenty years, with some countries likely to run out of wood and forest, further adding to the crisis of climate change. The emission of methane, a prime greenhouse gas, is also a problem. In South-east Asia, charcoal production from the mangrove forests that protect the coasts is usually both unsustainable and illegal.

And then there is health. The smoke from open fires and stoves, which causes respiratory ailments and cancers, especially among women and children, now claims over four million lives a year, the US government has calculated, '*More than AIDS, malaria and tuberculosis combined*'.

Used in modest amounts and sustainably sourced, charcoal is valuable and indeed vital to many, not least the artist, the blacksmith and anyone with a barbecue, but also in medicine as the 'activated charcoal' which binds to toxins in the stomach and prevents them being absorbed.

But there is little doubt that charcoal's alarming downsides have all too often been ignored and can outweigh its advantages - often a worrying balance.

PALM OIL AND RAINFOREST DESTRUCTION

Some plants, or at least their products, are ubiquitous. The modern world has an insatiable demand for the plant oils universally employed in the manufacture of processed foods, soap and cosmetic products. Of the various trees that yield oil from their seeds and fruits, **Oil Palm** (*Elaeis guineensis*) stands out for its sheer productivity, which annually can reach more than seven thousand litres of oil extracted per hectare. Native to the forests of west and central Africa from Gambia to Angola, this single-stemmed palm tree grows to 20 metres tall with large compound leaves and female flowers that produce 2-6 fruiting bunches containing up to 200 fruits. Local people in Africa had been using oil from wild palm trees for five thousand years, but its use increased after the Industrial Revolution.

It is hardly surprising that palm oil – the second largest vegetable oil crop after soybean – is now so ubiquitous in our homes. The trees grow on poor soils, the oil is semi-solid at room temperature, it has low production costs and a seemingly endless variety of uses, so that globally we each consume an annual eight kilos both in food and familiar personal and household cleaning products. Palm oil is in almost all processed food and has replaced animal tallow in cosmetics. There is also the vexed question of people avoiding saturated, and, even more so, trans fats. As an alternative to partially hydrogenated oils, such as in traditional margarine, palm oil has the right consistency but is unsaturated. After the food giant Unilever switched to using palm oil in 1995, so did everybody else, and in 2015 the

US Food and Drug Administration insisted that artificially produced trans fats must be removed from foods – to be replaced by palm oil.

Oil palms are still grown in Africa, but the plantations and oil production have largely shifted to other tropical regions, especially South-east Asia and notably the island of Borneo. Malaysia, where the industry was established under British colonial rule, used to be the largest producer, but since 2007 Indonesia has supplied over half the world's palm oil. It is Indonesia's main export and the growing economies of Asia now provide a ready future export market.

Unsurprisingly the IMF and EU and others have promoted the production of this ubiquitous commodity in tropical rural development schemes, where the wide establishment of plantations has greatly helped to alleviate rural poverty. The EU has even encouraged palm oil as a biofuel.

However, there are very significant downsides. The new oil palm plantations are being carved out of ancient rainforests that are a rich, irreplaceable resource and a buffer for Earth's climate. Big palm oil companies have also displaced local people, eroded their culture and subjected them to human rights abuse. Large-scale forest destruction, often by means of uncontrolled fires, releases the carbon dioxide and other greenhouse gases that drive climate change, while causing dangerous smog pollution that blankets major cities far from the burning forests. One specialized tropical ecosystem in particular, rainforest over deep peat deposits, can certainly never be replaced and peat fires continue to burn underground for years, releasing a stream of carbon into the atmosphere.

Above all, the cutting down of old-growth forests takes a terrible toll on

their teeming biodiversity, destroying unique habitats and devastating populations of plants and animals, of which orang-utang, clouded leopard and Asian rhinoceros are the most prominent – and the numerous as yet unsourced medicinal plants are the most precious.

Palm oil is listed on the packaging of almost every commercially available food and is hard to avoid except by keeping to a strict eating regime of unprocessed whole foods. Even when food contents are labelled, palm oil usually lurks inside the basic ingredients. Ecologically friendly palm oil is available from small producers in its native west Africa, but these sustainable sources cannot even begin to feed the huge demand.

Palm oil has certainly improved many lives, that is beyond question. But is the cost in loss of an even more precious commodity – tropical rainforest – too high a price to pay?

GUM TREES – A BURNING ISSUE

One of the most remarkable features of Australia's wealth of unique plant and animal life is the sheer number and diversity of the native **Gum Trees** (*Eucalyptus*). Almost entirely restricted to Australia, this group of over 700 mostly evergreen woody plants, ranging from shrubs to forest giants 100 m or more tall, occurs across a variety of habitats and climate zones, with many species adapted to hot and arid conditions.The trees often have a distinctive appearance: robust, sparsely branched trunks with peeling outer bark, narrow crowns, brittle hanging branches and usually spear – or sickle-shaped, leathery greyish leaves that cast partial rather than deep shade.

The great array of Gum Trees contributes an instantly recognizable image of Australia, and one, the **Coolabah**, or Dig Tree (*Eucalyptus coolabah*) usually growing by pool-sides and watercourses, famously stars in that most famous of Australian songs, 'Waltzing Matilda' growing beside a billabong or ox-bow lake. Forest and scrub dominated by *Eucalypus* comprises some three-quarters of the natural vegetation of Australia. Fire is ever-present in the ecology of the Australian scrub and forests, where the trees and their leaf and twig litter, packed with highly inflammable oils, can combust readily, and sometimes explosively. Most species regenerate after fires and there is evidence that after the arrival of Aboriginal people in Australia, the distribution of Eucalyptus expanded considerably. Not only do the seeds survive bush fires but they may even need the presence of chemicals in the smoke in order to germinate.

During the terrible bush fires in the

summer of 2019–20, all seemed lost over huge areas, but photographs taken soon afterwards showed healthy new shoots emerging.

Because *Eucalyptus* ecology evolved in tandem with repeated episodes of fire, future land management strategies – especially at a time of global warming – should almost certainly include far more use of firebreaks and controlled burning.

No longer restricted to Australia, and introduced on a large scale to many countries worldwide, the rapid growth and drought tolerance of *Eucalypus* has made them valued forestry trees. During the 20th century they were much promoted by the agronomists of the United Nations and other official bodies. At least 20 species have been widely planted in the Mediterranean region and they have extensively replaced native forests, especially in parts of North

Africa, where they were first introduced in 1854, and in Portugal, Spain and Italy. Foresters prize them for timber and wood pulp, shelter belts and windbreaks,soil stabilization, drainage of marshy ground, shade and ornament, and the production of the oil of eucalyptus used in medicine as an antiseptic and respiratory decongestant. They are sometimes coppiced, in other words regularly cut back to encourage regrowth of smaller trunks and stems, while mature specimens add charm and atmosphere to streets, seafronts or squares.

But the downside, and it is considerable, is that in summer-dry environments they deplete the soil of moisture. And, more significantly, the trees and their fallen branches and leaf litter readily catch fire – an essential adaptation in Australia but a menace in the already fire-prone Mediterranean regions. Furthermore the deep, oil-rich litter inhibits seed germination and thus suppresses native vegetation and prevents it from regenerating. They also cause problems in other regions. In Brazil, where 7 million hectares of Eucalyptus have been planted since 1910, they have replaced native vegetation such as the threatened Atlantic rainforest. In South Africa and elsewhere they are regarded as invasive species.

In the Mediterranean region, re-afforestation with these introduced trees, especially **Tasmanian Blue Gum** (*Eucalyptus globulus*), has also produced momentous changes in cultural landscapes, ancient vistas and the local ambience. '*A single eucalyptus will ruin the fairest landscape. No plant on earth rustles in such a horribly metallic fashion when the wind blows ... like the sibilant chattering of ghosts*' wrote Norman Douglas in *Old Calabria* in 1915. Yet they may sometimes be the only trees in a damaged or degraded landscape, and yield much-needed shelter and shade, as in parts of rural Sicily. '*The trees were only three, in truth, and eucalyptus at that, scruffiest of all Mother Nature's children. But they were also the first seen [since] six that morning. It was now eleven...*' wrote Giuseppe de Lampedusa in his classic novel *The Leopard* in 1958).

Love them or hate them, there is no denying that for more than a century and a half these trees from the other side of the world have made a major contribution to Mediterranean economic life, provided a wealth of raw materials, and helped to drain malarial marshes. And it is difficult to see how they could ever now be totally eradicated.

As with other plants, this villain can also be a hero, adding to our lives as well as threatening them, and thus, presenting us with a conundrum.

TOBACCO AND LIES

Take a look at any photograph of the 1920s or 1930s and the chances are you'll see people smoking – from New York 'Society' and the stars in Hollywood to humbler industrial workers, and from the Royal Families of Europe and political leaders like Roosevelt and Churchill to gangsters like John Dillinger and Bonnie and Clyde. After World War 1, during which reliable delivery of tobacco to the troops was regarded as important as food and ammunition, an incredible 92% of British men smoked.

The Tobacco plant (*Nicotiana rustica, N. tabacum*) belongs to the Nightshade family, many members of which contain often deadly poisonous alkaloids. One of these is nicotine, the active ingredient of tobacco, which is also an addictive stimulant. The slow-dried or 'cured' leaves of the plant are smoked, sniffed or chewed. Once regarded as medicinal, tobacco use is regarded as a prime cause of lung cancer and has been implicated in a range of ailments of the lungs, heart, circulatory system and liver. Indeed, the World Health Organization rates tobacco as the '*the single greatest cause of preventable death globally*' – estimated to have killed 100 million people during the 20th century. At the same time, tobacco cultivation detracts from food production because it requires large areas of land and heavy amounts of pesticides and fertilizers, themselves detrimental to human health.

Nevertheless, once Sir Walter Raleigh had brought back tobacco to England from the New World, it became fashionable and even essential. Most governments not only allowed it, they became the principal supporters of the tobacco industry – indeed in many countries, also the only suppliers. More recently, national monopolies were sold off for huge sums to big international tobacco companies. However, when governments no longer owned them they greedily taxed them. For instance, the British Government levies 80% tax on every packet, thus effortlessly collecting £12 billion, then spending just £750 million on 'smoking-related' health problems. In fact, Britain's National Health Service is made possible by tobacco revenues.

So, when in the 1950s medical research revealed the risks of smoking, governments did not ban tobacco as a dangerous substance or drug because electorally and financially they wouldn't dare. Instead, they went on to ban cigarette advertising, slap on increasingly dire health warnings, and, of course, increase their huge tax collecting, acting more like senior business partners than adversaries or watchdogs.

Then, in 1998, the heads of all the main companies solemnly swore on television to a Grand Jury in Washington that '*smoking was not addictive*'.

The next big lie was by governments. In their laudable efforts to reduce smoking, they turned pressure on the 'innocent bystanders', calling them 'passive smokers'. However, in nearly all circumstances the danger of 'passive smoking' is actually a myth. Except in the case of asthma or small children, tobacco smoke in the air is so diluted as to pose a minimal threat. Britain's

respected Hazleton Institute in 1998 revealed the real exposure of non-smokers to tobacco smoke the equivalent of smoking half a cigarette a month. In Sweden, exposure was close to undetectable.

The World Health Organisation then found the risk from passive smoking to be 'statistically insignificant'. Indeed, all modern buildings have to filter and clean the urban 'fresh air' they use. So we should really worry much more about the diesel engines in our streets than the smokers – and governments are at last addressing this problem.

But following the highly questionable epidemiology of the U.S. Environmental Protection Agency (who then admitted it also lied) governments have imposed smoking bans not only in the workplace, but in hotels, bars and restaurants – even parks – all over the world.

Yet tobacco companies and governments are still locked in a mutual embrace of mendacity. Like many couples, they deserve each other.

Tobacco and slavery

Tobacco was one of the crops for which slavery was, sadly, essential. European, and especially English demand expanded the American tobacco plantations in the 18th century, and the slave population increased hugely. A culture of expertise surrounded tobacco farming and as someone wrote '*the quality of a man's tobacco often served as a measure of the man*'.

Two of the most famous Founding Fathers of the United States were tobacco farmers who owned slaves, George Washington and Thomas Jefferson, the first and third Presidents. Like many other tobacco farmers, their plantations were financed by loans from England, which could cause real financial problems if tobacco prices dropped. George Washington, owing a huge sum, once excused himself by writing, '*Mischance rather than Misconduct hath been the cause of my debt. It is an irksome thing to a free mind to be always hampered in Debt*'.

The Tea Tax (page 139) is cited as the main reason for Britain losing the American colonies, but the colonists' tobacco debts were another powerful grievance.

While Bristol and Liverpool were the ports that ran the sugar and cotton trades and their attendant slavery, it was Scotland's port of Glasgow that dominated tobacco for 50 years, 1740 to 1790, trading more tobacco than all the other British ports together. The so-called 'Tobacco Lords' were celebrated for their entrepreneurial skills and endeavour - which unquestionably brought untold wealth to Glasgow and transformed a town into a large and prosperous mercantile city, littered with their magnificent mansions.

St Andrew's Square, with its superb church, was built by them to celebrate their

power and success, and the University of Glasgow received millions from them.

However, as are Bristol and Liverpool, the city is now confronting its slave-related past. There is a move to create a Museum of Slavery and even to change the names of Glasgow's streets named after 'Tobacco Lords' – like Buchanan Street, Dunlop Street, Ingram Street, Wilson Street, Oswald Street, Cochrane Street and Glassford Street.

From Bristol to Bordeaux and elsewhere, the former empires and modern enterprises of Europe are facing up to the cruel realities behind their past financial successes. Many would agree perhaps it's high time they did.

COTTON AND THE ARAL SEA

Human activity has always degraded landscapes. Greed, ignorance of ecological processes and worthy attempts to increase crop production frequently end in tears. Communist regimes, especially, have always had a tendency to grandiose dam-building and irrigation schemes – witness the present bombastic episode of dam construction on China's River Yangtze – that are out of sympathy with the environment, and in the long run fail the aspirations of local people. Too rarely do economists expose increased output to any sort of environmental audit. The Aral Sea (Aral'skaya More), on the borders of Kazakhstan and Uzbekistan, is, or was, one of the largest inland seas in the world. Its waters are shallow, averaging 16 metres in the early part of the 20th century. The sea has always fluctuated in size. As late as the Middle Ages, a connection may have existed with the Caspian Sea to the west.

Two rivers, 1,300 miles long, drain into the Aral Sea: the Amu Dariya or Oxus in the south, with a large delta, and the Syr Dariya or Jaxartes in the north-east. Both bring down copious quantities of sediment from the high mountains, but as long as enough water arrived, the salinity levels were containable. Evaporation is the only outlet for the water in the Aral Sea. Once the shores were home to a few nomads and fishermen, but after the foundation of the Soviet Union, fisheries were developed and fishing boats brought their catches to the thriving port of Muynak.

But in 1918,the new Soviet economic planners decided to divert the river water with canals to irrigate farmland for rice, melon, cereals and, above all, **Cotton**, the 'white gold', which the USSR wished to export. Typical of frantic early Soviet construction, the canals were poorly built and leaked. Half the precious water went to waste, and still does.

From the 1950s, mainly for cotton, huge quantities of water were being extracted from the rivers. The results, cynically predicted by the Soviet engineers, became all too obvious. Since 1960, a sea the size of Southern California has halved in area, and worse, its volume has reduced by 75% – equivalent to Lake Erie and Lake Ontario both simply vanishing. This is bad enough, but short-term economic gain has resulted in hideous environmental degradation. Now much of the Aral Sea is as arid as the surrounding deserts. The fishing has long gone, with the salinity of the remaining water far too high. The old rusting hulks of the last fishing boats litter the sand-filled channels that failed to save their industry. It was hopeless. The port of Aralsk is now seventy miles from the sea. The delta swamplands are all but dry. Barren salt-flats surround the remaining open water. Millions of tons of salty sand blow into the air. Even the irrigated farmland has become too salty for crops-including the precious cotton, with winters colder and summers reaching 49° C. This is desertification on a huge scale.

The human cost has been terrible too. The former fishing port of Muynak is now land-locked. It once employed 60,000 of its inhabitants to catch or process fish. Locals now face poverty and malnutrition, with the Red Cross and Red Crescent sending food parcels. Their health is also irreparably damaged by the corrosive salty dust that blows from the barren wastes around the shrunken sea. Drinking water is polluted. Tuberculosis, typhus, lung and oesophagal cancer are rife. Infant and maternal mortality rates are as bad as anywhere in the world.

Now climate change, with hotter and drier conditions, has exacerbated the problem, and heavy fertilizer and pesticide residues contribute to an appalling ecological and human disaster. Nature has once again struck back, demonstrating that even a structure as large as an inland sea is vulnerable – unwise to be seen it as just piece of state property.

Meanwhile, government scientists in the surrounding and now independent countries are agreed that more water must be allowed to reach the Aral Sea. But some suggestions, such as diverting other rivers, may now inflict worse ecological damage.

The old lake will never be the same and much will remain desert, although a dam completed in 2005 has re-invigorated the North Aral Sea. The water level has risen, salinity has decreased, zander or pike-perch (and other fish) have returned, and commercial fisheries again exist. The South Aral Sea, however, continues to shrink and the hotter and drier conditions of a warming climate suggest an uncertain future for the formerly extensive and productive wetlands and farmland sacrificed for a cash-crop monoculture of cotton.

GIANT HOGWEED - GIANT PROBLEM

GIANT HOGWEED, THE INVADER THAT BURNS

'Turn and run
Nothing can stop them
Around every river and canal their power is growing
Stamp them out
We must destroy them
They infiltrate each city with their thick dark warning odour'

From 'The Return of the Giant Hogweed' by the rock band Genesis

Few weeds inspire fear. Fewer still can boast of having their own song, but the mighty **Giant Hogweed** (*Heracleum mantegazzianum*) is definitely feared by many and also starred in the recordings and live performances of progressive rock band Genesis. Humorous, but with a dark message, 'The Return of the Giant Hogweed' ends with the monster plants dancing in triumph! Released on the 1971 album 'Nursery Cryme', the song arose from sensational newspaper stories in the summer of 1970 of children in London and elsewhere suffering burns after exposure to these invasive plants of river and canal banks, especially on their faces when they used the hollow stems as makeshift toy blowpipes, didgeridoos or telescopes. For a while there was mild hysteria, with appeals to destroy all Giant Hogweeds – which can be an imposing five metres tall with stout, bristly red-blotched stems and cartwheel-like heads of white flowers over half a metre across – and much talk of John Wyndham's classic 1951 sci-fi novel '*The Day of the Triffids*'. The media scare has surfaced repeatedly ever since, but in recent years this plant has proliferated to the extent that it has become a genuine problem.

During the half century since that early Genesis album, Giant Hogweed, in the carrot family or *Apiaceae*, has steadily increased its range in Britain, Europe and North America.

The lyrics suggest that the band may have known it, like our co-author John Akeroyd did, from their schooldays at Charterhouse in Surrey, where it grew vigorously in the 1960s. Genesis appeared well informed about the plant: its native home in 'the Russian hills' (it came to Kew Gardens in 1817 from the Caucasus), how Victorian 'fashionable country gentlemen' liked to grow it in 'wild gardens' and, more sinister, the way it can burn the skin in sunlight. Chemicals in the sap, furocoumarins, make the skin sensitive to the UV rays in sunlight, producing a painful red rash and watery blisters that can take weeks to heal, leaving brown marks.

Perhaps as result of climate change, the riverbanks that are Giant Hogweed's favoured habitat have more recently seen repeated flooding and the papery fruits, produced in their thousands, can float far on water. The deep roots then make the plant hard to eradicate or poison, but fortunately it is instantly recognizable and so can be approached with caution. In some places it forms veritable forests – an army of Giant Hogweeds is an impressive sight – and one can see the appeal to Victorian gardeners.

Armed with a bad reputation and undoubtedly dangerous if not treated with respect, Giant Hogweed has become a scapegoat for other white-flowered members of the Apiaceae umbelliferae family best avoided on sunny days, not least the smaller native **Hogweed** (*Heracleum sphondylium*) and other common wayside wildflowers such as **Angelica** (*Angelica sylvestris*) and **Cow Parsley** (*Anthriscus sylvestris*). Nevertheless, the Wildlife and Countryside Act 1981 wisely prohibits its introduction into the wild and puts controls on its spread, while the US Department of Agriculture classifies it as a Federal Noxious Weed, with restrictions on interstate movement. Not only gardeners but also beekeepers have been responsible for much of the spread of Giant Hogweed.

Plants & Us

Europe and North America are now unlikely ever to be rid of this enormous weed. Not for nothing in the 18th century did Linnaeus, (above)Father of Taxonomy, give those sturdy hogweeds their Latin name *Heracleum*, after the all-conquering Heracles or Hercules of Greek legend. And, because it was discovered and named only after his death, Linnaeus never even knew of the existence of the species we know today as Giant Hogweed!

What is a weed?

Giant Hogweed is just one of the thousands of plants that we call 'weeds'. It is often said that weeds are just plants in the wrong place. This is partly true, as many, to a greater or lesser extent, are a nuisance or indeed noxious. But a more accurate definition might be that weeds are just opportunist plants that occupy the disturbed habitats provided by farming, gardening, road building and other human activities. Some are recruited from naturally open and disturbed places like watersides, unstable slopes and shingle beaches, whereas others (maybe the majority in the modern linked-up world) have been introduced from other countries, regions or continents. Weeds also have a positive side. Many are closely related to crop plants – with which they have crossed in the past during the evolution of those crops – or are themselves a source of food such as wild grains and greens. They are a too-often neglected resource, and the great American essayist and orator Ralph Waldo Emerson was entirely correct to assert that a weed is merely *'a plant whose virtues have not yet been discovered.'*
Or, indeed, as we know, *'A weed is a plant in the wrong place'*.

TEA AND TREACHERY

In this book we feature five plants that have created some of our most familiar and everyday products – sugar, cotton, cocoa, tobacco and coffee. Sadly, all involved and relied on the creation of something evil – slavery. And it was slavery that was too often regrettably owned, organised, protected and condoned by Britain.

If we turn to another everyday product, tea, we could perhaps indulge in a sigh of relief. Surely a nice cup of tea didn't involve Britain and slavery? However, it turns out that it *did* involve Britain, and behaviour almost as disgraceful as the other four.

Drinking tea from the **Tea Plant** (*Camellia sinensis*) began in China thousands of years ago, initially for medicinal purposes. The first tea arrived in London in 1652, the same year as coffee and cocoa. By then, the British East India Company was competing with many similar European companies, of which the most formidable was that of the Dutch. This had at its disposal 140 trading ships, 40 warships, 20,000 sailors, 10,000 soldiers and 50,000 civilian employees. Britain was to clash with the Dutch, especially over spices, sometimes to the death (page 134).

At that time, all the tea came from China, which was desperate to maintain its monopoly and was very careful to keep its tea

planting and production techniques a close secret. Europeans who came to negotiate were allowed no further than a small wooden jetty in Canton harbour.

The trade in tea grew and grew, and by 1820 Britain was the biggest consumer and exporter, with tea 5% of Britain's gross domestic product. Curiously, because the tea ships needed to be weighted down for stability, the ballast chosen was porcelain. So Britain also became the biggest trader in what we still call 'china'.

But tea was about to present real problems for Britain. First, because of a foolish and tiny tax on tea in America, it triggered the 'Boston Tea Party' in 1773 on the issue of 'taxation without representation'. Three years later came the Declaration of Independence. Tea had lost Britain her precious American colonies (page 133).

Then the hugely valuable tea trade with China generated another problem. China had always insisted on being paid for its tea with silver. Now the scale of the transactions meant that the East India Company was running out of silver. The answer was iniquitous. Why not expand the opium drug trade? After all, the company already owned the monopoly for opium. And the obvious market was China itself. So a huge new industry in India was created; growing and harvesting the **Opium Poppy** (*Papaver somniferum*) and smuggling the opium drug into China. Over a million people were involved. And while making huge profits, Britain and its Company managed to pretend cynically that it was nothing to do with them!

Soon the Chinese began to realize that the British were turning their citizens into drug addicts on a vast scale. They objected strongly and even resisted, arresting British sailors and burning opium stocks on shore or in British storage hulks.

In 1840, the British shelled Canton and declared war, bombarding other coastal towns.

As part of the financial settlement, the island and port of Hong Kong was ceded to Britain and remained British for 158 years, until 1997. There were several more wars between 1856 and 1894, which an enfeebled China was bound to lose.

In spite of its profitable tea trade with China over many decades, Britain now also decided to break China's tea monopoly. Using tree plants found in Assam and also plants stolen from China, the Company set up tea production in India which soon overtook China. India and Sri Lanka are now the biggest producers, together with over 25 other countries.

For Britain, tea is still one of its favourite drinks, associated with soothing and invigorating comfort – and, indeed, 'just our cup of tea'.

But if we step back and think about it, just for a moment, we admit that Britain's role in the Opium Wars was something dreadful.

It is the equivalent of Colombia's drug cartel bosses, for other commercial reasons, forcing drugs on to the United States. And when the Americans first objected and then resisted, declaring war on the United States, shelling its coastal towns and, having won the war, demanding huge reparations and for good reason occupying New Orleans and keeping it as a Colombian colony for 158 years!

CHOCOLATE – 'FOOD OF THE GODS' – OR PRODUCT OF EXPLOITATION?

Most of us enjoy chocolate, highly popular both with children and adults, though it frequently causes the latter some guilt. It is made from the bitter seeds of the **Cocoa** or **Cacao Tree** (*Theobroma cacao*), which are fermented, roasted, dried and ground. The egg-shaped orange seed pods, growing 6–12 inches (15–30 cm) long, are distinctively borne on the trunk and branches of this small evergreen tree, restricted to the warmest zone of the Tropics between 20^0 north and south of the equator and requiring shade.

It originated in Central America, where archaeological evidence of its use goes back to at least 1900 BC. Mayan hieroglyphs from the 5th century record chocolate in both domestic and ceremonial contexts – prepared as a warm bitter drink. But chocolate was particularly prized by the Aztecs, who took control of much of the region in the 1400s. It was a luxury – the scientific name *Theobroma* means 'food of the gods' – that they imported from the hot lowland forests, offered as a tribute by the peoples they ruthlessly conquered. The Aztecs drank it cold and, lacking Old World spices such as cinnamon, they flavoured it with chilli, allspice, vanilla, honey and other local ingredients. It was a drink of the élite and for their warriors, who received it in their army rations.

The conquistador Hernán Cortés encountered chocolate – the name derives through Spanish from the Aztec *xocolatl* – served to him in golden cups at the court of Montezuma. Not long after, it arrived in Europe where it became a favourite drink of the Spanish court of Charles V, taken warm and sweet with honey or sugar and often flavoured with another Central American import, the aromatic pods of the climbing orchid **Vanilla** (*Vanilla planifolia*). Within a century this new drink had spread through Europe.

Yet chocolate was still not quite palatable enough. The creation of the modern drink is credited to Irish physician, botanist and collector, Sir Hans Sloane (1660–1753), famous for his library and 'cabinet of curiosities' that formed the basis of the British Museum and the Natural History Museum collections, and for the Chelsea Square that bears his name. Having encountered chocolate during a visit to the Caribbean, he simply added milk. It then became a drink of the fashionable coffee houses (page 238). It was not until the early 19th century that chocolate became not just a drink but also the familiar solid product we know and love. In 1875 the Swiss pioneered the use of powdered milk to make milk chocolate.

Today's global trade in chocolate is worth $50 billion, with most consumed in Europe and the USA. Chocolate is high in calories and, like all confectionery, blamed for rising rates of obesity and associated illnesses like diabetes and coronary heart disease. It contains variable amounts of fat in the form of cocoa butter, and most commercial chocolate contains both excess sugar and added vegetable fat. However, in small but regular quantities, dark chocolate is now seen as a healthy food, rich in flavonoids, anti-oxidants and anti-inflammatory chemicals, which may even help to lower blood pressure and to improve cognitive function. It is also a useful source of minerals, including zinc, and of Vitamins

B2 and B12, although it can induce allergies in some, and has been linked to heartburn, acne and gout.

Alas, chocolate has a much darker side than merely an association with obesity. Like the sugar (page 48) that has always sweetened the drink, it was a labour-intensive crop of the British, French and Dutch colonies, where it was harvested and processed by African slaves. From the 1890s production moved to West Africa and elsewhere, making chocolate a more widespread and affordable commodity, although dogged by reports of child labour. Some 60% of global chocolate production is now centred in West Africa, especially Cote d'Ivoire. Children still comprise much of the labour force and, in an echo of chocolate's sinister past, the industry has been associated with modern slavery and people trafficking.

None of these children will probably ever taste refined packaged chocolate, a luxury that we take for granted, but one for too long steeped in human cruelty and shaming exploitation.

COCA AND COCAINE

On the Eastern slopes of the Andes grows a small shrub which has made its mark worldwide in many more ways than one. The leaves of **Coca** (*Erythroxylum coca*) have been chewed by the mountain people of South America for centuries, because the alkaloids – including cocaine – in the leaves give them a sense of exhilaration and an increase in energy. The ruling Incas regarded Coca as sacred and it enabled their hardy subjects to endure high altitudes and back-breaking toil; and later the harsh conditions in the gold and silver mines of their Spanish colonial masters. The Spanish at first regarded chewing Coca as '*the work of the Devil*'. However, they then realized that the claims for its usefulness were true, and so they legalized and then taxed it. (Now, where have we heard *that* before?)

In one sense, coca and, or more especially, cocaine (first isolated in 1860) *was* a hero, because it became an anaesthetic for delicate operations on the nose and eyes. A prominent enthusiast was pioneering psychiatrist Sigmund Freud who, aged 28, wrote in 1884 a paper called 'Uber Coca', which he himself described as 'a song of praise to this magical substance'. Unfortunately, he succumbed to something that appears all too often in the cocaine story – addiction. Indeed, it took him twelve long years to break his cocaine habit.

The energy-lifting qualities of coca and cocaine have been utilised in several products. Few people probably now know of Vin Mariani, a French 'cocawine' created in 1863.

It was enjoyed and, moreover, endorsed by Popes, inventors like Thomas Edison, politicians like Ulysses S. Grant, and actresses like Sarah Bernhardt. But today many more people will certainly have heard of John Stith Pemberton's Coca-Cola with its 1886 recipe incorporating coca, which was only removed twenty years later.

Coca-based pills were sold all over America as a stimulant for workers, and a brand of tablets called 'Forced March' supported Ernest Shackleton and Captain Scott in their expeditions in Antarctica. The German army in 1944 was even working on a cocaine-based drug D-IX to give their soldiers 'superhuman strength'.

But the late 20th century saw cocaine become known as something else – a major recreational drug, and that was when it became a villain. In the United States and Europe it is second in popularity only to cannabis.

The Coca leaves are secretly harvested in Colombia, Peru and Bolivia, with most of the actual cocaine production in Colombia, where the drug lords have become very rich and powerful – and very brutal. Smuggling methods include vehicles and boats of all sizes, aircraft and even submarines. Often it is simply the human couriers, '*mulas*' or mules, who take their chances crossing the borders, for little reward and at great risk.

As cocaine became popular it started by being the recreational drug of the well-off, including the high-living habitués of New York's Studio 54 or rich stockbrokers, as portrayed in the film 'The Wolf of Wall Street'.

In the main method of taking it, typically the white powder is laid out in 'lines', 'bumps' or 'rails'. It is then sucked up the nose ('snorting', 'sniffing' or 'blowing') through improvised tubes or 'tooters'. The drug can bring on intense happiness and loss of contact with reality.

Unfortunately, anything other than the most casual use of cocaine can have serious medical problems. Prolonged use by addicts can cause fast heart-rate, hallucinations, paranoid delusions, unpleasant itching sensations, nasal deformities, tremors, convulsions, high body temperature, strokes and even fatal heart attacks. There are thousands of such deaths every year.

With Coca production uninhibited in South America and little progress in stopping it entering the United States, cocaine began to flood the US market in the 1970s, so the price dropped. Organised crime dealers needed to find new markets and 'crack cocaine' was born. Powdered cocaine was mixed with ammonia and boiled down into rocks that could be smoked, with a cracking sound. 'Crack' was more addictive than powdered cocaine and much cheaper, so it spread even further, especially among poorer addicts, and indeed in the 'crack epidemic' in the 1980s related to 32% of all homicides in the United States. Its effect on the African-American community has been devastating to this day, doubling the murder rate among young black men. Moreover, thousands of Mexicans also are killed every year in cocaine drug wars.

Worldwide, there are 18 million users of cocaine and the annual market in the drug is estimated at $100–130 billion. Perhaps, with the huge costs of policing, healthcare and social disruption, the time may have come for governments to reassess their attitude to cocaine and other drugs. Were illegal drugs to be legalised, controlled and administered through medical supervision and government legislation, the money would be available to benefit a wider section of society. And, since the profit on a gram of cocaine from production in Colombia to point of sale in the USA or the EU is over 30,000%, Coca growers might at last receive a fair price. As with Cannabis (page 11), any legalization debate is likely to continue for a long time.

Meanwhile, a leaf that once gave Peruvians a bit of an energy lift has sadly become a worldwide curse – indeed another plant villain.

PLANTS THAT KILL

At Alnwick Castle, the Duchess of Northumberland built 'The Poison Garden' after seeing an ancient derelict garden in Padua near Venice, built by the Medici family to find more effective ways of killing their enemies. She freely admits, 'I thought that most children would be bored by hearing about the curative properties of plants and so The Poison Garden unashamedly focuses on how plants are used to kill rather than to cure. Every plant inside has the power to kill in the wrong hands.'

Around 100 toxic, intoxicating, and narcotic plants are kept behind black iron gates, only open on guided tours. Visitors are strictly prohibited from smelling, touching, or tasting any plants, although some people occasionally faint from inhaling toxic fumes while walking in the garden. Favourite plants include **Monkshood** (page 76), **Angel's Trumpet**, **Deadly Nightshade**, **Castor Oil Plant** (page 31) and the **Opium Poppy** (page 50).

Whatever your religious beliefs (or lack of them) it is strange to think of any benign creator who would give us plants that kill, often with appalling suffering, and more

surprisingly, highly attractive plants bound to attract the human race – and particularly children.

In their fascinating book *The strangest plants*, Professor S. Talalaj, his wife and son record many such plants. The reputation in Java of the **Upas Tree** (*Antiaiaris toxicaria*) of being able to kill those who even approach it, has been proved to be an exaggeration, but there is no doubt about the lethal effects of its poison for anyone or anything struck by a blow-pipe dart tipped with its sap. Explorer Sir Charles Brooke recorded that in Malaya, 'A man next

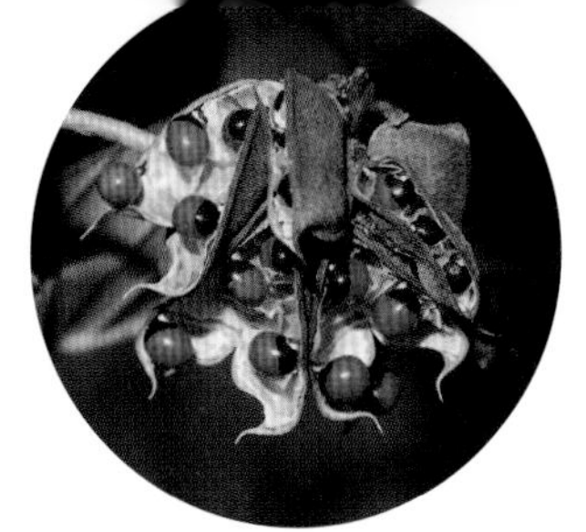

to me in a boat was struck in the hand. The poison ran so quickly up his arm that by the time the elbow was green, the hand was black. He died in four minutes.'

This deadly plant was also used in Malaya for execution, and horrifyingly to kill thirteen of the King's concubines for suspected infidelity. A sharp stick with Upas sap was ritually stabbed into their breasts, all of them dying in five agonising minutes.

The blow-pipe, often aimed with extraordinary accuracy from a range of a hundred yards, was a deadly weapon against animals and humans in the Amazon, too. It was judged by its native users as being superior to the white man's firearms because of its silence. The plant providing 'urari' was *Chondodendron tomentosum* and the natives even used it when fighting hand to hand by coating their fingernails with its deadly poison, now called 'Curare' by Europeans. In Africa, the juice of the fruit *Acocanthera shiperi* has long been used to transform arrows into deadly weapons.

A grisly role for the **Calabar bean** (*Physostigma venenosum*) was devised by the Nigerians, to determine the innocence or guilt of prisoners accused of crimes or witchcraft. They were forced to drink a potion that usually killed them. For the same purpose, for witchcraft suspects in Ghana, the extract from 'the ordeal tree' (*Erythrophleum sauveolens*) was placed under the eyelids with terminal results.

The **Prayer Bean** (*Abrus precatorious*) is another vicious killer, indeed just one seed can kill an adult. In India, it was long used as a secret poison. Incredibly, the seeds were also often made into colourful necklaces for children, with some predictable results.

What is the most dangerous European plant? Probably the **Monkshood** (*Aconitum napellus*), or **Aconite** (below), unfortunately such a pretty plant that it remains popular in gardens. It was also known as **Wolf's Bane** because it was used to kill wolves. In Ancient Greece, one of its most unpleasant roles was killing off old people who had become a burden to the state. For centuries in Europe, many battles were lost to those who had gained advantage by smearing aconite on their spears and arrows.

It is a strange conundrum that the most dangerous plants are often the most beautiful and therefore still grown in gardens – a hazard to us all. And some of them have been employed to kill people (page 77).

PLANTS AND MURDER

For all the beauty of plants, there is, of course, a darker side to their story, although they can hardly be blamed for their poisons. Many of them, after all, rely on a cocktail cabinet of chemicals to avoid being eaten by insects, birds and mammals. However, the history of murderous plant poisoners would be a hefty volume with Emperors, Empresses, Kings, Queens, dictators, soldiers, politicians, courtiers and courtesans filling its pages – either as victims or perpetrators.

The motives varied from power politics, ambition and financial gain to something more personal like covering up an affair. Imperial Rome was a veritable hotbed of such murders. Preferred plant poisons included **Henbane**, **Monkshood** ('mother-in-law's poison'), **Yew** berries and poisonous mushrooms. (Indeed, Pliny advised people never to eat mushrooms of any sort.)

Such murders would have great political effects. Agrippina poisoned her husband the Emperor Claudius with mushrooms to hasten her son Nero on to the throne. (Claudius's food taster was in on the deal.) Nero went on to use Agrippina's professional poisoner, Locusta (proprietor of a poisoners' school!), to get rid of his rival Germanicus and several others including, ungratefully but unsuccessfully, his own mother Agrippina. Many Roman Emperors murdered their rivals with plant poisons and several others themselves fell victim, including the Emperor Augustus killed by his wife Livia with poisoned figs.

While Rome was an epicentre of such murders, in the ancient world the tradition of killing 'celebrities' lived on – even if the victims didn't.

Thus, it is only too believable that Alexander the Great did indeed die by such foul play, or that Ptolemy XIV of Egypt was conveniently removed by his joint-ruler Cleopatra before her politically important lovers Julius Caesar and Mark Anthony turned up.

The decline of Rome in no way signalled

a decline in murder by poisoning. Chinese, Byzantine and Holy Roman Emperors, Islamic rulers and Imams, Kings, Queens, Dukes, Popes – all were victims or possible victims, let alone legions of lesser mortals.

When we come to the Victorian era, the poisons became ever more easily available. Two favourite poisons were now chemical – arsenic and cyanide. The other (see above) was plant-based, **Strychnine** (*Strychnos nux-vomica*), one of the plants whose poisonous seeds were used to kill rats and other pests. Horrifyingly in 1871, families in Brighton were sent parcels of cakes laced with Strychnine with a note saying, '*A few home-made cakes for the children. Those done up are flavoured on purpose for yourself to enjoy.*'

In 1910, Dr Crippen used that old stand-by **Henbane** (page 32) to help him to kill his wife, Cora.

Gradually, in many countries advances both in pathology and detection led to a decline in poisonings, but more recently new candidates have emerged. In one of the more spectacular incidents, **Ricin** (*Ricinus communis*) made from beans of the **Castor Oil Plant** (page 33) was used in 1978 in a tiny pellet which was stabbed with an umbrella into the Bulgarian dissident Georgi Markov on Westminster Bridge in London. Since then, in their quest to eliminate opponents on foreign soil, Communist regimes have abandoned plants and turned to ever more sophisticated materials like radio-active polonium which killed Alexander Litvinenko or nerve agent Novichok which nearly killed Sergei and Julia Skripal, but did kill an innocent local, Dawn Sturgess, in Salisbury in 2018.

It looks as if Putin's agents again used Novichok to poison Russian opposition leader Alexei Navalny in 2020. Nothing seems to change.

Mithridates and his antidote

Mithridates III (135–63 BC), King of Pontus on the Black Sea, who waged three wars against the Romans, lived in constant fear of poisoning. His father was poisoned and from his youth Mithridates studied poisons and would regularly take sub-lethal doses to confer, he hoped, a degree of immunity. He furthermore created his own super-antidote, mithridate, which it is said he took daily. The wise Pliny, unimpressed by this concoction, noted that it was composed of fifty-four ingredients. Another classical source indicated that almost all derived from plants, mostly medicinal herbs: frankincense, ginger, myrrh, pepper, poppy, rhubarb, valerian, etc., ground and mixed in honey. Mithridate or versions of it persisted in Europe until the 19th century. It was reputedly administered to Oliver Cromwell (who later declined a more effective drug, quinine, for his malaria (page 17), as a precaution against the plague).

PLANTS IN WAR

Plants and the wooded battlefield

Troy and the wooden horse

The Yew Tree and the longbow

Pomegranates, Pineapples and grenades

Oaks, the 'wooden walls of England

Cotton and its Civil War

Wood and aircraft

The Conker and the birth of a nation

PLANTS AND THE WOODED BATTLEFIELD

Sadly, for most of history, someone, somewhere, has been at war. It is not surprising that many campaigns and numerous battles were influenced by terrain, and of course, by the nature of the countryside – especially by woods and forests.

This is not just because they can form barriers like thick forests and impenetrable jungle. It's also that they concealed whole armies and masked their movements. Here are just a few that influenced our world.

TEUTOBURGER FOREST

In AD 9, Emperor Augustus was found literally banging his head on a wall and exclaiming, 'Quintilius Varus, give me back my legions!' A Roman force of three legions had confidently entered Germany's thickly wooded Teutoburger Forest to punish a non-existent revolt – a myth put forward to Varus by a Roman-trained traitor, Arminius.

Strung out thinly over twelve miles along a single muddy track, they were ambushed by German tribes and destroyed to a man – with perhaps 20,000 dead, including Varus and all his officers. This was one of the worst battle defeats the Romans ever suffered and effectively stopped Roman expansion across the Rhine.

THE MONGOLS AND THE SPRING OF GOLIATH

The Mongols lived and fought across the open grassy spaces of the Eurasian steppes. Once they reached Europe, they were in more wooded, marshy and mountainous countryside both in central Europe and further north, where forests of both broad-leaved and coniferous trees inhibited their mobility. This may have been why, although the Mongols would prove to be a persistent problem, Europe (except Russia) was largely spared after their initial major incursion in 1241–42.

When they came west again twenty years later, they moved south into the more steppic and desert country of Anatolia and the Middle East. There, at the spring of Ain Jalut ('Spring of Goliath') in the Jezreel Valley near Nazareth (now in northern Israel), the unstoppable Mongols met defeat at the hands of Sultan Qutuz of Egypt and his ally Baibars with an army of Mamluks, ironically themselves mostly sometime Eurasian slaves captured in the Mongol wars. And it was a wood that defeated them. Baibars used an old Mongol trick of feigned retreat, leading the Mongol army towards where the Sultan's main force was on higher ground – hidden in thick evergreen oak woodland. The resulting defeat marked the end of Mongol southward expansion in the Middle East.

The Mongols may not have liked woods, but they did create them. The early to mid-13th century invasions of Genghis

Khan, his sons and grandsons are estimated to have cost no less than 40 million lives, some 10% of the then world population. Without inhabitants, the forests reclaimed former agricultural land and the deserted farms and villages. And, thinking of today's worries about global warming, it has been calculated that this new forest biomass locked up some 700 million tons of atmospheric carbon – yet only a year's worth of petrol emissions today.

AGINCOURT'S TWO WOODS

Over-confident, very badly organised and inattentive was the huge French army that approached Henry V's tiny force at Agincourt in 1415 . They had paid little enough attention to the well-known threat of the

AZINCOURT
TRAMECOURT

English yew long-bows (page 88), in spite of two previous devastating defeats during the Hundred Years War, Crécy and then Poitiers. Thus, over-enthusiastic, they were hardly likely to survey the ground properly and to notice that as they advanced, the thick woods on either side would compress them into a narrow, boggy and crowded killing field, perfect for Henry's archers to rain death on them. The result was a third defeat and one just as bad as the others.

VIENNA WOODS

Austria's Vienna Woods (Wienerwald) are normally linked to the charming waltz by Johann Strauss ll. But in 1683 these green forests echoed to sounds of a fierce battle that saved the city and helped expel the Ottoman Turks from central Europe.

Here was a semi-wilderness with few inhabitants and paths, covered by dense forests of Beech, Hornbeam, Oak and scrub. But through this difficult terrain came an army of Germans, Austrians and Poles, under the overall command of the Polish King

Jan Sobiewski III, to try to defeat the huge Turkish army besieging Vienna. He chose to approach by this difficult route for surprise, hiding his troops among the trees.

The army emerged and charged down on the Turkish camp and siege works – '*as if a flood of black pitch was pouring downhill*', a Turk noted. It was a hard fight on a hot day, and by afternoon the soldiers were tiring. But then Sobiewski played his ace card. In one of history's most dramatic cavalry charges, some 9,000 Polish cavalrymen led by their remarkable lance-wielding *husari* (hussars) – heavily armed and armoured, draped with leopard or tiger-skin pelts and with great eagle feather wings attached to their backs – surged forward to finally break the Turks. They fled, leaving 15,000 dead and a field of tents rich in oriental silks and embroidery; but, best of all, their well-supplied baggage train – and bags of coffee beans.

It was one of the most decisive battles of the world, stopping a hitherto apparently unstoppable Turkish and Islamic expansion.

Opinion varies as to whether this victory first brought the coffee habit to Christian Europe, but Vienna's cafés remain as famous as Strauss's waltz – so too the all-concealing Vienna Woods. The story that the 'croissant', adopted from Turkey's crescent, came from Vienna's siege may be false. Rather, it honoured the bakers of Budapest in 1686 for thwarting a Turkish attack.

THE ROSES OF MINDEN

Every August 1st, some British infantry regiments parade with variously coloured roses to celebrate the Battle of Minden, fought between an Anglo-German army and the French and their Saxon allies. For some inexplicable reason, that same day red roses are delivered anonymously to the British consulate in Chicago.

In 1759, marching to battle, British troops plucked wild roses – probably the late-flowering, white-flowered **Field Rose** (*Rosa arvensis*) – from the Westphalian hedgerows and put them in their hats. They went on to show superb control against French cavalry. As a French Marshal later wrote bitterly, '*I never thought to see a single line of infantry break through three lines of cavalry and tumble them to ruin.*'

Sadly, victory was not won, because the battle also witnessed the cowardice or stupidity of Lord Sackville, who four times refused to advance to win the battle. He was court-martialled and dismissed with the words that he '*should never serve in any military capacity whatsoever*'.

Unfortunately, he did. Fifteen years later he was made Secretary of State for the American Department and proceeded, with his usual brand of arrogance and stupidity, to lose Britain its American colonies.

NAPOLEON'S MARCH TO MOSCOW

Most people know of Napoleon's horrific 1812 retreat through the snow from Moscow. But few realise that his advance was nearly as disastrous. Before the last two centuries, battles lasted no more than a day.

Why? Because, before railways arrived, supplies could not last longer. As it advanced, Napoleon's colossal 'Grande Armée' of 530,000 had intended to rely on their normal routine of 'foraging', or stealing, from the countryside they passed through. But, by chance, Poland and the Ukraine had just suffered a drought and a terrible harvest, so Napoleon's men and horses started to starve. Horses died and soon some men even went into the woods to commit suicide. By the time Napoleon reached Moscow his army had shrunk to 100,000. This teaches us that if you intend to rely on local produce, it pays to check the weather.

THE WILDERNESS

The 'Wilderness' was known long before the American Civil War. Near Fredericksburg in Virginia, German miners had tried to tame it and failed. In May 1864, two huge armies met there, 118,000 Union forces and 62,000 Confederates.

For armies trying to manoeuvre and fight, it was a nightmare. One Confederate officer wrote: '*Imagine a great, dismal forest containing the worst kind of thicket of second-growth trees, so thick with small pines, scrub oak, cedar and dogwood that one could barely see ten paces*'. Another described it 'as impossible to conceive a field worse adapted to the movement of a grand army'. He was right.

But for two days they fought there, with 18,000 Union casualties and 11,000 Confederate casualties. In a final horror, some of the wounded were burned to death in fires in the dry brushwood. It was a horrible, inconclusive battle, but with Grant's Union army undaunted and still moving forward, many regard it as the beginning of the end of the Confederacy.

BELLEAU WOOD

On his state visit to America in 2018, President Macron of France gifted to the United States a sapling of the **Sessile Oak** (*Quercus petraea*). It came from Belleau Wood and was a symbolic honour of thanks to America for one of its most ferocious battles

In June 1918, the Germans, with five divisions, launched a series of attacks near the Marne River, hoping to defeat the Allies before the arriving American forces could be fully used. Bearing the brunt of the assaults

were the U.S. Marines – and Belleau became a glorious part of their history. At first they were forced on the defensive, and when urged to fall back by the retreating French, retorted memorably, 'Retreat? Hell, we just got here!' Then they counter-attacked, with a two-time Medal of Honor recipient, First Sergeant Dan Daly, reportedly shouting at his comrades, 'Come on, you sons of bitches, do you want to live for ever?' The battle for Belleau Wood raged for three weeks with the wood lacerated by shellfire and the Marines, sailors and soldiers, sustaining significant casualties. It cemented the Corps' reputation forever, despite President Trump in 2018 disgracefully refusing to visit their Belleau Wood cemetery, as 'it was full of losers.'

KATYN WOOD

In 1943 an old man told the occupying Germans of a huge burial site in the thick woods at Katyn, near Smolensk. The bodies of 4,500 Polish officers, including five Generals, and many civilians were discovered and exhumed – in front of hastily-gathered international observers. Victims had all been shot in the back of the head. It emerged that, in 1939, when the Russians had taken over one half of Poland, they had put nearly 15,000 surrendered officers, politicians, administrators and policemen into three camps in Russia.

In 1940, under the direct orders of Stalin, who had no interest in the survival of such leaders in his planned post-war Poland, they were taken in groups into the forest and systematically liquidated.

The Germans, on their way to killing millions of innocent civilians, made a great and cynical propaganda fuss about the crime, although they must have been secretly impressed by Stalin's cold destruction of the leadership of a whole nation.

MALAYSIA AND SINGAPORE

The British thought that most of Malaya was 'impenetrable'. One officer said, 'Out on exercise, the General would say,"That's heavy jungle, this is mangrove swamp, so the Japs will never come this way." Just as Singapore was about to fall, I had to go through a mangrove swamp and hardly got my feet wet!'

Sticking to the roads in Malaya, the British had been repeatedly outflanked through the 'impenetrable' jungle by the advancing Japanese, leading finally to Britain's greatest and most humiliating capitulation at Singapore to a foe a third their number.

But, after months of retreating and further defeats, the British learned to live and fight in the jungle and, even more important, to defeat its greatest scourges, malaria and other diseases (page17). Soon they were to beat the Japanese at their own game.

HÜRTGEN FOREST

After the success of the D-Day invasion and Patton's brilliant sweep through France to Germany, the Americans might have thought that the last bit was going to be easy. But the dark, deep forest of Hürtgen finished such illusions. On September 19th 1944 started the longest battle the U.S. army would ever endure, in dense conifers punctuated with deep ravines, full of mud and snow, with few roads or tracks. The Germans, outnumbered five to one, had built bunkers, blockhouses, booby-traps and minefields among the trees whose thick cover negated American air and tank superiority. It was a grinding battle of attack and counter-attack, of mortars and machine-guns, rifles and pistols, shrapnel and deadly tree splinters. The bloody struggle raged for three months, and was judged by both sides a defensive victory for the Germans. The Americans lost 33,000 casualties, 9,000 from pneumonia, trench-foot and frostbite. The battle only ended when on 16th December the Germans launched their surprise attack just north, in the Ardennes – the 'Battle of the Bulge'.

THE ARDENNES

The hilly Ardennes were the site of not one, but two German armoured thrusts in World War 11, both times their woods hiding their intentions. The Maginot Line had been strategically designed to funnel invading German forces to the north of it, so it is amazing that the French Generals did not expect an attack though the Ardennes and then ignored their own reconnaisance pilots' reports of heavy traffic jams in the woods. As the Panzers then poured through, Churchill asked the French Generals, '*But, where is your strategic reserve?*' He considered the shrugged and feeble response, '*Aucune*' as his worst shock of the war.

From those same woods, four years later, a huge and undetected Panzer army, Hitler's last reserves, burst out and very nearly broke through the American lines to Antwerp, luckily stopped just in time in the 'Battle of the Bulge'.

Military strategists have far too often casually considered that woods and forests were 'impenetrable', only to be proved horribly wrong.

VIETNAM'S FORESTS

In war, if you consider the jungle as an enemy rather than a friend, there are three things you can do, and the Americans and their South Vietnamese allies tried them all . You can avoid going there. You can use artillery and aircraft to blast it, which they did, losing 5,000 planes and resulting in huge civilian casualties. Or you can literally try to get rid of it.

Using a herbicide called 'Agent Orange', the Americans sprayed the Vietnam countryside to defoliate tropical forests and crops so as to rob their enemies of cover and to reduce the food supply. Overall, the result was a human and ecological disaster.

Agent Orange, a mixture of 2,4-D (organo-phosphate herbicide still used to kill lawn weeds) and 2,2,5-T (organo-chlorine herbicide now banned in most countries) causes mutations and cancers. The mixture was also contaminated with the persistent toxic pollutant dioxin. Between 1962 and 1971, 20 million gallons were sprayed on 18% of Vietnam's forests, often at thirteen times the strength of herbicides sprayed in America.

One Vietnamese later said:

'We understood all too well its horrible destructive force. As soon as the planes passed over, the sky turned dark with a strange, thick milky rain. The jungle canopy broke apart, ulcerated, and fell to the ground. Leaves, flowers, fruit, even twigs, all silently dropped, green leaves turned black, crumpled. That brutal massacre of nature still disturbs my sleep.'

Vast swathes of agricultural land suffered permanent damage, four million Vietnamese civilians were exposed and nearly three million suffered often fatal illnesses, there was a spike in birth abnormalities, and thousands of U.S. and allied veterans even had medical problems. Lawsuits continue. Spraying Agent Orange also greatly devastated the rich forest biodiversity, and subsequent regeneration was often hindered through invasion by Bamboo and other aggressive tropical grasses such as Cogongrass (*Imperata cylindrica*).

Nowadays woods, forests and jungles have lost their historic ability to hide and disguise. Modern surveillance techniques like drones, radar, and infra-red imaging can detect men and machines only too easily. Bit too late for Quintilius Varus though.

TROY AND THE WOODEN HORSE

One morning, the citizens of Troy woke up to find something very peculiar outside their gates – a huge wooden horse, with no Greeks to be seen. It seemed, at first glance, to be the end of a ten-year siege. Homer, writing in his *Iliad* in 850 BC, four hundred years after the event, tells us that it all started when Helen, the most beautiful woman who ever lived, fathered by Zeus himself, was given by Aphrodite to a prince of Troy called Paris for judging that she was 'the fairest of the gods.' Helen, unfortunately, already had a husband, Menelaeus, King of Sparta, whose brother was, inconveniently, Agamemnon, mighty King of Mycenae. Unaware of the gods' divine involvement, the Greeks plainly considered Paris a mere seducer and kidnapper, and a fleet led by Agamemnon pursued him back to Troy. Helen was 'the face that launched a thousand ships.' The resulting siege of Troy by Greek ships and heroes lasted ten years.

Homer continued his epic story in the *Odyssey*, where he described the fall of Troy in what today we would call 'flashback'. The long siege had destroyed many of the heroes on both sides. So, when they found the Greeks tents burned, their camps abandoned and the wooden horse outside the gates, described by a Greek deserter, Sinon, as a gift to the Goddess Athena, it must have been quite a dilemma for the Trojans. However, after such a long and bitter war, you would have expected them to show a touch of prudent cynicism and suspicion.

The Trojans debated furiously. Should they destroy it or leave it for a few days under the hot sun of Asia Minor? Odysseus (whom Roman poets called Ulysses) and his small team of volunteer Greek fighters, concealed inside the horse, would have perished, and Troy would have survived.

A Trojan priest, Laocoon, did not believe Sinon and suspected a trick. In the immortal words of Virgil: '*Do not trust the horse! Whatever it is, I fear the Greeks, even when they bear gifts.*' His only reward was for him and his children to be eaten by two serpents that rose from the sea. After this grisly spectacle, even the most hardened sceptics were subdued. Nor was it any use that Cassandra, daughter of Priam the Trojan King, agreed with Laocoon and also warned against the horse. Unfortunately, she had been blessed by Apollo with the power to foresee the future correctly, but also cursed that she would never be believed. Indeed, she foretold the sack of Troy, but as usual nobody believed her, leaving her raving to herself in frustration.

The Trojans then foolishly dragged the wooden horse into the city and, in an orgy of drunken celebration, left it unguarded. The concealed Greeks slipped out, lit a signal fire for their fleet, and opened the gates for their now returned army. The sack of the city itself was so violent that the Gods themselves were said to be joining in. Nearly all the Trojans were killed, with their aged King Priam murdered on his own altar, and Cassandra sold as a concubine. Indeed, the Trojans should have been far more suspicious.

That's the famous story. How much of it can we believe? Some say the 'horse' was a battering ram, covered with dampened horse-hides to resist burning arrows. Others point out that ships were called *hippoi*, 'sea horses', their prows decorated with a horse's head. Whatever, the horse was indeed a potent religious symbol at that time.

And that fatal horse was made of wood– fir wood according to Virgil– probably timber recycled from the Greek warships, which according to ancient writer and botanist Theophrastus noted, were constructed of fir, probably **Greek Fir** (*Abies cephalonica*) from mountain forests.

Once again, a plant has influenced a battle – and ended a war.

The herb **Elecampagne** (*Inula helenium*) named after Helen, Helenakraut in German, was used to treat coughs caused by asthma, bronchitis, whooping cough and tuberculosis.

THE YEW TREE AND THE LONGBOW

It is amazing how slowly some lessons sink in, however painful those lessons may be.

Mankind decided quite early that it was safer to attack things at long range, whether food, animals or fellow human beings. Spears and catapults were all very well, but the bow and arrow emerged as the optimum weapon for hunter and soldier alike. It enabled the Parthians, Huns and other steppic horse-archers to overthrow the mighty armies of ancient Rome and equipped the nomadic tribes of the Eurasian steppes for centuries.

It was the English who brought this weapon system to devastating military perfection, and their enemies really had no excuse for being repeatedly surprised. Three times did France, with five times the population, suffer defeat at the hands of the English during the Hundred Years War, a conflict which lasted from 1337 to 1453, covering the reigns of no less than five English and five French kings.

It may have been snobbery, with the French knights in their expensive armour only willing to test their 'chivalry' against their social equals on the English side. To them, nobody else

mattered, least of all the archers, an ancillary force of 'social inferiors'. Tragically, they had entirely missed the point.

The English or Welsh longbow was a formidable weapon, carefully created from a stave of **Yew** (*Taxus baccata*) with its heartwood compressing and its sapwood tensing, creating tremendous power. The archers of the steppes had attained their firepower by a composite bow incorporating animal sinew, horn and glue, but the English based their longbow on plant tissue alone. An experienced archer could fire fifteen steel-tipped arrows a minute, capable of penetrating armour at 350 yards. The repeated 110 lb draw required great strength, and yeoman archers were required to train regularly. The new games of golf and football were banned as a distraction from archery practice. A disciplined body of English archers could fill the sky with lethal arrows.

The French chronicler Froissart recorded the deadly effect at Crécy in 1346. *'The Englishmen shot where they saw the thickest press. The sharp arrows pierced the knights and the horses, and many fell, both horse and man. And when they were down they could not rise again, the press was so thick that one overthrew another.'*

In the eight hours of the battle, the French charged 16 times, but were destroyed by the half million arrows that rained down on them.

The political and social effects on France were devastating. Among their 12,000 casualties were 1,200 knights and eleven princes, including blind King John of Bohemia, who had quixotically insisted on going into battle tied to two other knights.

Only ten years later, the pattern was repeated at Poitiers. Nobody seemed to be learning the lesson that this yew-powered projectile was now dominant. You would think that if many of your ancestors had been killed by a weapon, you would pay real attention. But no; decades later Henry V of England with 6,000 men faced more than 25,000 Frenchmen near the little village of Agincourt near Calais. No less than 5,000 of the English were archers. The battle was a deadly replay. Once again, a whole French generation was almost destroyed. Killed were the French commander, Charles D'Albert, and 500 members of France's noble elite, along with 5,000 other knights. The English lost less than 200 men.

When firearms arrived, English commanders were so irritated by the short range and slow rate of fire of the musket, that they tried to bring back the longbow – but now there were not enough men strong enough to work them.

But the yew tree had left its mark on the battlefield and on history. No other tree has killed as many people.

POMEGRANATES, PINEAPPLES AND GRENADES

The Mills bomb hand grenade that served the British Army well in both World Wars was known to Tommies as a 'pineapple', which it fancifully resembles. But the word 'grenade' itself comes to us from another fruit, the pomegranate, equally exotic and steeped in mystery and legend. Its name derives from the Latin *pomum* (fruit) and *granatum* (seeded), hence the old French name 'pomme-grenade', in modern French just grenade.

Native from Turkey to the Punjab, **Pomegranate** (*Punica granatum*) was cultivated from the dawn of civilization in Mesopotamia and Egypt, from where it reached India, China and the Mediterranean. A small tree less than 6 metres tall, it has dense spiny branches, small glossy leaves and scarlet flowers that develop into red, orange or golden apple-like fruits – huge berries with a hard rind and crown of persistent flower parts. Inside, each of the numerous closely packed seeds has a pink fleshy coat, sweet, but slightly tart as well.

The military hand grenade, which appeared during the 15th century, was gunpowder packed into a pottery container much like a pomegranate fruit in appearance – even with a crown through which the fuse passed. Later grenades were slimmer, of metal and filled with bullets – recalling the seeds in the fruit, and thus the name persisted. From the 17th century, an age of great sieges, grenades became heavier and so European nations recruited, from their strongest and tallest soldiers, specialised companies of grenadiers. Britain's Grenadier Guards, are a reminder of those times. The fruit – *granada* in Spanish – is on the Spanish coat of arms, and also lent its name to Granada in southern Spain, which too bears a pomegranate on its coat of arms, and the fruit is widely depicted in decorative motifs around the city. Alternatively, Granada may take its name from the Moorish Garnata, 'hill of strangers', and was known as Gárnata al-Yahud, Granada of the Jews, in the 11th century a dominant political and cultural local influence. Later its magnificent Alhambra citadel, palace and gardens, from which the Moors were expelled only in 1492, became the greatest gem of Spain's Islamic heritage

The pomegranate has long been a potent cultural icon in the Mediterranean and Middle East. King Solomon of Israel decorated the Temple in Jerusalem with pomegranate motifs, and bas-reliefs show Persian kings surrounded by maces topped by pomegranate-shaped heads. Indeed, the persistent flower parts that crown the fruit probably inspired the crowns of all kings.

Mediterranean peoples have esteemed them since antiquity as food, drink, flavouring and medicine, and as a symbol of fertility once sacred to Aphrodite and other gods. It has many mentions in the Bible and as good a claim as any to be the 'forbidden fruit' that Adam and Eve ate in the Garden of Eden.

What a pity such a useful fruit is associated with something as unpleasant as a hand grenade.

The Greek legend of Persephone

Hades, Lord of the Underworld and brother of Zeus, wanted Persephone, daughter of Demeter, Goddess of the Cornfield, for his wife. He seized her as she was picking flowers and carried her down to Hades. Demeter wandered disconsolate in search of her missing daughter until she learned that Hades was responsible. Enraged, she wandered the earth forbidding trees to fruit and cereals to grow. People starved, and all Mount Olympus was alarmed. Zeus asked Hades to return the girl but on one condition: only if she had not so much as tasted any food in the Underworld. She had nibbled a single pomegranate, eating just seven seeds. Thus, the gods agreed a compromise: she should remain in Hades for three months of the year – the short Mediterranean winter – as Queen of the Underworld.

The seven seeds probably represented seven phases of the moon before new corn sprouted.

OAKS, THE 'WOODEN WALLS OF ENGLAND'

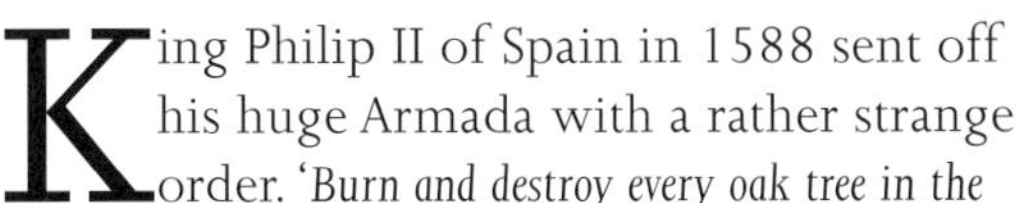

King Philip II of Spain in 1588 sent off his huge Armada with a rather strange order. '*Burn and destroy every oak tree in the Forest of Dean*'. On the face of it, this is very curious. Surely the first objective of the Armada with its 130 ships and 20,000 men was to link up with the Duke of Parma's 30,000 troops waiting in the Spanish Netherlands and invade England, topple Queen Elizabeth and restore the Catholic faith? The Armada never landed its men in England, of course, but the Spanish King's order reflected his knowledge of the huge importance to the Royal Navy of the oak tree.

The **Oak Tree** (*Quercus robur*) had been part of the fabric and folklore of Britain for centuries. It had been worshipped by the ancient Greeks, the Vikings and the Celts, and then by the Druids of England. Oaks had been involved in the lives of many Kings and Queens, not least Charles II hiding in one at Boscobel House after his defeat by Cromwell at the Battle of Worcester.

Oak has been used for furniture, construction (as in the House of Commons panelling) and the storage of wine and spirits. But it was its most vital use in the building of wooden warships that was so significant. Only the oak provided such a hard wood for the massive sternposts and other large pieces, together with the ribs and huge areas of planking. Soon the Royal Navy ships were nicknamed 'The wooden walls of England'.

But such ships used up an enormous amount of wood. Back in 1418, King Henry V was able to dominate the Channel with 30 ships like the *Grace Dieu*. But that one ship alone had consumed 2,735 oaks and 1,145 beech trees. The *Tudor Rose*, by 1545, had needed 14.5 hectares, or 39 acres of oaks and, with larger ships, this had doubled by the time of Trafalgar in 1805 – with Nelson's HMS *Victory* costing no less than 86 acres of oak forest. It was little wonder that Britain was beginning to run out of suitable oak trees.

Commemorating that escape by King Charles II after Worcester, there have been no less than eight ships named HMS *Royal Oak*. The last one was a battleship sunk at the naval base of Scapa Flow in 1939 by the daring U-boat commander Günther Prien.

So important was oak to the Royal Navy that 'Hearts of Oak', reflecting the strongest part of the tree, is the official march, with the chorus:

'Hearts of oak are our ships,
Hearts of oak are our men.
We always are ready, steady boys, steady,
To charge and to conquer, again and again'.

Just months before Trafalgar, Napoleon nearly had a chance to overcome Britain's 'wooden walls'. The American Robert Fulton suggested using his new steamboats to tow an invasion fleet across the Channel when the English ships were against unfavourable winds. Napoleon replied, 'What, sir, would you make a ship sail against the wind and currents by lighting a bonfire under her deck? Excuse me, I have no time for such nonsense.'

So for another hundred years Britain would continue to rule the waves, albeit with steel and steam. But many centuries of the hearts of oak had made it possible.

COTTON AND ITS CIVIL WAR

Many people might ask, 'Why would one part of a country wage war on another, and stronger one – with the risk that it would lose everything?' The answer – cotton and slaves.

Cotton, the earliest known plant fibre to have been utilised, has long been the most important both in volume and economic value. Early societies discovered cotton independently in the Old and New Worlds, with archaeological evidence in the Indus Valley from 5,500 BC and in Peru from 4,000 BC. In historic times cotton probably spread from Egypt, reaching Spain via the Islamic world in 900 AD and then the rest of Europe. Cortes later encountered New World cotton in Mexico in 1519, when he was presented with a gold-encrusted cotton robe in Yucatan.

All the four cultivated species of **Cotton**(*Gossypium*, in the mallow family, Malvaceae) are bushy annual plants that require warm weather and well-drained soil rich in humus, and there were millions of acres in America to provide that. Cotton itself is largely cellulose fibres that grow from the seeds to form a white woolly 'boll', within a seed-pod that serves both to protect and disperse them as a unit. Intensive labour was needed to gather the seed bolls and extract the fibres, and black slaves from Africa provided the workforce. Cotton started as very expensive to produce because the essential 'ginning' – the separation of the seeds from the hairs or lint – took so long. For instance, from raw material to thread, wool took two days, linen four days, silk six, but cotton fourteen. Two innovations were to transform the situation.

In Britain, America's biggest market, Richard Arkwright had installed his first mill with his 'spinning Jenny' in 1770.

Now 50 unskilled workers replaced 2,500 'spinsters', so production of cotton cloth could drop radically in price. At the same time in Savannah, Georgia, Eli Whitney had solved the ginning problem and his simple rotary machine meant a slave could 'gin' not one pound of cotton a day but 50. With prices reduced, both the production of raw cotton and its conversion to cotton cloth boomed – between 1774 and 1850 increasing 150-fold. After the abolition of the slave trade, from 1808 legally slaves could not be imported, but they could be bred. By 1860, four million black slaves were owned by white men. Two thirds of all raw cotton came from America, its biggest export, and two thirds of the world's cotton goods were made near Liverpool in Britain.

Thus the Southern states of America were wedded to their slaves and 'King Cotton'. Their way of life would have to be protected, they thought, by force of arms.

The war with the North that they initiated by attacking Fort Sumter in 1861 was based on several delusions. One was 'one Southerner can whip five Yankees', another was that the British were so dependent on cotton that they must intervene on the South's side. However, there were other harsh realities that took a long time to face. The South had half the available manpower to fight (obviously the slaves were not part of that), and as an agrarian society its industry was feeble. It had no shoe factories, no linen mills for tents, no pharmaceutical factories even for quinine, no glassworks, no steel rolling mills, not even its own salt. Above all, its railroads, now vital for modern warfare, were short, patchy and disconnected and there was not one workshop that could repair a locomotive – let alone build one. This transportation weakness, above all, would lead to fatal shortages for the Confederate army – of food, ammunition, uniforms, boots and wagons.

Strangely, most of the men who then fought so bravely for the South were poor whites who did not own any slaves. The rich men on their plantations who did own slaves often avoided doing any fighting and just ran away from Sherman and his 'March to the sea' Critically, in spite of hardship in Lancashire, the British did not intervene and began to look at Egypt for its cotton.

The result was a tragic four-year Civil War in which three million Americans fought and that killed 620,000 of them, wounding a million more. It wrecked the South and its way of life, but did at least free the slaves – albeit to suffer many more decades of cruel discrimination.

But the really bizarre irony is that, seven years after the end of that Civil War, thanks to share-cropping and mechanisation, the South was producing the same amount of cotton as before – and this time, without any slaves at all.

WOOD AND AIRCRAFT

Looking at modern aircraft, it is hard to remember that for much of their early history planes were made of wood. In Seattle, a town once created by cutting giant Redwoods, Firs and Spruces back from the waterline and founded by the timber industry (page 134), rich lumber merchant William E. Boeing decided to go into flying in 1917, starting to build aircraft at his wooden boat works on the Duwamish River. Boeing became one of the giants of aviation, famous for the B-17 Fortress, B-29 Superfortress and B-52 bombers and the pioneering 707 and Jumbo 747 airliners.

From the 1930s, most aircraft were built of metal, but not all. During WW2, the shipping losses to U-boats in the Atlantic were sufficient for the U.S. government to consider huge aircraft to transport men to Europe. The eccentric Howard Hughes got together with ship magnate William Kaiser to design a huge flying boat with eight engines. To avoid using strategic steel and aluminium, the Hughes H-4 Hercules was to be built of wood. Naturally as its fame spread, it was called 'The Spruce Goose', although it was mostly Birch wood. It took so long to build that this colossal plane only flew once, about a mile, in 1947 and was declared redundant as the war had ended two years earlier. Now displayed in the Evergreen Museum in Oregon, while magnificent, it is one of aviation's great white elephants.

But there was another aircraft built of wood that was to prove a triumph, the De Havilland D.98 Mosquito. Designed privately by Geoffrey de Havilland against initial

British government opposition, this beautiful twin-engine aircraft proved to be the fastest aircraft of its time, a versatile and outstanding success as a fighter, night-fighter, light bomber, photo-reconnaissance plane, bombing pathfinder, torpedo bomber and carrier plane. As with the Hughes Hercules, the plane was mostly of Birch wood, built as a monocoque with

Ecuadorian Balsa, strengthened in key stress points with Spruce, Ash and Walnut and sealed with a special British-created Resorcinol waterproof glue. A big advantage was that sub-contractors could be quickly found who were familiar with working with wood like furniture factories, cabinet makers, car builders and even piano makers, meaning that the plane entered service very quickly, with over 7,000 being built.

The Mosquito was an immediate and dramatic success, soon nicknamed the 'Wooden Wonder', and carrying out some of the most daring raids of the war. A furious Reichsmarschall Hermann Goering, head of the Luftwaffe, after being twice bombed by Mosquitoes, used it scathingly to criticise his own aircraft builders, including Messerschmitt who had failed to build a similar wooden plane, partly because of the lack of water-proof glue.

'It makes me furious when I see the Mosquito. I turn green and yellow with envy. The British, who can afford aluminium better than we can, knock together a beautiful wooden aircraft that every piano factory over there is building, and they give it a speed that they have now increased yet again. What do you make of that? There is nothing the British do not have. They have the geniuses – and we have the nincompoops!'

Some modern aircraft are built with wood, but never such a successful warplane.

Linen from **Flax** (*Linum usitatissimum*) was used to cover the wings of all early aircraft. Irish linen from Northern Ireland was used so much by the British that there was a saying, '*We won the war on Irish wings*'.

THE CONKER AND THE BIRTH OF A NATION

All over Britain each Autumn children pick up shiny brown horse-chestnuts, drill holes in them, attach them to string and then try to smash the 'conkers' wielded by their friends.

The conker, which arrived in western Europe from Turkey in 1576, appears a harmless enough fruit. The conker tree or **Horse Chestnut** (*Aesculus hippocastanum*) is a native of mountain valleys in Greece, Albania and Bulgaria, then under Turkey's Ottoman Empire. In the four centuries since its introduction to Britain, this handsome tree – so conspicuous in bud, leaf, flower, fruit and autumn colour – has become an evocative icon of the countryside, parks and streets, providing the ammunition for innumerable 'conker fights.' Yet the fruits have had an unexpected influence on world affairs via the munition factories of World War I.

And, by an irony of history, the Islamic world should rue the day they reached the West.

The story starts three and a half centuries after the tree arrived in western Europe. On 1 July 1916, waves of British soldiers attacked firmly entrenched German lines at the tragic Battle of the Somme. One reason for their failure to break through, despite weeks of horrific casualties, was the inability of the artillery to destroy the German barbed wire and bunkers.

Many shells fell short or failed to explode. The Minister of Supply, David Lloyd George, desperately needed to source better munitions, especially cordite, the propellant of artillery shells, of which Britain would eventually fire off 258 million! For cordite, he needed a huge quantity of acetone, a solvent essential for its manufacture, of which there was a shortage.

Lloyd George and Winston Churchill, who, in charge of the Navy, was equally anxious about shell quality, turned for help to a 'boffin'. Zionist and chemist Professor Chaim Weizmann of Manchester University took up the challenge. He used his process of bacterial fermentation that he had discovered in 1912 to ferment maize starch to yield acetone. But stocks of maize were running low, due to the German U-boat campaign lacerating merchant shipping from America. Weizmann needed a new source of starch and suggested conkers, free and plentiful. Soon an extraordinary national collection campaign was underway, and in autumn 1917 children from all over the country gathered sacks of the precious fruits for processing factories in Dorset and Norfolk – sending their conker parcels to Government offices in London for secrecy. Acetone was now available, cordite production assured, and in November 1918, Germany surrendered to the victorious Allies.

In reality, the fermentation of conkers yielded only a small proportion of acetone. Nevertheless, a grateful Lloyd George, by now Prime Minister, wanted to reward Weizmann. He asked the Professor (Herod and Salome spring to mind) if there was anything he could do for him, no doubt thinking along the usual lines of a knighthood or even a peerage. *'Yes, there was,'* Weizmann said, *'I would like help to establish a homeland for the Jews in Palestine'*. He was sufficiently persuasive that the Prime Minister replied, 'We'd better go and talk to Foreign Secretary Arthur Balfour.' And that, wrote Lloyd George, *'was the fount and origin of the Balfour Declaration'* that established the modern state of Israel and *'left a permanent mark on the map of the world.'*

A permanent mark it was. A major problem was that the fledgling state of Israel, the product of an almost casual gesture about conkers, then grew too slowly. In vain did Weizmann appeal in 1920, *'Jewish people, where are you?'*

Few Jews in Europe, especially in Germany, where they were prominent, wealthy and influential, had any intention of abandoning their successful lives for some poor, hot, barren settlement. So, tragically, most were trapped and died in the Holocaust. Israel also grew so slowly that it became the focus of resurgent Arab nationalism. Since 1948, when Chaim Weizmann duly became its first President, the apparently laudable concept of Israel's 'promised land' has sadly spawned wars, permanent refugee camps, terrorism, oil crises, suicide bombers, Al- Qaeda, 9/11 and terrible conflicts in Iraq and Afghanistan.

Seldom has an apparently unrelated decision had such a profound influence on our world.

PLANTS IN PERIL

PLANTS IN PERIL

Life on Earth is sustained by plants. Conserving them is one of the most important and urgent issues facing people worldwide, for they are now threatened as never before. Many forms of environmental damage are to a greater or lesser extent reversible, but extinctions are final. We always need to be vigilant but, on the plus side, plant conservation is now central to much of the ancient science of botany, and many of the richest plant sites are now relatively safe with rare plants rescued or their numbers and habitats restored.

Nevertheless, some of the oldest natural forests on Earth are still being felled, as in Brazil, and rare or threatened habitats such as temperate rainforests and grasslands, coastal mangrove swamps, seagrass meadows and dry tropical rainforests, together with tens of thousands of plant species worldwide, are regarded as being in danger. There are far too many plants for which botanists have little information to assess their conservation status while new plant discoveries continue to be made every year – and these are often already under threat.

One particular threat has the greatest potential for damage. As many scientists have emphasized for the last 30 years, and members of the public led by activists like Greta Thunberg are saying today, plants and all Nature are now in peril from a warming climate. Plants have existed on Earth for 470 million years and have witnessed many episodes of environmental change, especially to the climate. Although such change has always been a factor in Earth's geological history, we are now in an extreme warming phase, possibly caused and certainly exacerbated and accelerated by a global industrial society that persistently burns fossil fuels. A huge rise in the levels of heat-trapping carbon dioxide in the atmosphere since the beginning of the modern industrial period in the late 18th century has been associated with an increase in catastrophic floods, wildfires, desertification, salination and falls in water tables. The threat is increased by poor management and uncontrolled human settlement of natural habitats like fire-prone forests in Australia, California and the Mediterranean region. And as such threats expand, we may already be in another of Earth's great Ages of Extinction.

Habitat destruction, poor use of crops and agricultural land, especially the reduction in numbers of crop varieties and the rise of sometimes enormous monocultures of potatoes, bananas and other food staples, together with the increased ease of global transport and the inadequate monitoring of borders, have greatly facilitated the spread of plant pests and many diseases. All over

the world, over-exploited soils treated for decades with chemicals are losing their structure and ability to sustain crop yields. Meanwhile, deforestation continues. Crops extend deep into tropical forests, replacing naturally sustainable resources and vital ecological 'goods and services' with cash crops of soya and palm oil, and even cut flowers. The precipitous decline in insect numbers, leading to the loss of many pollinators of crops, will eventually lead to the collapse of some food supplies.

We will certainly pay a high price for the cumulative damage to our environment, not only in loss of the diversity of plants, animals animals and habitats, but also in the consequent huge economic losses and damage to human society. The health and integrity of Nature, especially plants, underpins our whole civilization and its wealth. The emergence of the Covid-19 virus is as much an environmental crisis as a medical one. Destruction of natural habitats, especially tropical forests, creates the conditions for invasive weeds and animal pests, as well as the spread of viruses and other animal diseases that can transfer across to humans.

Instead of persecuting nature we must learn to embrace its infinite benefits and resources. One of the most valuable trends in recent years has been the growth of ethnobotany – the study of the interaction between plants and people. This has given the traditional branches of botany – field studies and the taxonomy or naming of plants – a boost that enables them to flourish and to complement the modern molecular-based plant sciences. Ethnobotany has especially revealed how communities of native people living far outside the confines of conventional modern societies, Those whose rights, values and very survival have been so hard pressed by 'civilization', have profound, practical insights into the wise management of habitats and uses of plant resources. For too long these wild or semi-wild gifts have been unsustainably exploited, damaged or destroyed. Now, bringing on board new crops, new drugs and new ways of working with, rather than against nature, will benefit us all.

In the following pages are examples of where plants of major environmental and economic value are in peril, more often than not through human selfishness, greed, ignorance or poor planning.

If the plants disappear, then the very base of Earth's eco-systems will also go and with that, all present surface terrestrial life forms,

And that, inevitably, includes us.

A terrifying thought.

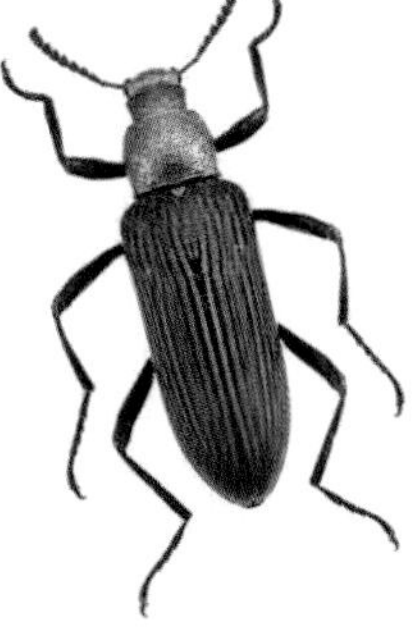

THE POTATO AND IRELAND

In 1845, Ireland had a huge population of nearly nine million, compared with just sixteen million in the whole of England, Wales and Scotland. Such a number of people could only be sustained by the **Potato** (*Solanum tuberosum*), 'the lazy crop', which thrived in a cool wet climate, could be left in the ground while the men went to work at other jobs, and was productive enough to be grown in little plots of land, so-called 'lazybeds'. The poor, especially, were largely dependent on this one staple, a food source that had ironically led to a quadrupling of the population of Ireland over the previous century. This single crop was very vulnerable to diseases, which arrived often enough – Dry Rot, Leaf Curl (spread by aphids) and the mould *Botrytis cinerea*. And, of course, the population would be equally vulnerable to any failure of the plant.

Which is exactly what happened. A sudden, new and devastating disaster struck; potato blight (*Phytophthora infestans*), a tiny fungus believed to have originated in Mexico, which overnight could turn healthy potatoes into black, evil-smelling rotting mush. It reduced the 1845 Irish crop by half. The next year it was catastrophic – with three-quarters lost. The removal of a staple food, one rich in starch, protein and vitamins, caused immediate starvation, and on top of that, precipitated diseases like typhus, scurvy and dysentery.

Unsympathetic landlords and British bureaucratic ineptitude failed to deliver the necessary famine relief, and a million died. These disasters were quickly followed by the population trying to escape with mass emigration. Another million left for America, England, Canada and Australia, but escape was not always enough. The 'Famine Ships' sat in North American harbours with their hapless passengers dying of disease on board, or in quarantine stations tantalizingly in sight

of freedom. Indeed, they were soon called 'Coffin Ships'. By 1848 Ireland had lost one quarter of its people, and emigration continued for decades.

Potato blight brought widespread misery to Scotland as well, and to many parts of Europe. But the potato and its blight would forever be linked to Ireland's tragic history. Few organisms or crop failures have had so great an impact on the human story. A good question might be: would the Irish have broken away from Britain, starting with the Easter Rising (below), without the bitter grievance they felt over the neglectful attitude of the British about the Potato Famine?

Another great long-term effect was political – and in the United States. The large numbers of Catholic Irish to arrive altered the racial and religious tone of America, which had been largely White Anglo-Saxon Protestant. The Irish also brought a degree of hatred into American politics. They may have affected attitudes to the South in the Civil War; they could have delayed American entry into both World Wars, and some of the forty million Irish-Americans, many of whom have never even been to Ireland, still harbour a real grudge against Britain a century and a half later. Seldom has a plant had such a tragic influence.

The GPO 1916 reproduced by kind permission of Thomas Ryan RHA

The battle of the cabbage garden

Weakened by deprivation and disease, Ireland in 1848 was in despair. An ancestor of one of our authors, William Smith O'Brien, Member of Parliament for Limerick, was horrified by the famine and led a revolt against English rule. Promised 5,000 'fully armed men', in humiliating reality the rebels mustered only 32 armed men and another twenty 'prepared to throw stones'. On July 29th 1848, this motley band intercepted some mounted constabulary who retreated into a

Mrs McCormack's cottage. 'The Battle of

OLIVES AND THE FATAL SPITTLEBUGS

Imagine the Mediterranean without the olive tree. Olives, alongside bread and wine, are an ancient staple and have long formed the basis of both human survival and rural prosperity in the region. Pressed olives yield an oil that is the essential ingredient of Mediterranean cuisine and a major item of trade for millennia. The **Olive Tree** (*Olea europaea*) itself is a quintessential feature of the landscape, perfect for the typical regional climate of hot, dry summers and mild, moist winters. From the 15th century, Portuguese, Spanish and English mariners took the olive around the world, especially to California, Chile, South Africa and Australia.

Up to 15 m tall with a broad crown and massive twisted trunk, gnarled grey bark and narrow, evergreen silvery-grey leaves, olive trees are covered in May with small creamy-white scented flowers, and in autumn with greenish, purplish or black fruits, each like a miniature plum enclosing a hard stone. Cultivated throughout the Mediterranean lowlands and up to 800 m in the hills, it also persists in abandoned terraces and fields, scrub and woodland, and even in built-up areas, or as a wild plant of cliffs and rocky places.

The olive's knotted trunk and its tenacity echo the harsh terrain and the struggles of country people. Lawrence Durrell wrote in *Prospero's Cell* (1945), before tourism and farm subsidies brought unforeseen wealth to Greece, of how '*the olive is for the peasant both a good servant and a hard master... Its crop is irregular, and ... bread and oil as a diet hardly leaves any margin for thrift.*' Today irrigation allows a more regular crop, and EU subsidies have encouraged extensive plantings of smaller, easily harvested trees. Modern olive groves can have a slightly regimented look, but mature and ancient olive trees, some over 1,000

years old, have special charm. Yet too many older terraces, often rich in wildflowers and wildlife, have been lost and one needs to travel far to see traditional flowery groves as in Greece's Mani peninsula and the island of Lesbos.

But now a terrible threat hangs over these charismatic trees and the industry and economy they support. In Italy, particularly in olive-producing Puglia in the 'heel', over eleven million of the region's sixty million olive trees have already been lost to bacterial infection, not least many ancient gnarled 'ulivi secolari'. The wilt disease *Xylella fastidiosa* blocks the water-conducting cells and is spread from tree to tree by a small native sap-sucking insect, common froghopper or meadow spittlebug (*Philaenus spumarius*), familiar to many when immature, hidden in a foamy blob of 'cuckoo spit'.

Until this disaster began in 2013, Puglia produced 40% of Italian olive oil. Infected trees are being cut down and burned, and since 2015 all trees within a hundred metres have to be removed and destroyed. It has since also been reported in Tuscany, Spain and France. There appears to be no means of stopping the disease, although it may partly depend on factors such as drought and attacks by other pests. Luckily, some trees are resistant and are being selected for propagation.

Thought to have arrived from Central America, this dangerous bacterium can infect over 200 different plants and has already devastated vines in California and citrus trees in Brazil – but the Mediterranean's olive tree will prove a more serious casualty. Should it disappear or merely be decimated, Mediterranean Europe will suffer incalculable economic damage and lose an international cultural emblem that has linked people, food and landscape since Antiquity.

The olive's yellowish wood makes handsome furniture, and its prunings provide kindling and food for livestock. The Romans anointed their bodies with olive oil, and it is still used in medicine and to make soap. An olive branch has been a symbol of peace since ancient times, as in victors' crowns at the original Olympic Games. The Bible has many references to Olive, the most famous telling how Noah released the dove from the Ark to seek dry land as the flood receded. It returned with an olive leaf in its beak. Farming could begin again.

BANANAS AND THEIR FUNGAL ENEMY

Despite being largely restricted to the tropics, bananas are surprisingly the world's most eaten fruit, and also the fourth most valuable food crop (after wheat, rice and maize). And like so many plants important to us, they are under threat.

Bananas may look like trees but are in fact the largest of all herbaceous (non-woody) perennial plants, up to 10 metres tall with great overlapping leaf-bases and a distinctive cone-shaped terminal bud that protects the male flowers. The separate whorls of female flowers develop and ripen into the familiar bunches or 'hands' of bananas, each fruit in fact an enormous elongated berry.

The bananas we eat today derive from the wild and anciently cultivated **Banana Plant** (*Musa acuminata, Musa balbisiana* and their hybrids), which came originally from South-east Asia. Bananas may have first been domesticated in New Guinea 10,000 years ago, from where after 1,000 BC they spread to India and China. Mariners distributed rootstocks around the Indian Ocean in the 5th–15th centuries and the Arab conquests took them through the Mediterranean region as far as Spain. In the 16th century bananas arrived in the Caribbean and tropical Americas, where Ecuador is now the largest exporter, and were later taken to Australia. However, the international banana trade only took off in the late 19th century when the Americans developed refrigerated ships.

After Edward Fyffe began importing bananas on a large scale in 1901, several British railway companies built 'Banana Vans'. These were ventilated and heated by steam to continue the ripening process during transportation.

While the British importer, Elders and Fyffe (now the Fyffe Group) was a respectable company, the American equivalent was not. The United Fruit Company was formed in 1899 and it soon dominated the banana trade in Central America, where it ended up owning 3.5 million acres (14,000 km2) and was, for instance, the biggest landowner in Guatemala. Its monopoly was backed by a stranglehold on transportation, with its own railways and a fleet of ships.

More sinister, it was dubbed 'El Pulpo', the octopus, blatantly bribing and controlling governments in Central America and the Caribbean. It engineered several political coups and even American invasions to further its ends and was involved in a banana strike in 1928, which led to the 'Banana Massacre' when Colombian troops – at the behest of the company – opened fire on the workers. It was those countries that were dominated by the company that were called 'Banana Republics'.

The United Fruit Company must sadly rank with Britain's East India Company (page 70) as disgraceful examples of commercial and political exploitation and colonialism.

Bananas comprise a variable group of species and cultivars. The 'Cavendish' group, yielding a cheap uniform product, provides nearly half of today's 100 million-ton global banana crop and almost all of those we buy and eat in the West. 'Cavendish' was bred by Joseph Paxton at Chatsworth House in

Plants and Us

Derbyshire, where he was Head Gardener for William Cavendish, the 6th Duke of Devonshire (page 297). In 1836 Paxton first harvested fruits from a plant, originally from China, which he had propagated in his pioneering heated glasshouse at Chatsworth. Since then it has travelled the world.

Widely grown in tropical regions, bananas are mostly consumed locally and a mere 17% of the crop – but a portion worth \$8 billion a year! – is for export, mostly to the USA, Europe and Japan. A natural convenience food – flavoursome, sweet and soft, bananas are full of fibre, minerals and vitamins. They are also regarded as very healthy, eaten by athletes and others to restore energy and potassium levels.

In tropical countries, the similar but non-sweet starchy bananas or 'plantains' are a carbohydrate food staple, one that once proved useful to slave owners in the Caribbean sugar plantations. In Ethiopia the related **Enset** or **False Banana** (*Ensete ventricosum*), a drought-tolerant root crop native to East Africa, feeds no less than 20 million people.

All is not well, however, with the ubiquitous crop of 'Cavendish' bananas. In the 1940s and 50s a wilt fungus, Panama Disease (*Fusarium oxysporon*), effectively wiped out the previous mainstream banana cultivar, the thicker-skinned, sweeter 'Gros Michel' or 'Big Mike'. Now *'Cavendish'*, similarly propagated from suckers, grown in huge monocultures with over-application of fungicides, and lacking the resilience of genetic variation, is itself now under threat. A new strain of Panama Disease, spreading through Asia since the 1990s, has reached Mozambique and Colombia and is likely to spread further, after it reached Queensland in 2015, Australian scientists developed a genetically modified 'Cavendish' banana, but this may be difficult to market because of public suspicion of GMOs.

Panama Disease is not the only threat. A leaf-spot fungus, Black Sigatoka or Black leaf streak (*Mycosphaerella fijiensis*), discovered on Fiji in 1963, has spread to all banana-producing regions to become the main banana fungal disease. It is less virulent but can reduce yields by half and cause premature or uneven ripening. This could mean that 'Cavendish' may not actually disappear, but in a few years may become economically unviable.

It is important in the longer term that plant breeders get away from 'Cavendish' to explore the untapped resource of genetic diversity available in wild bananas or locally cultivated 'land races' in South-east Asia, even including red and blue varieties. If the global crop does again fail, it will spell catastrophe for poorer tropical countries.

Despite the world being so reliant on a single crop, governments have been complacent – as they have with human diseases – and bananas have received too little research effort compared with other crops. 'Cavendish', like 'Big Mike' a generation earlier, has the great commercial advantage that it can be picked green and then ripen in transit. That is undoubtedly a key feature for future breeding. And perhaps future types of bananas may even taste better!

ELM TREES AND THEIR FATAL DISEASE

Do you even remember the magnificent **Elms** (*Ulmus*) the once ubiquitous trees that added such charm and grandeur to the countryside, or the sight of them lining streets and avenues? Their long story has often been associated with mortality – including that of people – both their association with country churchyards and an alarming habit of dropping branches suddenly and dangerously with no prior warning like a creaking in the wind. The wood, hard and not splitting easily, traditionally provided wood for chairs, wheel rims, and ironically, coffins – probably including those for some of their unfortunate victims. Hollowed out and laid end to end, they also once served as water pipes.

There is evidence for the susceptibility of elm trees to disease from as far back as the Neolithic era. But real disaster arrived in the 1960s with the sudden appearance of 'Dutch Elm Disease', not from the Netherlands but from Asia, whence it was introduced into Europe and America in epidemics which wiped out a shocking number of these beautiful trees. The name refers to the team of Dutch plant pathologists, Bea Schwarz, Christine Buisman and Johanna Westerdiijk and their untiring efforts in the 1920s to elucidate the disease and save Europe's elms. Note that the elms are complex and variable group to classify and some are much less resistant to the disease than others.

Dutch Elm Disease is caused by a microfungus, *Ophiostoma ulmi*, spread by Scolytus elm bark beetles. The tree tries to block the fungus by plugging its own xylem water distribution system, which stops water and nutrients reaching the rest of the plant, eventually killing it. The disease had first been detected in Europe way back in 1910, and this went on to devastate the **American Elm** (see Panel), but it was a more virulent strain, *Ophiostoma novo-ulmi*, brought in on timber from North America, that started major devastation in Europe from the 1960s. France, for instance, lost a tragic 97% of its elms.

In Britain alone, twenty-five million of these lovely trees died, leaving few survivors, and even most of the fifty that Prince Charles had planted at Highgrove were soon to perish. The so-called 'English Elms' (probably introduced by the Romans) of the Midlands and southern England all but disappeared other than a few hedgerow suckers. Vistas immortalized by our greatest landscape artists were lost forever.

Of course, Europe and America have tried to save their elms, and by all sorts of

means. Pruning the dead timber proved too expensive except where the trees had almost iconic value. Chemical spraying with DDT and dieldrin came next, but there was strong opposition because of the poisoning of birds, and it has been discontinued in favour of herbicides successfully injected into the trees. This expensive option has worked on a local scale, notably in Brighton, situated by the sea in a basin surrounded by protecting hills. Since 1998 the city has maintained a national collection of elms, together with a series of disease control measures. Another successful direction is a biological vaccine developed by the University of Amsterdam, 'Dutch Trig' trials with **American Elm** (see Panel) have proved more than worthwhile, reducing losses in Denver from 7% to 0.5%.

As a long-term approach, The Conservation Foundation has co-ordinated the identification of surviving elm variants such as 'Huntingdon Elm' and other apparently resistant elm populations and individuals to propagate, cross and select trees for the future. Over 3,000 apparently healthy elm trees have been planted out across the UK.

Combinations of these methods may work, but sadly it will take a very long time for these great trees to ever appear again as plentifully in our countrysides, towns and parks.

American Elm (*Ulmus americana*), native to eastern North America, was very important to the USA and its history.

- The Liberty Tree in Boston was an elm under which the colonists met to defy Britain.
- Dutch Elm Disease first arrived in 1928, was initially contained and then spread. Of the 77 million trees in North America in 1930, over 75% had gone by 1990.
- The elms of The National Mall in Washington were stricken in 1950, but saved by a combination of treatments.
- 'Elm City', New Haven, Connecticut, lost all its elms before 1950.
- Elm Street is an epitome of American suburbia, hence the resonance of the horror film series *A Nightmare on Elm Street*.
- The inner bark of the similar American native **Slippery Elm** (*Ulmus rubra*) is a mucilaginous herbal remedy long used to alleviate minor ailments of the skin, upper respiratory tract and digestive and urinary tracts. Mucilage is a complex carbohydrate secreted by certain plants.

ASH AND ITS DIEBACK

It would be easy to suggest that it is only man that can ruin the plants and trees in a much-loved countryside. Not true. As we have seen with the elm trees, nature can be equally devastating. With the Elm, the threat, a microfungus, was carried by beetles. In the case of the **Ash** (*Fraxinus excelsior*) it is another fungus, one blown by the wind. That said, the fungus in both cases seems to have been introduced by people.

The so-called ash dieback or chalara originated in Asia, where the native trees, Manchurian Ash and Chinese Ash, were able to resist the fungus *Hymenoscyphus fraxineus* (formerly *Chalera fraxineus*). But when the fungus arrived in Europe, there was no such immunity in the local ash trees, and about thirty years ago, starting in Poland, the devastation began.

The fungus spends the winter on dead leaves on the ground, then from June produces tiny white fruiting bodies and spores. The trouble is that these spores spread widely because they can blow with the wind from miles away before landing on the leaves of healthy ash trees, penetrating and eventually blocking the trees' water transport systems and killing them. The first signs appear in late summer with blackening and wilting of the leaves and shoots, and brown discoloration of the outer and inner bark. Scientists have worked out some other key factors: spores do not survive for more than a few days; trees need a high dose of spores to get infected; once infected, the trees cannot be cured although not all will die, indicating genetic variation for tolerance.

It is thought that in Britain we will eventually lose up to 90% or more of our native ash trees, with devastating results for the landscape, biodiversity (1,000 species live in association with ash) and the wood industry – and costing £15 billion to manage. The loss will be calamitous, as ash is a dominant tree of lime-rich and damp but well-drained soils, and on limestone rocks and cliffs, especially in the west and north of Britain and in Ireland. Europe has three native (and two naturalized American) ashes, and more than half of the 60 ash species known worldwide are cultivated in Britain. Several are already affected and nearly all may be at risk. Ash dieback has yet to be reported from North America, but the history of Dutch Elm Disease (page108) provides a salutary lesson in potential for cross-Atlantic infection.

It is not just the wind that can spread the spores. People visiting the countryside have been urged to brush soil, leaves and twigs off footwear and wheels of all kinds – cars, prams, bicycles, and especially from off-road mountain bikes. Imports from the Netherlands and elsewhere have since 2012 been strictly regulated, a measure which if imposed earlier might have prevented the epidemic in the first place. Nor should the UK- a country where native ash come up like a weed in woods, hedges and gardens - ever have imported such large quantities of ash saplings.

The government in Britain is working with Forest England and others in a research programme to establish a new generation of healthy ash trees, by monitoring the spread of the disease, carrying out mass screening to find resistant individuals and populations, and promoting a Living Ash Project to secure the supply of resistant trees in the UK and Ireland. Another approach will be cross breeding with tolerant species, especially the two East Asian ones.

All these measures are long-term. Sadly, it may take fifty years or more for the countryside in Britain and elsewhere to feature these beautiful trees that we used to take for granted.

BEES AND POLLINATION

One of the greatest threats to plants (and so to us) is the widely observed decline in the populations of bees and other insects. Indeed, years ago Albert Einstein put it brutally, '*Mankind will not survive the honey bees' disappearance for more than five years.*' Today, the increasing plight of the bee population and its alarming decline in numbers should be of great concern to governments and to us all. Incredibly, bees are responsible for pollinating a third of all the food crops we eat in their role as pollinators (see panel). Furthermore, bees also pollinate our oilseed crops are and these seeds provide a great deal of the world's supply of fat, and food for livestock. The problem even extends to what most of us wear. Cotton is grown for both oilseed but more so for fibre, and thus trouble for bees spells trouble for the cotton industry.

Is the widespread use of insecticides to blame? The jury is still out, but many scientists, notably UK insect guru Prof. Dave Goulson, think they are playing a major role in the decline of our most precious pollinators, as well as other insects. From the 1990s it became apparent that neurotoxic neonicotinoid insecticides – synthetic forms

of nicotine were killing large numbers of bees. Much more toxic to insects than the notorious DDT, they were banned by the EU in 2018 but are widely used elsewhere. They are not only absorbed by plants, so contaminating the pollen and nectar on which the bees feed, but persist in soil and water, where they accumulate with repeated use. And plans to include these water-soluble chemicals to control sea-lice on salmon farms suggest that the threat will not be going away.

But bees are being weakened too by stresses such as *Varroa* mites which suck their fat storage bodies and spread viruses. Originally found in the Asian honey bee, a more virulent strain has spread worldwide. Some wild honey bees seem to have evolved immunity, but careful breeding programmes may be the only long-term answer for hive honey bees. In the UK, other threats, which include *Acarapis* mites living in the bees' respiratory system and Bee Paralysis Virus (CBPV), causing trembling, hair loss and loss of the ability to fly, appear to have expanded in recent years, perhaps related to the importation of queen bees from other parts of Europe.

And, potentially even more disastrous, the bee-predating Asian giant hornet is beginning to colonize Europe and North America, although fortunately still rare. Meanwhile many thousands of beehives are mysteriously just being abandoned in episodes of so-called 'Colony Collapse Disorder'.

Bees are by no means the only plant pollinators. Both in Europe and in America (where honey bees were introduced), native bumblebees and various solitary bees shoulder much of the burden. Others include butterflies, moths, wasps, beetles and ants, while in the Tropics birds like hummingbirds, honeyeaters and sunbirds play a major role, attracted especially to red flowers. Even animals have a role, especially bats but also monkeys, lemurs, possums, rodents and lizards, even snails. But bees are the most ubiquitous and efficient pollinators whose future we are able to influence.

So we had better start exerting that influence before it is too late for us all.

Just some of the crop plants in danger of lack of pollination by bees

Alfalfa (Lucerne)
Apple
Almond
Apricot, Nectarine and Peach
Artichoke
Aubergine (Eggplant)
Blackberry, Loganberry and Raspberry
Blueberry
Cabbage, Broccoli, Brussels Sprouts, Cauliflower and Kale
Carrot
Cashew
Celery
Cherry
Citrus fruits
Clovers
Dill and Fennel
Garlic
Melons and Watermelons
Mustards
Oilseed Rape
Onion
Passion Fruit
Pear
Plum
Pumpkin, Squashes and Zucchini

BOX AND ITS ADVANCING ENEMIES

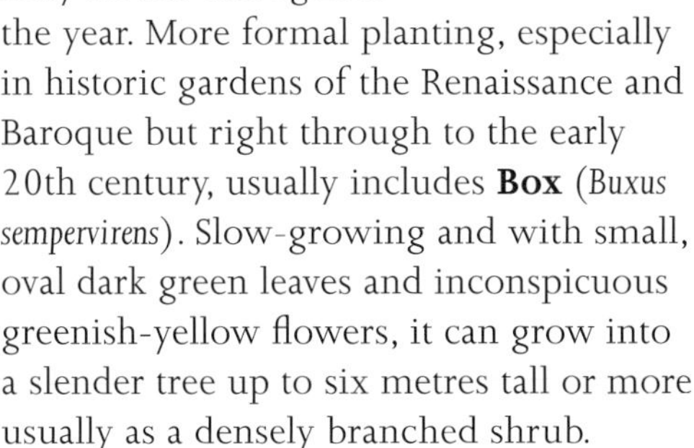

Gardeners employ all sorts of shrubs and trees to plant and train as hedges, especially evergreen shrubs that provide a leafy screen throughout the year. More formal planting, especially in historic gardens of the Renaissance and Baroque but right through to the early 20th century, usually includes **Box** (*Buxus sempervirens*). Slow-growing and with small, oval dark green leaves and inconspicuous greenish-yellow flowers, it can grow into a slender tree up to six metres tall or more usually as a densely branched shrub.

Gardeners have prized this evergreen shrub since at least Roman times when Pliny the Younger in the 1st century AD enthused in a letter to a friend about the Box hedges at his Tuscan villa 'clipped into different shapes' – so easily trained into a hedge or topiary, or as a neat edging or backdrop for paths, beds and parterres, especially the compact, dwarf cultivar 'Suffrutescens'. The native home of Box is scrub, forest clearings and thickets on dry, stony, or lime-rich soils in the hills and lower mountains of southern Europe and SW Asia, where after the winter the leaves often scorch a striking yellowish-bronze. It is widespread but only locally common, and in some areas, such as limestone plateaux in the Cévennes of SW France or Box Hill in Surrey, the only site in the UK where Box forms woodland, it creates a distinctive landscape.

But it is a plant that is much more associated with gardens than the wild. In fact, gardens without Box hedges would be unthinkable. Or would they? For in recent years this ubiquitous garden stalwart has come under severe threat from several fungal parasites and animal pests. From the 1990s, Box in European gardens has suffered from box blight, a rapid dieback brought about by the fungus *Cylindrocladium buxicola*, which has since spread to North America. Another fungus but one long present, *Volutella buxi*, browns the leaves but causes much more minor and local damage.

The most recent threat is the larvae of the box tree moth (*Cydalima perspectalis*), originally from eastern Asia but invading Europe since 2006, which can completely defoliate Box hedges and even attack the bark. In the UK, this moth is widespread in London and parts of southern England but increasingly present elsewhere – attracting the largest number of enquiries about pest damage that the Royal Horticultural Society receives from concerned gardeners.

It is spreading rapidly too across Europe and is suspected of being introduced to the Caucasus with box plants imported from Italy to Sochi to landscape the 2014 Winter Olympic Games! The moth and larvae do fortunately have several predators, although avoiding the box blight fungus will require the breeding of resistant cultivars or even the total or partial replacement of Box with other evergreen hedge plants such as **Yew** (*Taxus baccata*). The fine-textured, hard cream-yellow wood of box is prized for carving and turning on the lathe, and it is a traditional material for cabinet makers' inlays, musical instruments, shuttles for silk weaving, and wood-engraving blocks.

GRAPES AND PHYLLOXERA

Today we are sadly becoming used to seeing introduced plant pests and diseases cutting a swathe through crops, garden plants and native or planted forest trees. The damage to local and national economies and landscapes can be profound, and it is sobering to reflect that we once nearly said goodbye to vineyards. For just over a century and a half ago, a diminutive but virulent insect threatened the loss of all the grapes, vineyards and wine production in Europe and, especially, the Mediterranean region where the trio of wine, olive oil and cereals had formed the staple crop since ancient times.

Wine produced from the fermentation of grapes has for thousands of years been one of humankind's greatest pleasures. Cultivated from at least 4,000 BC in the Caucasus and soon adopted by the Mesopotamian and Egyptian civilizations, the woody, climbing **Grape Vine** (*Vitis vinifera*) and its familiar bunches of fruits feature prominently in the Bible and much other ancient literature. The Phoenicians, Greeks and Romans spread vine cultivation around the Mediterranean and over western Europe as far as Britain, and later, especially in the era of European colonial expansion, vines and wine production became cosmopolitan. Hundreds of cultivars have been bred of table, dried or wine grapes, differing in both the growth and form of the plants and in the flavour of the raw and fermented fruits.

All was well until the mid-19th century when the introduction of new vines from North America – a centre of wild grape species diversity – to Europe led to the introduction of grape phylloxera (*Daktulosphaira vitifoliae*), a sap-sucking bug related to the greenfly and other aphids, to which the native Grape Vine proved highly susceptible. The insects induce deformations of the roots and facilitate the entry of bacterial and fungal plant disease. Spreading through France and across Europe from the 1860s, these tiny creatures devastated whole vineyards and threatened the entire European and Mediterranean grape harvest, also that of California. The 'Reconstitution' of the grape and wine industry was made possible by grafting vines on to rootstocks of phylloxera-resistant North American grape vines, crossing with these vines, or growing the native American species themselves. Most of today's vines have been grafted on to American rootstocks, a complete change from the viniculture systems that had been in place for millennia.

Phylloxera hit the French economy hard, as wine production fell by over three-quarters, leading to increased immigration of workers to North Africa and America, with some wine makers decamping to enhance the industry in Chile. At least two thirds of European vineyards were destroyed, although many were later replanted with grafted stock. Californian vines were also replanted, although from 1919 the industry suffered even worse damage from Prohibition (page 176).

There remain today a few scattered pockets of vineyards still unaffected by phylloxera, usually on the poorest soils, including the white Asyrtiko grape on the volcanic Greek island of Santorini, and vines on the volcanic ash slopes of Mount Etna in Sicily; also, some Reisling vineyards in the Mosel region of Germany, where the soil is poor and slaty. In the southern hemisphere, more isolated by harsh geographical zones, Chilean and many Australian vines remain phylloxera-free.

NEMATODES - THE HIDDEN ENEMY

Nematodes are one of the greatest threats to plants, yet most people have never heard of them. In fact, nematodes or roundworms have been described for centuries, at least the visible ones. In the Book of Numbers in the Bible, 'Fiery serpents' are mentioned, which may have been the 30-inch long tropical Guinea worm (*Draculunculus medinensis*) we know today. Great scientists of Antiquity like Hippocrates, Aristotle and Galen recorded nematodes, including the roundworm (*Ascaris lubricoides*) of the human gut, sometimes 14 inches long. Concerning plants, in his *Love's Labour's Lost*, Shakespeare writes '*Sowed Cockle, reap'd no corn*', alluding to Ear cockle or Seed Gall ruining crops of wheat and rye, which we now know is caused by the much smaller, 5mm, nematode *Anguina tritici*.

It is amazing how people don't know about nematodes – because with an estimated 40,000 species they are among the most successful and ubiquitous living things. They live inside other life forms in farming soil, in frozen wastes, hot deserts and tropical jungles, up mountains and at the bottom of the sea. One species apparently lives only among the fibres of German beer mats. With 60 billion for each human, they account for about 80%

of all animals on earth. For plants they can sometimes be a benefit, breaking down the organic material in compost or attacking plant pests such as cutworms and weevils, but they are usually a real problem, with few plants and crops that do not suffer from their presence.

Most plant-parasitic nematodes or eelworms are very small, tiny, which is why it took science so long to focus on them. It was not until 1743 that the English biologist and Jesuit priest John Turberville Needham (1713–83) used his new and superior microscope to observe eelworms, 'aquatic animals, like worms, eels or serpents', inside the galls that they induced on wheat plants. In America, pioneer plant pathologist Nathan A. Cobb (1859–1932) led a generation of nematologists to banish any scepticism about the effects of what he called 'the devastating eelworm'.

Gradually puzzled farmers slowly recognised the hidden enemy they were up against. They realised that the practice of crop rotation had been unconsciously in part to offset the build-up of nematodes in their soil. In Germany, they even injected cyanide and other gases to try to kill the nematodes before planting sugar-beet. High resolution microscopic filming reveals nematodes using a long sharp 'stylet' to stab into plant cells, incidentally allowing other harmful viral, bacterial or fungal diseases to follow.

Incredibly, the 4,100 known species of plant-parasitic nematodes do about $100 billion's worth of damage to crops each year. Indeed, there is scarcely a crop in the world not affected, and all the most economically important ones are vulnerable – potatoes, wheat, rice, maize, sugar-beet, soya, vines, cotton, citrus fruits, tomatoes, nuts, bulb crops – and literally hundreds of crops are at risk.

To counter nematodes attacking field crops, one of the most successful chemical weapons is aldicarb, buried as a granule in the furrow at planting. Aldicarb protects emerging young roots from nematode and certain foliar insect and spider mite damage. Treated crops are able to develop strong roots and vigorous foliage, and out-yield unprotected crops (see above). But Aldicarb is a restricted-use product and can only be used on registered crops.

As well as such chemicals, there are other solutions, fumigants and resistant cultivars, and there are even fungi present in the soil that trap them in minute lassoo-like loops before then digesting them. Nevertheless, the farming community looks to be locked in this battle against a hidden enemy for years to come.

PLANTS OUT OF SIGHT - OUT OF MIND

The world has gradually begun to wake up to the many plants in peril – at least on land. Deforestation, pollution and climate change are now everyday topics of conversation. But most people would be amazed to discover that many of the plants most vital for our future and that of our world are hidden – because they are under water in the sea. Here are some of their very important stories.

GREEN ALGAE : PLANKTON, CORALS AND OXYGEN

'Pond scum' is an old-fashioned insult usually applied to thieves, vandals and other disreputable folk. The words bring to mind stagnant, grubby green ponds or perhaps larger bodies of water like low-grade boating lakes. In fact, the green colour comes from an interesting, beautiful and varied group of more than 7,000 so-called 'lower plants', the Chlorophytes or Green Algae, regarded in modern classifications as being distinct from the true plants. They may sometimes create unprepossessing scum or blankets but en masse they form one of Earth's vital life support systems. And, like so many of the organisms generally referred to as 'plants', they are today under threat.

Green Algae were the progenitors of all the land plants and thus the flowering plants that now dominate the continents and are the main subject of the this book. They obtain their energy from sunlight via photosynthesis, having, like the true plants, the same green pigment, chlorophyll, and like plants they very often possess cellulose cell walls and store food as starch. Most consist of microscopic single cells or groups and colonies of cells, although several are substantial green seaweeds, like the **Sea Lettuce** (*Ulva lactuca*) of seaside rock pools, with quite complex structures. Some Green Algae exist inside the tissues of minute or larger animals, notably within the cells of the reef-forming corals. In the tissues of lichens, they exist in a specialized intimate association with a fungus. Individually they may be small, but together they make up 1% of global biomass and in fact contribute more to carbon fixation through photosynthesis than all the forests on land.

The most abundant Green Algae are the Diatoms, each one a single cell enclosed by the interlocking halves of a transparent silica shell, like a tiny Petri dish. Diatoms are found wherever there is fresh or salt water but are most abundant in the plankton of the oceans, where algae are responsible for releasing well over half of the oxygen produced by all the photosynthesis on the planet. We truly need them, but most of us are unaware of them – or of the warnings of scientists recording a fall of some 40% in plankton numbers since 1950, probably largely in response to warming oceans.

Another important group are the Dinoflagellates, also one-celled but with two flagella (Latin *flagellum*, little whip) which enable them to move through the water. They attract attention only when present in excess – the so-called 'red tides' which release toxins that poison fish and make shellfish unfit or even dangerous for human consumption. Dinoflagellates without a flagellum also live inside the cells of marine animals, most importantly in symbiosis with the tiny colonial animals that comprise corals, beneficially exchanging nutrients and giving some coral species their green, yellowish or brownish colour. If environmental conditions deteriorate, when the water is polluted, full of sediment or too warm, the corals expel these algae and become bleached, effectively dead – which is another consequence of global warming already happening in some regions. We lose coral reefs at our peril for they are immensely productive and shelter a third of the world's fish species. Australia's Great Barrier Reef alone has 350 coral species, 4,000 mollusc species and 1,500 different fish, some 8% of all fish species in the world.

The dinoflagellates in plankton are important primary producers in oceanic food chains and they constantly recycle nutrients. But we take all these Green Algae and other plankton – basically a living, breathing soup for granted, and rarely give them a thought. With the other forgotten undersea plant heroes – the seagrass meadows, the kelp forests, the richness of intertidal seaweeds, even the microscopic algae forming a film on those seaweeds – they provide a vital support system for all life on Earth.

SEAGRASSES AND THEIR UNDERWATER MEADOWS

For most people it is conventional wisdom that flowers grow on land, or maybe in ponds, streams, rivers, or lakes, while in the sea they are replaced by the flowerless seaweeds. But some seventy specialized species of flowering plants have evolved to live submerged in sea water. These seagrasses are superficially similar to some of the seaweeds and thus largely overlooked, even by scientists. Yet they are so successful that the extensive marine 'meadows' they form are among the most productive habitats on Earth, supporting rich assemblages of marine animals and absorbing large amounts of the carbon that would otherwise contribute to 'greenhouse gases'.

The seagrasses are, in fact, not grasses at all and are more closely related to the lilies. Typically they have creeping underground stems or rhizomes, ribbon-like leaves and inconspicuous flowers that are actually pollinated under water, and they mostly live in clear shallow seas of the warmer temperate and tropical regions. One of them, however, **Eelgrass** (*Zostera marina*), is widespread on the coasts and estuaries of the North Atlantic and North Pacific, where its extensive beds – like miniature green forests – support a rich and varied fauna of invertebrates and fish. English marine biologist, C.M. Yonge, vividly described cuttlefish hunting their prey amid the greenery, '*their striped bodies appearing through the leaves of eel-grass like tigers in a jungle*'. Eelgrass meadows provide protection, nurseries and food for fish, notably Atlantic cod, and at low tide are feeding grounds for ducks, geese and wading birds. They store carbon, and also absorb pollutants, build up sediment, reduce coastal erosion, and purify and oxygenate seawater.

A larger plant, **Posidonia** or **Neptune Grass** (*Posidonia oceanica*) covers much of the seabed of the shallower waters of the Mediterranean and will be familiar to anyone who has taken a seaside holiday, there the meadows forming dark underwater patches. Quantities of silvery-brown fragments of the plants' leaves, which grow up to a metre long, pile up on the strand, along with the sea-washed brown fuzzy balls unkindly known in Spain as *pedos de monjas* or 'nuns' farts'. Like eelgrass, as well as supporting wildlife and fisheries, the plants protect against coastal erosion, Posidonia form a

It is gratifying that Carlsberg, brewer of legendary beers – whose ads once had Orson Welles sonorously intone 'Probably the best beer in the world' – is now working with WWF to protect depleted seagrass meadows. In fact, the company and its Carlsberg Foundation has a distinguished history of support for research in the plant sciences (including studies by John Akeroyd and colleagues on the flora of the Greek mountains).

In the UK, 'Project Seagrass' brings together WWF, Sky Ocean Rescue and Swansea University, initially using 1.2 million seeds to re-plant eelgrass off Pembrokeshire in Wales, and by 2050 restoring 2,500 hectares of seagrass meadow around the British Isles. Carlsberg is helping to finance the project with an on-pack donation of 50p from every special edition Carlsberg beer pack.

Carlsberg has also released new research ahead of Earth Hour to mark the launch of its WWF partnership, which should inspire British people to take actions with the power to make a big impact on the environment. Carlsberg and WWF have created Carlsberg's 'Together Towards ZERO' programme, which sets carbon reduction targets to keep the rise in global warming below 1.5°C.

The research, which examines British attitudes and behaviour towards the planet, both pre- and during COVID-19, has found that more than two in three (70%) of us are now more optimistic for the country's green future than they were a year ago, with 80% vowing to make lifestyle changes to protect the planet, and 86% saying their children and grandchildren are their motivation. Seagrass conservation will provide a valuable contribution.

Does this make Carlsberg the most ecologically helpful beer company? Probably!

mass or *matte* of living and dead rhizomes and roots – growing up through the accumulated sediment, a metre or so a century – which provides a substantial carbon sink. Posidonia beds are important for marine archaeology as the vegetation blanket and low oxygen levels help to preserve water-logged wrecks even from ancient times.

In tropical waters, as their names suggest, other seagrasses such as the **Turtlegrass** (*Thalassia testudinum*) and **Manatee Grass** (*Syringodium filiforme*) of the Caribbean and Gulf of Mexico, are food for larger herbivorous animals, many of them threatened species such as turtles and marine mammals. And from Africa to the western Pacific, a seagrass with paddle-shaped leaves, **Dugong Grass** (*Halophila ovalis*), is a major food source for dugongs, whale-like mammals living in shallow tropical waters.

Despite their ecological and economic value, seagrasses have received too little attention from scientists and governments. Above all, their importance lies in their sheer productivity, often greater than that of cereal crops, with an acre of seagrass meadow able to sequester annually 740 pounds (336 kilos) of carbon. It has been estimated that seagrass meadows capture up to 83 million tonnes of carbon per year, at a rate five times higher than that of tropical forests.

However, seagrass meadows have declined progressively in the last hundred years, with over 30,000 square kilometres already lost this century. They are vulnerable to increasing human coastal activity: marinas, and other infrastructure, increased turbidity, nutrients from the land that produce smothering algal growth, and damage from dredging or shellfish farming, quite apart from a long-term threat from rising temperatures and sea levels.

Seagrasses may be unfamiliar to many but their meadows are a vital resource that needs to be protected. The sad thing is, so few people are aware of their importance.. Seagrasses have long had numerous sustainable uses by local communities, and in Europe were once gathered for fertilizer, house insulation and bedding for people and animals. Eelgrass traditionally stuffed mattresses, including those of French soldiers during the First World War, and was used to pack fragile china and glass. During the 1930s a wasting fungal disease caused by a slime mould, *Labyrynthula zasterae,* wiped out as much as 90% of the Eelgrass beds on both sides of the Atlantic and it has since been largely replaced by artificial materials

SEAWEEDS AND THEIR HIDDEN FORESTS

When people talk about forests they are usually referring to the tropical rainforests, temperate deciduous forests in Eurasia and North America or the belt of coniferous trees across the far north. Many would be surprised that as on land, forests also occur in the sea: the mangrove forests of tropical coastlines (see page 5) and, in the colder waters of both Hemispheres, extensive forests of the flowerless algae and related organisms that we call, rather insultingly, 'seaweeds'.

The most familiar of these, visible at low tide, are the long brown wracks that are attached to and festoon coastal rocks, sometimes supported in the water by gas-filled bladders. They occur with a variety of attractive smaller green and red seaweeds, which we can often see in rockpools along with assorted marine animals such as sea snails and crabs. Seaweeds are beautiful, economically productive and vital for the

health of the seas. They are also threatened, not least because few people give them a second thought.

The largest brown seaweeds are the kelps or oar-weeds and their allies, some as large as trees, which form their submerged forests in the cold and cooler waters of both hemispheres and are only revealed at the lowest tides. They form a fascinating group that modern research suggests sits slightly apart from the true plants. Their green chlorophyll is masked by other pigments, especially brown fucoxanthin. (Similarly the red pigment phycoerythrin masks the chlorophyll of red algae, the most numerous group of seaweeds.)

Like the forests of trees on land, the forgotten undersea kelp forests have a canopy, but one with great seaweed fronds rather than leafy branches. These forests have layers of vegetation comprising the green and red seaweeds that grow on the large basal holdfasts and stout stems or 'stipes' of the kelp. This vegetation provides food and shelter for communities of diverse marine animals from sponges, molluscs, sea urchins and starfish to fish, seabirds and otters.

Kelp forests may not be familiar to many people but they provide important environmental 'goods and services'. Forming one of Earth's most productive ecosystems, they help to keep seawater clean, fix and accumulate carbon, protect coasts from erosion and support fisheries by providing fish feeding grounds and sheltered nurseries for young fish and shellfish. Rich in iodine and other nutrients, dried kelp or *kombu* is popular as food in Japan and increasingly so elsewhere.

The North Atlantic coastal waters, home to one of the richest seaweed floras, have many great kelp forests, up to 4 metres tall, growing down to 30 metres in depth and dominated by **Oarweed** (*Laminaria digitata*) and **Tangle** (*Laminaria hyperborea*). With the several species of **Wrack** (*Fucus*) of the intertidal zones, this is a significant habitat belt around the coasts of Western Europe and eastern North America. Elsewhere, **Giant Kelp** (*Macrocystis pyrifera*), the largest seaweed of all (above) with fronds 40 metres or more in length, is found along Pacific coasts of North and South America and the coasts of South Africa, Australia and New Zealand.

Giant Kelp forests in particular face threats from pollution, sedimentation, increased sea temperatures, human alteration of their habitats and local over-harvesting for fertilizer and carbohydrates called alginates (widely used in dentistry, skin care products, brewing and for thickening a range of human and pet foods, with potential as biofuels). A decrease in their extent has been observed in regions as far apart as the UK, southern Australia and California.

Fragile and vulnerable to climate change, in Tasmania, for example, the kelp forests were once large enough to feature on nautical charts – but over 95% of them have disappeared since the 1940s, perhaps due to warmer sea temperatures and an increase in the numbers of sea urchins that can overgraze young kelp to the extent of creating 'urchin barrens'. On western US coasts, the sea otters that feed among the floating fronds of Giant Kelp control the urchins. Once hunted almost to extinction for their fur, the otters have recovered their populations over the last century – a critical factor in the survival of the kelp forests.

Wisely harvested, for they regrow rapidly, kelps offer a significant renewable resource with a range of uses. In the Far East, red algae comprise a major crop that yields food (see Panel), including jelly-like agar, which is also the medium for culturing microbes for science and medicine and for the micro-propagation of plants. We need algae and must protect them, but because they are hidden, they face a greater threat than most other plants.

The English scientist who became 'Mother of the Sea'

Several red seaweeds are traditional foods, especially in Japan but also for example in Ireland, Scotland and Jamaica. **Dulse** (*Palmaria palmata*) is eaten fresh or dried as snack or added to enhance the flavour of various dishes, and dried **Irish Moss** or **Carrageen** (*Chondrus crispus*) is boiled to make a blanc-mange-like jelly.

One of the most valuable edible red seaweeds is **Laver** (*Porphyra umbilicalis*), which forms thin tough sheets up to 20 cm across attached to rocks and stones. In Wales it is made into laverbread or *bara lawr*, served rolled in oatmeal and fried with bacon, and in countries of the Far East the closely related **Nori** (*Pyropia tenera*) is widely eaten. In Japan this wraps the sushi parcels that are a such a feature of that country's cuisine. It was, however, an English phycologist (a botanist who studies seaweeds), Dr Kathleen Mary Drew-Baker, who in 1949 single-handedly rescued the Japanese nori industry.

After the Second World War not only was Japan short of food but also the nori harvest had declined. Dr Drew-Baker carefully worked out the complex life history of *Porphyra*: the sheet or thallus produces both spores and reproductive structures with sexually produced spores that germinate and bore into bivalve mollusc shells to form tiny plants, which themselves give rise to another generation of sheet-like plants.

Japanese marine biologists built upon this research to raise and artificially seed nori plants on to nets where it could grow rapidly to maturity.

Today, Japan's nori industry, with farms covering 600 km (230 square miles) of coastal waters, is worth $1 billion a year, half of the East Asian production. Kathleen Drew-Baker continues to be revered in Japan as the 'Mother of the Sea', a much deserved accolade.

PROTECTION AND THE TROUBLE WITH TRAVEL

For millions of years, evolution has devised ingenious ways of preserving and protecting plants against the ravages of climate, disease or predators. Some plants are equipped to cope even with the most extreme environmental conditions, including severe atmospheric pollution or the presence of toxic salt, arsenic, lead and zinc in soil and water. All plants are engaged in an ongoing struggle, analogous to an arms race, against attack by fungi, diseases and by insects and other animals.

The more we learn, it is clear that the protective devices which plants employ can be most remarkable. Leaves attacked by caterpillars emit chemicals that alert other tissues of the plant and also those of neighbouring plants to produce substances injurious to the insects. For example, Acacia trees are adapted to quickly emit ethylene gas when giraffes start eating their leaves, so adjacent acacias promptly pump unpleasant toxins into their own leaves, and the giraffes move off 100 metres or so before trying to feed again. Oaks and other woodland trees carry bitter toxic tannins in their bark and leaves to kill or deter a range of chewing insects. Willows produce bitter salicylic acid,

nightshades a range of alkaloids. Clovers and other plants release cyanide when bruised. The bitter flavours that plant breeders have removed from modern vegetable varieties are themselves part of an armoury to make these plants unpalatable to animals. Several other plants, including elms and pines, call upon something even more amazing. When a caterpillar bites into a leaf, the trees can exactly identify its saliva and release the precise pheromones that will attract predator parasitic wasps that arrive and lay their eggs in offending enemies. Often these warning messages go out to other plants, not only via inter-locking root systems but also across an interlinked web of fungi (*mycorrhiza*) on the roots and in the soil.

Such methods of self-protection have developed and depended on most plants, especially trees, remaining in one place and undisturbed for millennia. For a long time this was helped by humans, the bulk of whom, at least since the last Ice Age, hardly ever moved more than a few miles from where they were born, lived and worked. But over the five centuries since Columbus

first crossed the Atlantic in 1492, the blink of an eye in botanical terms, a new factor has emerged – large-scale international transport and travel. This has inadvertedly created some of the world's great ecological and agricultural disasters.

The whole precious balance of plants and their habitats and the other plants, animals and fungi with which they interact has been upset. Invasive plants and other organisms are now one of the major causes of loss of native biodiversity worldwide as they disrupt ancient established ecosystems and displace native plants. They have the same effect on farming and forestry. In the Mediterranean region, species of Eucalyptus trees introduced from Australia have replaced native forests; in Britain and Ireland the

introduced Purple Rhododendron covers moors and invades woods and plantations, while Giant Hogweed strides along river-banks. Weeds now occur worldwide or right across whole temperate and tropical climatic zones.

Even more dramatic for humans, many diseases have migrated too. The blight that caused the infamous and devastating Irish Potato Famine arrived from Mexico; Dutch Elm Disease came with a fungus from Asia, ravaged the Elms in America and then came to Europe on imported American timber; the tiny Phylloxera bug came into Europe on American vines (themselves more resistant to the sap-sucking aphid attached to them) and proceeded to destroy the European wine industry; Bananas are under threat from new strains of wilt fungus from Asia and Fiji; Ash trees, resistant in Asia to the fungus which causes die-back, are not resistant in Europe and so are dying, while iconic Olive trees are disappearing in Italy, Spain and France because of the wilting disease which arrived from Central America, ironically spread by the native meadow spittlebug. Box

trees are being ruined by a moth from Asia, supposedly first brought in on hedges for the rather casual reason of landscaping President Putin's 2014 Sochi Winter Olympics! The list of such unforeseen disasters is endless.

All of these examples show that plants and trees that have for millennia successfully managed to survive where they were, are then at terrible risk when humans with their ships, railways and, more recently, aircraft, bring in dangers for which they are not prepared. And, alongside the injurious introductions, people increasingly inflict damage on a regional scale: climate change, the clear-felling of forests, the destruction of ancient grasslands by expanding agriculture and the over-collection of our precious resources of wild medicinal plants.

Fortunately, plants are resilient and retain the ability to continue to evolve in order to react in the face of human destruction. A recent report from the mountains of SW China nicely shows such evolution in action. A species of fritillary, the lily-like bulb *Fritillaria delavayi*, used in Chinese medicine as a cough and chest remedy, has two flower colour variants: bright greenish-yellow or dull greyish to brown. The camouflage of these duller plants makes them far less visible among the grey

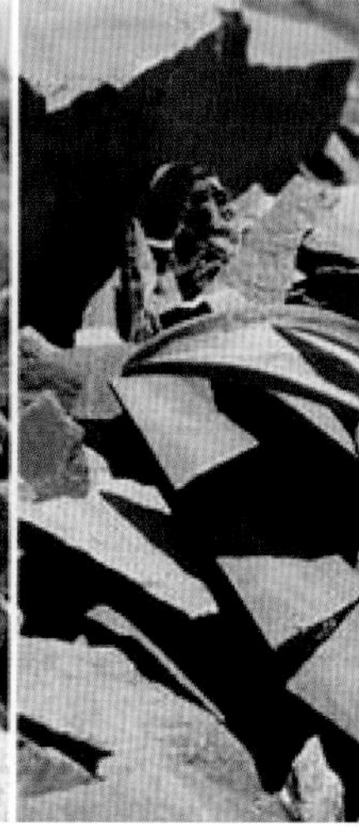

stones of the high-altitude screes in which they grow. Botanists have worked out that the plants are, incredibly, evolving to look dull and invisible to protect themselves (above) where there are high levels of bulb collection for the lucrative medicinal trade.

Charles Darwin, an optimist at heart, would have been thrilled by such episodes of 'natural' selection. They are the future.

Sadly, globalization and international transport have proved to be one of the great enemies of wild and crop biodiversity and conservation.

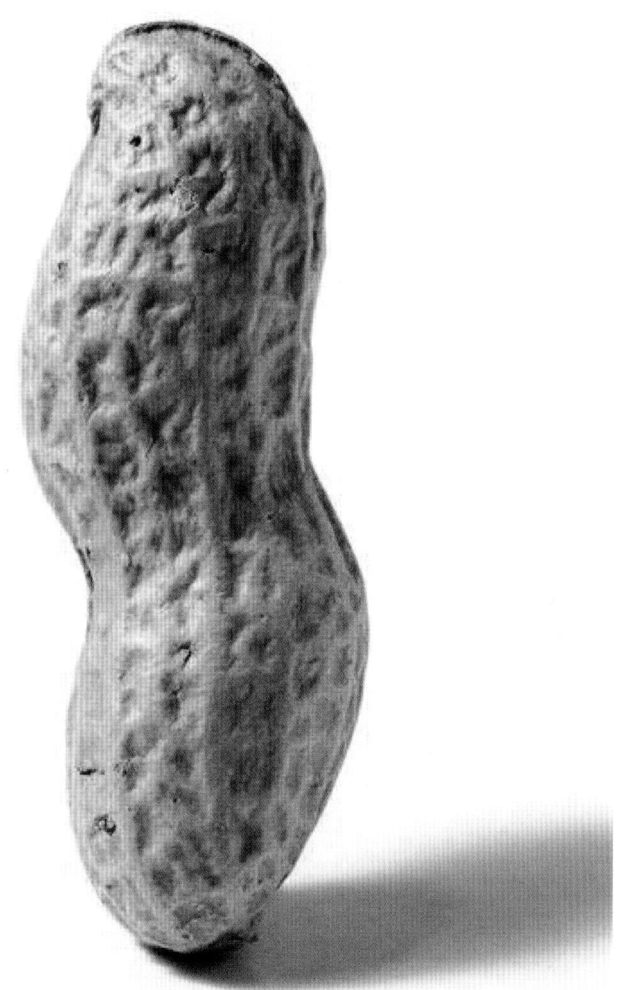

PLANTS AND MONEY

Holland and Tulipomania
India and the evil hedge
Frankincense and Myrrh
The Nutmeg and New York
Tea and Britain's American colonies
The 'Timber Rush' of America
Liverpool as 'Timbertown'
Burdock and 'Hook and Loop'
Mulberry and silk
Plants as marketing tools
Peanuts and the GroundnutScheme

HOLLAND AND TULIPOMANIA

The theft of plants and trees from suburban gardens is probably viewed as a modern crime. Yet such misdemeanours go back a long way. Indeed, a theft 400 years ago of a collection of bulbs ultimately created a crisis for a whole nation. And the Netherlands, only just free of the Spanish yoke, could ill afford the turmoil of what became known as 'tulipomania'.

Of all ornamental plants, tulips have captured the most imagination. From the steppes and stony hills across a broad belt from the Aegean to Afghanistan and Central Asia, tulips began to trickle into Europe from the mid-16th century via diplomatic links between the Turkish Sultan, Suleiman the Magnificent, and the Holy Roman Empire. In particular, Charles de l'Ecluse (better known to botanists as Carolus Clusius) spread tulips throughout Europe and promoted many of the spring bulbs we plant today. Born in France, he travelled and studied widely in Europe and in 1593 came to Leiden to establish a new physic garden, bringing with him both years of scholarship and a prized collection of tulip bulbs from Vienna.

Clusius was very well-known for championing tulips and produced an early classification – but his greatest influence was inadvertent. Someone sneaked into his garden and stole his tulips. Soon they were out, 'distributed in the trade'. Breeders set to work on natural variations and soon a range of garden forms was available, some rare and most highly prized.

In Holland in the early 1600s, tulips became more and more fashionable. Painters extolled their virtues and prices of the bulbs rose, especially those of the more extravagantly marked parrot tulips, with their intricate white or yellow 'breaks ' or feathery patterns caused by viral infections, then a complete mystery even to scientists. Tulips rapidly became status symbols reflecting the new wealth derived from the Dutch East Indies trade. Propagation was slow, but buyers could rely upon small daughter bulbs or 'offsets', which yielded faithful replicas of a carefully bred and selected parent bulb, to recoup their investment.
As tulip expert Anna Pavord notes, these '*were the equivalent of the interest earned on the capital invested in the bulb.*'

Tulips were sold by the weight of the bulb, rather like truffles, and by 1634 they were changing hands for 5,000 guilders each, literally the price of a substantial town house in Amsterdam. For Holland, 'tulipomania' had arrived. The craze went far beyond those with a fondness for plants and gardens. People from all walks of life, not just the conspicuously wealthy, speculated wildly on the bulbs, properties were mortgaged, individuals bankrupted and livelihoods lost. And pure greed rapidly overtook sensible investment or even social aspiration and status.

In 1635, a single bulb was sold for 4 tons of wheat, 8 tons of rye, 1 bed, 4 oxen, 8 pigs, 12 sheep, 1 suit of clothes, 2 casks of wine, 4 tons of beer, 2 tons of butter, 1,000 pounds of cheese and one silver cup. It really was 'the flower that made men mad.'
Like all such investment pyramids, 'tulipomania' had to end in tears, and early in 1637 the bottom dropped out of the ridiculously distorted market as professional speculators began to offload tulips. The

government tried to step in to call a halt, but was unable to control the wave of legal recrimination by aggrieved punters with 'negative equity.' So ended what is considered to be the first speculative bubble.

The bizarre crisis substantially dented the Dutch economy at home and abroad and allowed rivals such as England to move into lucrative overseas markets, an excuse for repeated, futile and expensive naval conflict between the two countries in the 1650s–70s.

All in all, 'tulipomania' did great harm to The Netherlands. But in this case, there was a silver lining. The tulip would turn out to be the basis of the country's huge modern flower industry.

Tulip fanciers never learn, for the story has an ironic footnote. Turkey, the country that had given its own national flower to Europe, had its own outbreak of over-zealous tulip speculation in the early 18th century, coinciding with the last embers of Ottoman power and perhaps a symbol of its final decay – when in 1719 Prince Eugene and the Austrian army finally expelled the Turks from Hungary. At about the same time France suffered a mild bout; and England too, where from the 1680s, gardeners were obsessed by tulips. Wit and social commentator Joseph Addison, himself a keen gardener, wrote in *The Tatler* in 1710, as the craze faded, of a gentleman who bemoaned the tulip bulbs his cook had mistaken for onions to "*make me a dish of pottage that cost me above a thousand pounds*"!

INDIA AND THE EVIL HEDGE

Most of us think of hedges as just barriers of vegetation separating our gardens from those of our neighbours. Some, of course, are more ambitious like the Maze at Hampton Court. But there was one that was both massive in size and evil in its purpose.

India was the 'Jewel in the Crown' of the British Empire, her richest and most populous country and the largest market for English products. It's extraordinary to think that it was salt that helped to lose this 'jewel'.

Salt, sodium chloride, is now so easily available and cheap that we never think about it. We even call it 'Common Salt'. But it was not always so. We all need salt - it plays a vital role in our physical health. Our bodies store only six ounces of it. If we sweat, we lose it. In hot climates and with physical effort, 2 to 3 ounces can be lost in just a day. If not replaced, the results are serious or even catastrophic. Blood pressure falls, the brain is starved of blood; lassitude, apathy, muscular weakness and then unconsciousness follow.

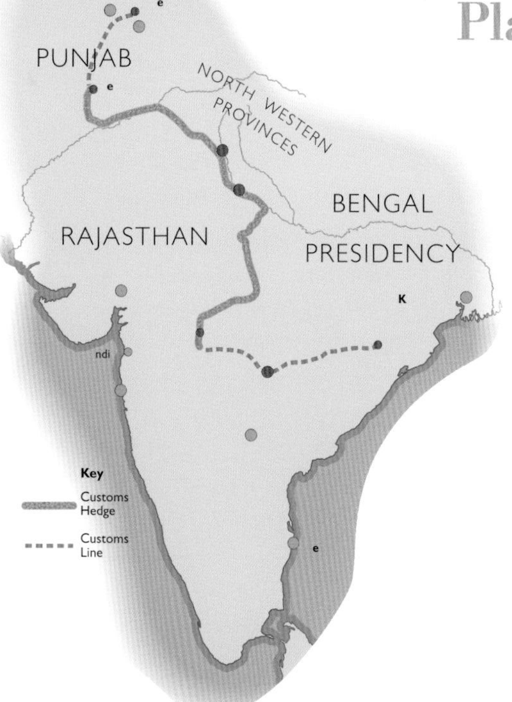

Before the saline drip was invented, it was impossible to feed unconscious people – so they simply died.

Nowhere was salt more critical than in India, hot and with a mainly vegetarian populace unable to replace salt by eating meat. So it comes as a shock to find that from the earliest days of the East India Company, the British decided to tax it, and, indeed, to make it the largest source of revenue. It is even more startling to find that the British schoolboy hero, Robert Clive, victor of Plassey, was to enrich himself so quickly and outrageously in the 1760s from salt revenues so as to arouse suspicion back in England.

Through the Salt Tax, the British allowed the poor of India to be deprived of salt, even in times of famine when the price of salt for a family could rise to half its income.

When faced with the inconvenient situation that the Indian rulers who were beyond British territorial control refused to tax the salt for their own people, the British then did something at once technically brilliant but morally appalling. Outraged, Sir John Strachey (Lytton's uncle) wrote, *'There grew up gradually a monstrous system of which it would be almost impossible to find a parallel in any tolerably civilised country.'*

He was referring to the Imperial Customs Line, and more particularly, to the 'Great Hedge of India', which began in 1854 as a dry hedge, annually involving 150,000 tons of thorny material. A live hedge proved cheaper and more effective. No less than 14 feet high and 12 feet deep, it was made of **Babool**, (*Vachellia nilotica*), **Indian Plum**(*Oemleria cerasiformis*), **Karonda** (*Carissa carandas*) and **Prickly Pear**(*Opuntia*), locked in with thorny creepers. As part of the 2,500 mile Custom Line, the hedge was soon a colossal 1,500 miles long, making it the second largest man-made structure on earth, only surpassed by China's Great Wall. It took 14,000 armed men to maintain and to patrol it, with a customs gate nearly every mile – all just to stop salt smuggling.

The Line and the Hedge were abandoned in 1879, but only because the tax-free Indian states had now been seized and the tax differences removed. But the inhumane Salt Tax remained to plague India for decades, part of a hated policy. Because, in addition to the Tax, India's own salt works were forcibly closed down to protect the price of the Cheshire salt being shipped thousands of miles from Liverpool. Hard-nosed business was allowed to wreck humane social thinking and sensible politics. Lack of salt in the great famines of 1866 and 1879 meant that horrifyingly more Indians died through the Salt Tax than Jews did in the Holocaust.

Surely, someone in government should have remembered that a century earlier ill-judged taxes had lost Britain her American

colonies. And in France, the savage 'Gabelle' salt tax had helped the rulers literally to lose their heads in the Revolution.

The hatred caused by the Salt Tax was exactly why Gandhi chose salt as a symbol for 'passive resistance', culminating in his peaceful and hugely popular 200-mile march in 1930. He led thousands of his followers to pick salt from the beach at Dandi, where they were brutally attacked by the authorities, with two killed and 320 injured.

Just seventeen years later, centuries of British rule ended. Britain's greedy attitude towards salt and its huge and disgraceful hedge had more than played its part.

FRANKINCENSE AND MYRRH

The Bible tells us that the baby Jesus was visited by Three Kings or Wise Men 'from the East'. And that they were bearing gifts of gold, frankincense and myrrh. Of these, the two spices would in fact have been the more valuable – as they had been for centuries. Some thousand years before, the Queen of Sheba had visited King Solomon with these gifts, valuable trade products of her kingdom, Saba, in present-day Yemen.

In Oman, Yemen and Somalia grows a small tree of dry rocky places (*Boswellia sacra*, in the tropical Bursaraceae family), and the fragrant resin that exudes from cuts made in the bark gives us **Frankincense.** Its main use was religious, being burned in ancient temples, as it still is today in Roman Catholic and Orthodox churches. Its transportation was long and difficult, with its enormous price making it an obvious target for marauders on the way. Frankincense, one of few desert products of any value, is today threatened by over-collection.

Myrrh, too, is a resin, which oozes from the cut bark of *Commiphora myrrha*, another small but spiny tree from the same family and region. It, too, was hugely valuable and was also used in religious ceremonies, especially in Egypt. Burned as incense, its aromatic smoke was meant to please the Gods. It also played a role in mummifying, myrrh being often used to help conserve the embalmed body.

The practical advantages of these two exotic and very expensive desert spices are not immediately apparent as being useful for a tiny baby. Indeed, the Bible does not record what Joseph and Mary did with their astonishingly valuable gifts – unless they sold them.

If they had done that immediately, so valuable were the spices, the couple could not only have upgraded to get a decent room for the night, the money could have bought the inn, or for that matter, probably the whole of Bethlehem!

THE NUTMEG AND NEW YORK

It is hard for us now to grasp the huge economic and political importance of spices. Ever since people learned to cook, spices have had an ever-increasing role, not just to flavour but to help to preserve it. In the first millennium BC, the spice trade from the east was already fully developed via Arab intermediaries. In 950BC, the Queen of Sheba anxiously visited King Solomon. Why? she was worried his fleet would bypass her kingdom (now Yemen), ruining her wealth as a spice route. The Romans were prolific users of spices and, although their use briefly declined in the Dark Ages, the spice trade revived again through contact with the Islamic world. The cynical Fourth Crusade was mounted by Venice, in reality, to capture Constantinople as a spice centre. The growth of Venice and Genoa was mainly based on the spice trade, and the cultural explosion of the Renaissance was only possible because of the massive wealth that spices created.

From the 15th century, at first it was Portugal and Spain, dividing up the world, that dominated the trade, but two new players, England and Holland, soon intervened. For year after year, they competed and fought, especially over the 'Spice Islands' of Molucca and Banda (now in Indonesia), and it was nutmeg that provoked the confrontation – and one of the strangest twists of fortune in history.

To speed up the journey to the 'spiceries', sailors searched for the 'Northeast' or 'Northwest passage'. England's Henry Hudson was attempting this, when he arrived in 1609 up a river the Native Americans called 'Manna-hata'. Now we call it the Hudson River and its main island Manhattan. Then it was the ever-present rivals, the Dutch, trading for fur, who created their own New Netherland there.

The tiny nutmeg island of Run in the Banda Islands was covered in **Nutmeg trees** (*Myristica fragrans*). The nutmeg fruit in fact yields two spices: the nutmeg seed itself and mace, its fleshy reddish covering. Run had been ceded to the British in 1616 by the Bandanese islanders. As the only one of the islands not under their control, it was besieged by the furious Dutch. A British hero, Nathaniel Courthope, led the defence for three long years until he was trapped and killed. Some of his followers and other British traders were horribly tortured by the Dutch at the 'Massacre of Amboyna'. The atrocity created hatred and a long-term desire for revenge. It took years of conflict for Britain to take back Run by the Treaty of Westminster in 1654, and she did not keep it long.

In Manhattan, that other Dutch island, director-general Peter Stuyvesant had done a good job building up the colony, but probably did not realise that he was about

to lose it because of bitter struggles over the nutmeg trade – four decades earlier and ten thousand miles away. Charles II's brother James, Duke of York, captured Manhattan, and, at the Treaty of Breda in 1667, the Dutch were given the choice of which island to keep. They decided that Run was much more valuable, and so the British acquired the whole of New Netherland, re-naming it New York.

Run is today just a tiny, sleepy island, its nutmeg monopoly and wealth long lost to Grenada and other places.

Indeed, the national flag of Grenada depicts a nutmeg! New York, while no longer British, has proved rather wealthier and more significant on the world stage.

TEA AND BRITAIN'S AMERICAN COLONIES

On the night of 16th December 1773, Boston Harbour was littered with tea chests and the surface of the water was covered in tea. For Britain, tea was on its way to losing America.

It may seem strange that it was tea that lost Britain her American colonies. And two men can be blamed. First, in 1767, Chancellor of the Exchequer Charles Townsend thought he had hit on a good way of raising money in the colonies. He decided to tax 'small unimportant things' like lead, glass, salt, paper and tea.

Three years later, Lord North, a Prime Minister, acidly described by the famous writer, Dr Johnson, as '*filling a chair with a mind as narrow as a neck of a vinegar cruet*', compounded the error. All the Townsend duties were repealed, except for the Tea Tax – which

would now cost more to collect than the revenue it would raise. In spite of the fears of Members of Parliament that there would be trouble, Lord North kept the tax, '*as a mark of the supremacy of Parliament and as a declaration of their right to govern the colonies*'.

Keeping the tax on tea was also an attempt to help the East India Company, which was in financial trouble in spite of its growing but secret involvement with the Chinese opium trade. The British, in addition to sending tea direct to America, also decided to control smuggling – which annoyed most of the merchants there, especially in Boston, where they were actively engaged in the trade.

So, opposition to the Tea Act grew

rapidly and finally exploded in Boston where three British ships laden with East Indian tea were anchored – the *Dartmouth*, *Eleanor* and *Beaver*. After a mass meeting, one of the ships' Captains, Francis Rotch, rode off to ask Governor Hutchison for exemption from the tax. When he returned to report that this was refused, a thousand men, many disguised as Indians, burst from the meeting, ran down to the harbour, boarded the ships and hurled the offending 298 tea chests into the water.

John Adams, normally a moderate, was right when he said, 'The people should never rise without doing something to be remembered, something notable and striking. This destruction of the tea is so bold, so firm, intrepid and inflexible, and it must have so important consequences, and so lasting, that I can't but consider it an epoch in history'.

In fact, it was 'taxation without representation' which caused the real indignation. Britain did not make the same mistake in Canada. Six years later, America declared its independence, and six years after that had won it by force of arms.

It would have been much better if Charles Townsend and Lord North had not tried to raise a bit of cash from tea.

Perhaps it is not surprising that Americans, on the whole, prefer coffee.

THE 'TIMBER RUSH' OF AMERICA

Most people know about the great 'Gold Rush'. It transformed California, with San Francisco's population jumping from 200 in 1847 to 100,000 just three years later.

It all started in 1848, when store-keeper Sam Brennan brandished a bottle filled with gold from Sutter's Mill, shouting, 'Gold! Gold! Gold from the American river!' The *New York Herald* printed the news, and the stampede was on – one of the greatest acts of mass greed in history.

From all over the world, 300,000 gold seekers poured in and San Francisco Bay was soon littered with 200 ships abandoned by their crews for the gold fields.

Early prospectors did well, retrieving by hand the easy pickings on the ground, and panning for nuggets in streams. But later, it was necessary to use more sophisticated methods of diverting rivers into sluices, and even using high-pressure hoses to reveal

the gold. Of the tens of thousands of gold seekers, many made no real money. However, the merchants supplying them *did* – selling them shovels, picks, food and whisky. The biggest beneficiaries were the loggers. The 'Timber Rush' ended up ten times more valuable than the 'Gold Rush', as huge quantities of wood were desperately needed for houses, stores, factories, mines and railroads. At first the wooden ships were broken up, but they provided a fraction of the need. It was the Pacific Northwest that would really benefit.

When the first loggers arrived at the shoreline of Washington and Oregon, they were stupefied by the density of the forests and the immense size of the trees, twice the height and five times the width of familiar trees like **Eastern White Pine** back east. At first they felled the trees that grew right down by the waterside. These included giant **Coast Redwood** (*Sequoia sempervirens*), **Sierra Redwood** (*Sequoia gigantea*), **Douglas Fir** (*Pseudotsuga taxifolia*), **Sitka Spruce** (*Acea sitchensis*), **Sugar Pine** (*Pinus lambertiana*), **Western Red Cedar**(*Thuja plicata*), **Western Larch** and **Lodgepole Pine.**

Little settlements were created like Seattle and Portland. But in order to bring trees from deeper in the forest, the 'Skid Road' was developed, made of foot-thick logs, twelve feet long laid crosswise like railroad ties or sleepers, and half buried in the ground. Along these roads cut through the forest came teams of sixteen oxen heaving a chained-together string of a dozen enormous logs.

Soon other methods to get the logs to the sawmills were invented. Logs came out of the forests smoking down long dry

chutes. Water-filled 'flumes', much as we see in a modern swimming pool, snaked out of the hills and ravines bringing logs and lumber down at 50 miles an hour. On the skid roads the oxen were replaced by 'donkeys' - not the animals, but Dolbeer's small stationary steam engines capable of pulling the heaviest log out of the forest. Later, geared Shay locomotives would arrive to haul whole trains of logs out of the wilderness.

Thus it was that, with these innovations, the logging and timber industries became the biggest in the North-West – ten times more valuable than the Gold Rush which they served.

In the little towns, the 'skid roads', as the brightly lit honky-tonk streets were soon called, provided everything the loggers would need – dentists, barbers, tailors, restaurants or tattoo parlours. But what a lumberjack really wanted, of course, was to be found in the saloons. The grandest of all was 'Erickson's' in Portland's North Side, with the biggest bar in the world, over 200 yards long, jammed with men, together with a concert stage and dozens of gaming tables.

But, after lonely weeks in the forest, whiskey was not enough. Naturally, many of the buildings in the Skid Roads were devoted to the provision of female company. Until the 1860s, most settlements had the ratio of one woman to ten men. Some philanthropic people devised schemes to bring respectable young brides out from the East, but others indulged in the less complicated tradition of the setting up of Skid Road bawdy houses, with many becoming some of the richest people in town.

The Skid Roads, in both senses, have long gone and the cities they helped to create, Seattle, Portland, Tacoma, Everett, Vancouver are now huge and respectable. Only the derogatory term 'Skid Row' reminds us of that dramatic and hell-raising era when timber was king, and the phrase'on the skids' came to mean someone going downhill.

LIVERPOOL AS 'TIMBERTOWN'

The great port of Liverpool is famous for many things – The Beatles and the 1960s 'Mersey Sound', two fine Cathedrals, two famous football teams and, less happily, the slave trade. But so strong was the city's connection to wood in the 18th century that it also earned the nickname 'Timbertown'.

Liverpool earned this name as it was the main port for wood imports. While London and the East and South coast ports monopolised the Baltic trade in softwoods, Liverpool dealt with the whole of the rest of the world and its wood, a trade that was rapidly expanding. It took great skill to deal with the complications of importing from far-off places, identifying the many and various specialist woods, finding markets for them and then supporting the effort with documents, insurance and banking. The excellent reputation of Liverpool's timber system and its expertise gradually encouraged importers of other materials to seek help and advice. It even gave birth to some of the merchant banks

that we still know today. Grindlays, William Brandt's and Anthony Gibb all grew out of timber trading. William Rathbone II started as a sawyer in a Liverpool timber yard, went into timber trading, and Rathbone Brothers became bankers in 1752.

One of the first specialist woods to arrive was **Mahogany** (*Swietenia mahagoni*), unfortunately as ballast in ships on the third, return leg of the 'Triangular trade', the dreaded 'Middle Passage' being for slaves from Africa (page 48). But there was no end to the varieties of wood soon to be traded in 'Timbertown'.

CONIFEROUS SOFTWOODS:
Douglas Fir (*Pseudotsuga menziesii*, Pacific coast of North America). Ladder makers, gymnasium equipment, door and window makers, the Ministry of Defence for fitting out almost anything.
Western Hemlock (*Tsuga heterophylla*, Pacific Coast.) Ladders and doors again, Newell posts, spindles and balusters for stairs.
Western Red Cedar (*Thuja plicata*, Pacific coast). Greenhouses and conservatories, orangeries. shingles and shakes for roofing, cladding and window blinds.
Silver Spruce (*Picea engelmannii*, Alaska). Masts and spars for racing dinghies. Oars. Sound

boards for musical instruments . Food boxes for the MOD. Aircraft construction and restoration.
Yellow Cedar (*Cuppressus nootkatenis*, Pacific coast.) Rudders and centre plates for racing dinghies.
Parana Pine (*Araucaria angustifolia*, Brazil). Staircases. Small step ladders. Broom handles.
Pitch Pine (*Pinus rigida*, eastern North America). Staircases, windows. Joinery.
Shortleaf Pine or Southern Yellow Pine (Eastern and south-eastern USA). Staircases and joinery.
HARDWOODS

Then there were the **hardwoods**, from deciduous trees, with equally diverse uses:
Keruing (*Diptocarpus* species, Malaysia). Lorry bottoms. Grain floors. Agricultural joinery. Gates. Sheep pens. Thresholds.
Jelutong (*Dyera costulata*, Malaysia). A very soft wood. Pattern and model making. Historically, until the 1960s its latex was used for chewing gum.
Meranti and Lauan (*Shorea* species, Malaysia). Hardwood joinery.
Ramin (*Gonystylus*, East Malaysia). Mouldings. Caravan manufacturing.
Oak (*Quercus*, UK, Europe, temperate Asia and North America). Great all-round hardwood. Joinery. Construction. Shipbuilding. Furniture. Flooring. Barrels. Historically used for the spokes of cartwheels - the felloes (rim) being **Ash** and the nave (hub) being **Elm**, until the 1960s imported from Japan for high-class internal joinery.
Ash (*Fraxinus* species, from same areas as Oak and with similar uses), but Ash is more flexible and more resilient to impact and therefore good for tool handles, snooker cues and historically tennis rackets and skis. It is less moisture-resistant than Oak.
Maple (*Acer* species, North America, especially Canada). Flooring, particularly sports flooring. Furniture. Kitchens. Butchers' blocks. Musical instruments. Historically, London Tube train floors and escalator treads. Piano actions. Bobbins and shuttles.
Cherry (*Prunus serotina*, eastern North America). Furniture. Toys. Panelling. Flooring.
Walnut (*Juglans regia*, Eurasia; *Juglans nigra*, North America). Furniture. Panelling. Flooring. Gun butts.
Tulip Wood (*Liriodendron tulipifera*, eastern North America). Furniture carcassing. Joinery.
Beech (*Fagus sylvatica*, Europe). Joinery. School furniture. Kitchen utensils. Turned objects.
Wawa (Nigeria) and **Obeche** (Ghana) (*Triplochiton scleroxylon*, West Tropical Africa). Mouldings. Saunas. Furniture carcassing. Caravan manufacture.
Iroko or 'African Teak' (*Milicia excelsa*, West Tropical Africa). Windows. Garden furniture. Decking. Gates. Boat building.
African Mahogany (*Khaya senegalensis*, Tropical Africa). Joinery. Cabinet making.
Utile (*Entandophragma* species, West Tropical Africa). Joinery. Cabinet making. Windows.

There are many, many more timbers imported for a variety of uses, such as **Niangon** (*Tarrietia utilis*), **Mengkulang** (*Tarrietia* species), **Yang, Karri** (*Eucalyptus diversicolor*), **Jarrah** (*Eucalyptus marginata*), **Elliottis or Slash Pine** (*Pinus elliottii*), **Hickory** (*Carya* species), **Sassafras** (*Sassafras albidum*), **Alder** (*Alnus* species), **Aspen** (*Populus tremula*), **Cottonwood** (*Populus* species), **Basswood** (*Tilia* species), **Birch** (*Betula* species) – some 6,000 timber tree species have been used over the centuries and, in all, about 30,000 species are recognized in the trade.

BURDOCK AND 'HOOK AND LOOP'

Children have always enjoyed the game of throwing bristly wayside seeds or seed-heads at one another – or on to long-suffering dogs to see if they will stick. This ability to attach and hold on tight is how many plants disperse their seeds – one of many remarkable adaptations that they possess for survival and spread. A particularly effective missile for children to throw is **Lesser Burdock** (*Arctium minus*) and related species of hedges and woodland edges, with clusters of purplish flowers and spiny egg-shaped seed-heads ('burrs'), in the dandelion and thistle family (Asteraceae or Compositae). The plant's variety of popular and local names thus includes much variation on a theme, for example Sticklebacks, Sticky Jack and Sticky Willy. However, the remarkable fact is that these adhesive burrs are the very origin of hook and loop fastening.

Following a hunting trip in the Jura Mountains in 1941, Swiss engineer George de Mestral found that the fur of his dog was covered with Burdock burrs, each with an envelope of narrow, spine-like scales ending in a neat and tiny hook. The inquisitive and inventive de Mestral examined these under a microscope and noted how they readily stick fast to animal hairs and the wool or other fibres of clothing. This gave him the idea of employing paired hook and loop surfaces as a convenient and speedy fasten and release alternative to buttons and zips for clothing. He experimented using cotton strips, but as this natural plant fibre wasn't stiff or strong enough, eventually settled on the then novel synthetic fibre, nylon. Later, polyester was used.

After ten years perfecting the hooks and loops, as well as the machinery to weave and produce the new fabric, de Mestral was ready to patent his invention. Not until 1955 did it receive one, but the wait was worthwhile for it would make his fortune. He called his invention 'hook and loop,' and his company and specific brand of hook and loop 'Velcro' from the French velours (velvet) and crochet (hook). It received a boost in the the 1960s after being adopted by both trendy fashion designers and by NASA for astronauts' clothing.

Today we cannot imagine life without this handy stuff, an everyday practical feature of outdoor clothing and scuba gear but also shoes, bags and medical devices such as blood pressure monitors.

Note that real burrs picked up on a country walk are especially hard to remove from hook and loop fabrics!

MULBERRY AND SILK

In about 2,700 BC, the Yellow Empress of China, Xilingshi, was drinking tea under a Mulberry tree when a white caterpillar cocoon fell into her cup. When she tried to pull it out, a long filament emerged – silk. Her husband, Huang Di, the Yellow Emperor, famous for many inventions, domesticated the silk worm (*Bombyx mori*) and created a silk industry whose secrets China was able to keep from the world for another 2,000 years.

Not a plant product as such, silk depends on cultivation of the **White Mulberry** (*Morus alba*), a small tree in the fig family (Moraceae), which is intimately linked with the silkworms feeding on it and the industry it created.

Silk brought the rich civilization of ancient China into contact with those of the Middle East and the Mediterranean region. From the 2nd century BC a web of trade routes linked China, Korea and Japan with Central Asia, India, Persia and the Roman Empire, and later the Byzantine and Ottoman Turkish Empires and western Christendom. Routes were both land-based, with caravans crossing central Asia, and on the sea, with Arabian and Indian mariners exploiting seasonal monsoon winds to sail across the Indian Ocean. Silk was but one lucrative commodity, alongside foods, spices, medicinal plants such as rhubarb (page 214), precious stones and technological innovations that travelled via these extended routes, as well as culture, religions and, unfortunately, bubonic plague. In 1877, it was the German geographer Baron Ferdinand von Richthofen (uncle of Manfred, the 'Red Baron' World War I air ace) who first coined the useful term 'Silk Road' or 'Seidenstrasse'.

The Chinese closely guarded the secret of silk and prevented export of silkworms or their eggs on pain of death. Thus, the Roman and Byzantine Empires were dependent on the Silk Road for their supplies, although silkworm's White Mulberry food plant had probably already arrived in the Mediterranean

world and Europe. Silkworms can survive to some extent on the leaves of other mulberries including **Black Mulberry** (*Morus niger*). This tree was well known to Roman writers and may have arrived after Alexander the Great's conquests of the lands we now know as Afghanistan and Pakistan. Alexander's soldiers would have been familiar with mulberries, eating them as dried winter and travellers' provisions, when they crossed the Hindu Kush and other mountains, where mulberries still grow.

In 552 Emperor Justinian connived with two Nestorian Christian monks, who had visited China and observed silk production there, to smuggle some silkworm eggs to Constantinople, reputedly hidden in walking canes and probably from the Central Asiatic fringes of the Chinese Empire. This state-sponsored industrial espionage and skulduggery (rather like that of the Chinese today!) would initiate a western silk industry, at first a Byzantine imperial monopoly, which soon spread to the Levant, Greece and elsewhere. Later the Arabs spread silk production through the Middle east and further west, and from the early Middle Ages both the Venetians and French would plant White Mulberry trees widely to support the prosperous Mediterranean silk industry.

Lyon became a centre for silk production, as did the Luberon and Cévennes massifs to the south. In the Cévennes, employing 300,000 people, silk was until the early 20th century a mainstay of the rural economy alongside Chestnuts.In southern Europe mulberry trees are still widely grown and pollarded for animal fodder or to provide summer shade on sidewalks and café terraces, and they often indicate areas of former silk manufacture.

Although silk has largely been replaced by modern synthetic fibres, it remains in demand and China and India produce annually most of a global total of 80,000 tons. The modern version of the Silk Road is a China-sponsored railway system that takes goods direct to Europe in a fortnight, three weeks less than the journey time of a container ship.

Black or White: two species of Mulberry Tree

White Mulberry (*Morus alba*) is a small tree 10–20 metres tall, with broad, lobed, almost hairless heart-shaped leaves. The stalked, elongated raspberry-like fruits are white to pink or purplish, and sweet even when unripe, although not great eating.

Black Mulberry (*Morus niger*), a smaller tree with more contorted branches and leaves that are downy beneath, has almost stalkless, broadly egg-shaped, dark reddish-purple fruits, which when ripe make excellent jam.

White Mulberry certainly provides the better food for rearing silkworms. In the early 1600s, King James I of England (James VI of Scotland), well- read and meaning well but often pedantic and misguided, ordered large numbers of Black Mulberry trees to be planted to form the basis of a native English silk industry. Alas, he chose the wrong species of tree. No wonder a French observer dubbed him *'the wisest fool in Christendom'*! Happily, a number of old Black Mulberries survive from Jacobean times and still bear fruit. A National Collection of Mulberries is held by Queen Elizabeth in the gardens of Buckingham Palace.

PLANTS AS MARKETING TOOLS

Considering their huge importance in our lives, it is unsurprising that plants have played a major role in promoting products, especially the ones we eat and drink. However, there are some such marketing campaigns that border on the outrageous or even amusingly fraudulent.

Carnations and Mother's Day

Theoretically, Mother's Day is a celebration honouring the mother of the family, as well as motherhood, maternal bonds and mothers in society. It is celebrated on various days in many parts of the world, most commonly in the months of March or May. Today it has little to do with ancient traditions like the Greek cult to Cybele, the Great Mother of the Gods, the Roman festival of Hilaria or the Christian Mothering Sunday, once a commemoration of Mother Church, not motherhood.

The modern Mother's Day began in the United States at the initiative of Anna Jarvis in 1911 who persuaded President Woodrow Wilson to declare a public holiday to honour her peace activist mother Ann. She chose carnations to be the flower to celebrate the day. But she strongly regretted its early commercialisation, and devoted the rest of her life campaigning against it, writing to price-gouging florists, 'WHAT WILL YOU DO to rout charlatans, bandits, pirates, racketeers, and other termites that would undermine with their greed one of the finest, noblest and truest movements and celebrations?' She would have been absolutely horrified by its huge, industrial promotion nowadays, with flowers, cards, telegrams and family outings and events. However, most mothers truly enjoy them!

Roses and St Valentine's Day

In 496 AD, Pope Gelasius 1 established the Feast of St Valentine of Rome to be held on February 14th each year. Apparently Saint Valentine had restored the sight of the daughter of his Roman jailer, later writing to her as 'Your Valentine' before being executed as a Christian in 269 AD.

By the 15th century, St Valentine was being connected to courtly love and by the 18th century in England couples were expressing their love by offering each other flowers, usually roses, sweets and cards, soon called 'Valentines'.

Just as with Mother's Day, huge commercialisation has followed, with flowers and cards. For the restaurant industry, February 14th can be a bumper evening and with bumper prices.

However, restaurateur friends of the authors report that not all their guests seem deliriously happy!

VALENTINE'S EVENING

What she's thinking:	**What he's thinking:**
How gorgeous – all these roses!	How embarrassing, all these roses!
Gosh, the place is crammed!	We'll never get served.
What an incredible menu!	Thought they'd never bring it.
I wonder how many couples here are in love?	I wonder if the other blokes are enjoying this?
If I eat any more, I'll burst.	If I drink any more, I'll never be up to it.
I wish he'd say something romantic.	Oh God, she's gone all dewy-eyed.
I wish he'd put his hand on mine.	I wish she'd take her hand off the table.
I wish he'd slip a ring on it	I wish they'd bring the bill.
Gosh, this is lovely!	Gosh, this is agony!
I wish he'd propose.	I wish we could go home.
I'm so glad we came here.	Thank God it's only once a year.
I suppose he might propose later.	I suppose I'll have to leave a tip.
What a lovely evening!	What an amazing con!
I wonder what it cost?	I wonder if I can ask her to chip in?
Gosh, what a place to come and dine!	It's cost a bomb, the food and wine.
How nice to be his Valentine!	Saint Valentine? No friend of mine!

Plants and Us

Tea and the 'China Clippers'

In 1850, Great Britain dominated the tea trade, being the biggest importer of tea, the biggest re-exporter and the biggest single consumer. Tea had been of huge importance to Britain. It had helped to lose the American colonies, had created opium wars and had temporarily ruined China (page 70).

For decades the tea from China had been arriving in Britain in the East India Company's dumpy, slow and safe ships. But from 1840, sleeker, faster ships were introduced and the brief reign of the 'China Clippers' began. There was no real justification for faster ships. Tea, properly packed, lasted for years. But a kind of snobbish race began, very like rushing newly-shot grouse down to London's restaurants on the 12th of August, or the race for Beaujolais Nouveau. People were happy to boast that they had paid more to drink tea delivered by the *Ariel*, *Era* or even the most famous of them, the *Cutty Sark*.

All in all, it was probably a good thing that this rather silly habit was killed off in 1869 when steamships and the new Suez Canal made the 'China Clippers' redundant.

Spinach and the decimal point

In 1870, German chemist Erich von Wolf was researching the amount of iron in spinach and other green vegetables. When writing up his findings in a new notebook, he misplaced a decimal point, making the iron content in spinach ten times more generous than in reality. While Dr von Wolf actually found out that there are just 3.5 milligrams of iron in a 100 gram serving of spinach, the accepted number became 35 milligrams thanks to his mistake. The mistake was later detected, but the myth continued, not least because of 'Popeye – the sailor man.' Based on the misconception, the cartoon character ate vast amounts of spinach, 'I'm strong to the finish, because I eats my spinach'. So popular were the cartoons that in America spinach sales grew by a third.

Carrots and night-fighters

During the German night bombing Blitz on London of 1940, the British had a secret weapon – their night-fighters were equipped with a new Airborne Interception Radar or AI. It proved highly effective in the hands of aces like 'Cat's Eyes' John Cunningham, who shot down 19 German bombers using the radar, once three in one night.

Cunningham's clever 'Cat's Eyes' nickname, implying he could see in the dark, was part of Britain's Ministry of Information's ruse to hide the technical reason for the RAF's successes.

They exaggerated the importance of the Vitamin A in carrots, from being good for the eyes to actually improving night-time eyesight. Advertisements and posters reinforced this notion with headlines like '*CARROTS keep you healthy and help you see in the blackout*'.

It is a moot point whether the Luftwaffe ever really believed that they were up against British pilots with eyesight fiendishly improved by eating lots of carrots. But it must have been a boost for carrot farmers.

Vines and 'Beaujolais Nouveau'

Each year in France, on the third Thursday of November, over a million cases of wine leave the countryside for Paris. The 'Beaujolais Nouveau race' is on, and incredibly, millions of bottles of it will soon be consumed all over the world. What started as a local event in Beaujolais and Lyon became an annual worldwide ritual, with the wine rushed to its destinations, and often by bizarre means – not only planes and trains, but racing cars, motorcycles, balloons, helicopters, rickshaws, and even Concorde one year.

While the craze proved a huge boost for the sale of Beaujolais wine, Nouveau's success is puzzling to any serious wine lover, who would regard such a young wine, literally weeks old, as a viticultural joke.

However, in America it is claimed that its taste is the nearest thing to white wine, the country's normal preference, especially when served chilled. And it can arrive conveniently in time for Thanksgiving. But the temporary publicity dominance of Beaujolais Nouveau, now far less popular, also proved to be a two-edged sword. The young wine has damaged the image of the more serious Beaujolais wines, which are only now regaining their reputation.

However frivolous the race may have been, it still remains one of the strangest marketing successes in history.

Pears and Babycham

For women in the 1950s, asking for a drink in public was a dilemma. There were no wine bars and there was not much choice in a pub between beer and hard spirits. A drink created from pears was to solve that.

Francis Showering was one of four brothers from a 200-year-old brewing family in Shepton Mallet in Somerset. They also had extensive pear orchards and Francis worked to create a successful version of the French drink, Perry. So he came to London to find an advertising agency, meeting Jack Wynn-Williams. Together they created Babycham, together with a little chamois figure. Launched as a 'genuine champagne perry', in 1957 it was the first alcoholic drink advertised on British television with the line 'I'd love a Babycham!' It was an enormous success, especially with women, and is judged one of the most spectacular market coups in history.

A rather charming story is that Jack Wynn-Williams later came to a marketing meeting with the Showerings. He was asked if he liked the blue Rolls-Royce that had brought him from the railway station. 'It's yours', said Francis, handing him the keys. 'For all your help.'

While Babycham sales eventually lost ground to wine and other drinks, its financial success propelled the Showerings to create a huge drinks and food empire, eventually to be Allied-Lyons, later acquired for £14 billion by Pernod-Ricard. Not bad for some pear tree orchards!

PEANUTS AND THE GROUNDNUT SCHEME

Peanut Butter is hugely popular in the North America and Britain, and most of us enjoy peanuts as a snack with our drinks. Peanuts are a huge global industry based on crops grown in several countries, including India, China, Indonesia, Australia, some West African states and the USA. Famously or, rather infamously, East Africa was once touted as another source. But it was not to last.

Someone called the BBC in 1964 to say, 'The Beatles film is the greatest waste of money since the groundnut scheme.' Soon after, Spike Milligan called Concorde a 'flying groundnut scheme'. It would take decades for the world to stop describing the 'Tanganyika Groundnut Scheme' as a perfect example of bureaucratic incompetence and waste. What on earth were they all talking about?

With Britain financially broke and still enduring food rationing, in 1946 Clement Attlee's Labour government thought up a scheme to create vegetable oil in Tanganyika, now Tanzania. It was partly to reduce financial reliance on the United States and also to appear to help a British colony by growing food there.

A mission was duly sent out and reported over-enthusiastically that three million acres should be cleared for the cultivation of **Peanuts** or **Groundnuts** (*Arachis hypogaea*). This useful member of the bean family (Fabaceae) was cultivated for over 2,000 years on the lower slopes of the Andes and from the 16th century spread far by the Spanish and Portuguese. The 'nuts' are in fact seeds contained in pods similar to those of beans or peas, but unlike these they are hard and produced underground. The peanuts are both oil- and protein-rich. In post-War Britain the oil was seen as important for production of margarine, with the residue used in 'cattle cake' animal feeds.

The proponents of the scheme also claimed that the soil was suitable, in spite of the large amount of clay – peanuts grow best on lighter soils. This was just one of the mistakes that would doom the project.

Clearing the land was the next problem and mistake. The country had no heavy equipment like large tractors and bulldozers to achieve this. Eventually some army surplus ones arrived from Canada and America, but many were quickly wrecked by inexperienced local drivers. There was one effective idea to clear the land by using two bulldozers to drag a long heavy ship's chain between them through the bush. This was then delayed by someone in London cancelling the purchase order for the chain because he thought it was a joke!

More problems: The existing railway line had been washed away, leaving only one dirt road to the scheme's site until a new railway and port could be built. There was no source near the scheme of drinking water, and when water was trucked in, the usefulness of its reservoir was rather marred by the locals using it as a swimming pool.

By 1949, two years into the scheme, things were plainly going very wrong. Only a fraction of the planned area had been cleared, and the soil and climate had proved unsuitable. Some peanuts were finally harvested, but the trouble was, they had cost six times what they could be sold for.

Eventually the whole scheme was abandoned. It had cost war-impoverished Britain nearly £40 million in precious reserves – £4 billion today. No wonder the 'Groundnut Scheme' became not only an insult but a byword for all ill-conceived, economically flawed, grandiose projects.

In fact, totally nuts!.

Nuts about nuts!

It's easy to see why the British chose peanuts for a doomed African venture. Peanuts, also known as Groundnuts, Monkey nuts and Goobers are one of the world's most popular snacks,with annual production of 47 million tons, with China producing 36% of them. America is a big producer and exporter, too, and the best-known American peanut farmer was, of course, President Jimmy Carter (pictured right) who had a 2,000 acre Farm in Georgia. The United States consumes $800 million's worth a year, only beaten, amazingly, by the 95% of Canadians who eat peanuts regularly, with 80% of them eating peanut butter every week!

PLANTS AND PLACES

The Rose of England
Scotland and the Thistle
The Leek and the Daffodil
The Cherry Blossom of Japan
Brazil and its musical tree
Alma-Ata, Apple City and world health
The 'Big Apple' and its naughty roots
Ireland and the Shamrock
Hollywood and the Holly places
The Lime trees of Berlin
Elms and American towns
Lebanon and its great Cedars
New Zealand and the Silver Fern
Freetown's Freedom Tree
Canada and the Maple Leaf

THE ROSE OF ENGLAND

Among the four nations that comprise the United Kingdom, England all too often plays down its national identity. Many people proudly boast of their Irish, Scottish, Northern Irish or indeed Welsh ancestry, even if this is only partly true, but rarely will you hear somebody say with confidence 'I am English' or refer to an English ancestry. Although you do hear 'I'm a Yorkshireman' from the inhabitants of God's Own County!

But there is one enduring symbol of England that all can recognise, our national flower, the rose. There are two familiar types of rose, the colourful, much crossed and selected garden rose (*Rosa*), usually with double flowers; and the pale pink or white wild roses, the commonest of which is **Dog Rose** (*Rosa canina*), with saucer-shaped single flowers. Under the blue skies of June, all over England, hedgerows – where they have not been grubbed out for intensive farming – scrub and woodland margins are splashed pink with the arched sprays of these wild roses, what the poet Rupert Brooke called the 'Unofficial English Rose'.

In the mid-15th century, after the Hundred Years War finally ended, the two branches of England's ruling Plantagenet dynasty, the Yorkists and the Lancastrians, fought for supremacy in what were later called 'The Wars of the Roses'. At the Battle of Bosworth near Leicester in 1485, Henry Tudor defeated the Yorkist Richard III and seized the crown for the Lancastrians. As Henry VII, he established his own dynasty, the House of Tudor, which created modern England. A careful and thrifty administrator, he restored peace and strengthened the nation's laws, economy, trade and diplomatic links, ensuring a rosy future.

To reunite England, he married Elizabeth of York and symbolised their union by then combining heraldic emblems to represent the two warring factions, the White Rose of York and Red Rose of Lancaster in a new emblem of a white rose superimposed upon a red one - the 'Tudor Rose', henceforth the heraldic emblem of England. No such bicoloured rose actually exists in nature, but the device was clearly based on the simple flowers of the wild roses of England that would have been familiar to all.

The Tudor Rose features on the Royal Coat of Arms of the UK in combination with the Thistle of Scotland, the Leek of Wales and the Shamrock of Ireland. It is also prominent on the scarlet dress uniforms of the Yeomen Warders or Beefeaters of the Tower of London and the Yeomen of the Guard who protect Queen Elizabeth, and can be seen on many coats of arms, flags and badges.

Probably scarcely noticed, it is even on the flag of the Borough of Queens in New York City, originally established in 1683 as Queen's County, while the adjacent Borough of Brooklyn was King's County.

SCOTLAND AND THE THISTLE

The Thistle, the earliest known example of a national flower, is today famous worldwide as a much-loved icon of Scotland.

The widespread and beautiful **Spear Thistle** (*Cirsium vulgare*), with large purple flower-heads, is a deep-rooted spiny weed of waysides and meadows. Back in medieval times it must have given farmers grief, and yet its good looks, vigour and tenacity endeared it to others, not least the nobility – who may have appreciated the symbolism of its regal purple colour. Spear Thistle – the native thistle on British coins – is generally accepted as the true thistle of Scotland, although gardeners and even botanists refer to the taller and more robust, woolly-leaved, non-native **Cotton Thistle** (*Onopordon acanthium*), which is probably the thistle of Lorraine (see panel), as 'Scots Thistle'.

Legend links Thistles to Scotland in the Battle of Largs in the Firth of Clyde in October 1263, when King Haakon IV of Norway attacked Scotland with a huge fleet to consolidate Viking control of Scotland's western coasts and islands

It's said the Norsemen removed their shoes to creep silently by night up to where the Scottish army was encamped. One of the attackers stood on a thistle and his loud cry of pain alerted the Scots. They then won the subsequent battle, after which the west became Scottish, not Norwegian. Haakon and his fleet sailed away to Orkney to over-winter, but he died there before fighting could resume the following spring. His successor compromised and the 1266 Treaty of Perth leased the Western Isles to the Scottish crown for an annual payment.

By 1470, thistles were on the silver coins of King James III and shortly after appeared on Scottish emblems and the national coat of arms. In 1687, James VII (James II of England) revived the old chivalric order as the Order of the Thistle, with robes with thistles on the collar, and the motto '*Nemo me impune lacessit*' ('No-one provokes me with impunity'), appropriate for a plant so well defended by spines! The Order is still held by a select group of 16 men and women who have made a significant contribution to Scottish life.

Today the thistle features wherever Scots live or work, at home and abroad. It also lends its name to bars and businesses, Thistle Street in Edinburgh, and the Glasgow football team Partick Thistle, known as 'The Jags' after the Scots word jag or jaggie (meaning prickly).

Spear Thistle is deservedly less popular in North America, where it was introduced in colonial times. Known there as Bull Thistle, it's an invasive and troublesome weed, unpalatable to livestock, of pastures, road verges and disturbed ground.
But wherever it grows, the flowers are an excellent source of nectar for bees and many other insects.

The French Connection
Thistle is also the floral emblem of the Lorraine region of France and features on the coat of arms of Nancy, the seat of the Dukes of Lorraine. About thc same time as it was stamped on James III's silver coins in Scotland, it was displayed on the city's banners at the Battle of Nancy (1477) when Lorraine defeated the more powerful Burgundy. In Burgundy itself, the village of Chardonnay (French: *cardon*, thistle), is the original home of the popular grape variety.

THE LEEK AND THE DAFFODIL

Like other nations, Wales has as its emblem a national flower – the daffodil. However, in addition, it has a vegetable emblem, the leek. This may have arisen because, curiously, in Welsh these two plants have similar names, *cenhinen* for leek and *cenhinen pedr* for daffodil, literally Saint Peter's leek. But it may just be that daffodils, both the garden plants and the small Welsh native **Wild Daffodil** or **Lent Lily** (*Narcissus pseudonarcissus*), with their pale yellow flowers and deeper yellow trumpets, are not only showier than leeks, but are usually in flower by March 1st, St David's Day. A second wild daffodil, **Tenby Daffodil** (*Narcissus obvallaris*), is named after the Pembrokeshire seaside town, but is now known to occur across SW Wales. A small, elegant plant with greyish leaves and all-yellow flowers, it is unique to Wales, although similar plants are apparently known in Spain, the native home of most of the world's wild daffodil species.

Both plants belong to the very same plant family (Amaryllidaceae), but whereas daffodils are poisonous, the widely-eaten **Leek** (*Allium porrum*) provides an important ingredient of the national dish of Wales, the hearty lamb and vegetable stew called *cawl*.

The daffodil did not become a popular Welsh symbol until the 19th century, but leeks go back much further. Indeed, legends claim that either the 6th century patron saint of Wales, St David, or the 7th century King Cadwaldr, encouraged Welsh soldiers to wear leeks on their helmets during a battle against the English, so as to distinguish them from their foes. This story can only be traced back to the 16th century and arose perhaps because the Tudor monarchs were Welsh in origin – and promoted the leek by making their guards wear it on Saint David's Day.

A slightly more plausible tale is that the

Welsh longbowmen who made so decisive a contribution at the Battle of Crécy in 1346 (page 88) were fighting in a leek field. Today the leek is on the cap-badge of the Welsh Guards, and is still worn by soldiers in Welsh regiments on St David's Day and by Welsh fans at Rugby International matches. The episode is alluded to in Shakespeare's *Henry V*, set seventy years later, in a comic interlude when Captain Gower asks his friend, the Welsh soldier Fluellen, why he wears a leek, as it is by then October and 'Saint Davy's day is past'. When Pistol, who had mocked the leek and disliked its smell, appears, Fluellen soundly berates him with words and his cudgel, forcing him to eat the raw oniony vegetable. Finally, Gower dismisses the disreputable Pistol:

'Go, go; you are a counterfeit cowardly knave. Will you mock at an ancient tradition, begun upon an honourable respect, and worn as a memorable trophy of predeceased valour …?'

All too often overcooked, leeks are not everybody's favourite food and many young people especially, reading *Henry V*, will have sympathized with Pistol, his punishment reminding them of their school dinners with badly prepared leeks, still gritty with soil. Well-cooked, leeks can compare well with any vegetable and were indeed the favourite of Rome's eccentric and cruel Emperor Nero, who believed they helped his singing voice, of which he was extremely proud.

CHERRY BLOSSOM AND JAPAN

There is probably no stronger link between a country and a plant than that of Japan and the springtime blossom of the **Flowering Cherry Tree** (*Prunus serrulata*). In ancient Japan, the arrival of the cherry blossom or Sakura had great importance because it announced the end of winter, the beginning of new life and rice-planting, and was used to plan the harvest. Its fleeting beauty, moreover, was celebrated as a metaphor for life itself – and was praised in poetry of the era.

Nowadays the Japanese turn out every year in huge numbers in parks, shrines and temples to gaze at the blossoms, while foreigners flood in from all over the world to see them. The blossoms are not only stunning, but highly symbolic, appearing often in art and literature as well as decorating numerous consumer goods.

So important is the blooming season that the Japanese Meteorological Agency issues detailed weather forecasts for the *Sekura zensen* or 'Cherry Blossom Front' as it moves northwards up the islands.

The lovely blossoms last only last two weeks, and their very transience and their exquisite beauty and volatility have become associated with mortality and the graceful acceptance of destiny and death. But sadly this created in the 1930s an unpleasant attitude that perhaps modern Japan might

like to forget. In 1930, *Sakuraki*, a Cherry Blossom Society of fanatical young officers was formed to try to take over Japan and set up a totalitarian state. Then, during the ensuing wars with China and the West, the Cherry Blossom was constantly used as a symbol to spur on civilians and the military alike, with a 'Song of Young Japan', exulting

in being ready to 'scatter like the myriad cherry blossoms'. Later, with Japan losing the war, young Kamikaze suicide pilots, with blossoms painted on their doomed aircraft, were urged to 'bloom like flowers of death', with one of their squadrons being called *Yamazakura* or 'Wild Cherry Blossom'. Their last Kamikaze plane, rocket-powered, was called the *Ohka*, another word for Cherry Blossom.

Even more sinister was 'Cherry Blossom by Night'. This military operation against America was devised by Unit 731, a notorious germ warfare unit with the dubious credit of killing 400,000 Chinese civilians with bombs loaded with bubonic plague, cholera, smallpox, anthrax and botulism. The plan was for Japanese submarines to arrive off San Francisco and Los Angeles and launch plague-contaminated fleas. Only the ending of the war by the two atomic bombs stopped this vicious operation.

How sad it is that such a lovely symbol of hope and renewal should have been for two desperate decades so misused.

BRAZIL AND ITS MUSICAL TREE

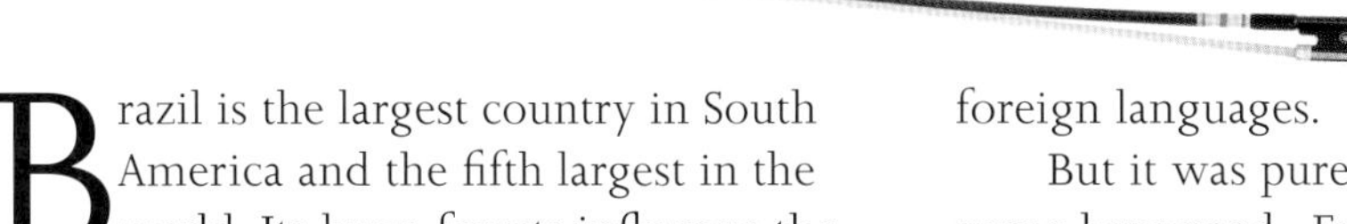

Brazil is the largest country in South America and the fifth largest in the world. Its huge forests influence the world's atmosphere, and it boasts the largest river, the Amazon. With 212 million people, it is also the Continent's economic powerhouse. As one prominent Brazilian pointed out: *'The biggest economy in South America is Brazil, the second is São Paulo county, the third is São Paulo city and the fourth is Argentina.'*

For a 'corporate identity' specialist, Brazil's name is excellent. It is short, memorable and easily pronounceable in foreign languages.

But it was purely by chance that the name happened. Early Portuguese settlers wanted to call it Terra de Vera Cruz (Land of the True Cross). But there were others – less religious and more practical – who pointed out that the only worthwhile economic benefit achieved in the colony so far was the red dye and wood exported from the local tree, called **Pau Brazil** (*Caesalpinia echinata*). Why not call the huge country after the useful little tree?

And indeed they did!

The Brazilwood tree (as opposed to the Brazilnut tree) provides the only wood suitable for violin bows, with the correct density, straight grain, no knots and the preferred colour. Sadly, the tree is under threat from encroaching agriculture and urban development. Other endangered 'music trees' are the **Maracauba** (used for marimba keys), **Lignum Vitae** (recorders) and **African Blackwood** (clarinets, flutes, oboes and bagpipes). Fender's iconic guitars are threatened by a beetle attacking the **Swamp Ash** from which they are made. So important are all these trees to the musical world that there was even a special tree conservation programme called SoundWood created by Fauna & Flora International, whose founding Patron was Yehudi Menuhin, with supporters like classical cellist Robert Cohen and the late and great jazz clarinettist Acker Bilk. SoundWood engaged instrument makers, logging companies, musicians and school children around the world to raise awareness of the threats pushing valuable music wood species to extinction. FFI continues to conserve these threatened tree species within its wider biodiversity conservation partnerships.

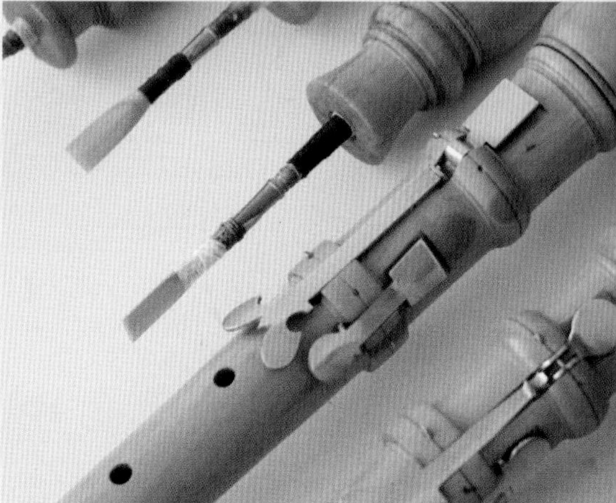

ALMA-ATA, APPLE CITY AND WORLD HEALTH

Apples are a major commercial crop and this familiar firm globose fruit has long been a popular food and cultural icon, from ancient Greece to today's Apple Inc. corporation. Apples remain a huge global commodity, with a total crop of more than 80 million tonnes, more than half grown in China, some 5 million in the USA and 3 million in Turkey. The greatest diversity of the 30 or so wild apple species is found from Turkey to Central Asia, where apples were first cultivated perhaps 4,000 years ago and from where they spread to Europe and later, in the 17th century, to the USA.

The **Apple Tree** (*Malus domestica*) is grown wherever there's a temperate climate. Crosses with wild crab apples and further crossing and selection by farmers and growers have given rise to the 7,500 or so orchard and garden cultivars of the domestic apple. Its most ancient ancestor is now known to be *Malus sieversii*, which grows in forests on the lower slopes of the Tian Shan Mountains of Kazakhstan. In fact, apples lent their name to Kazakhstan's largest city and former capital Alma-Ata, which means 'Father of Apples'.

The native forests of apples and other fruit-trees in the nearby mountains remain an important genetic resource for apple breeders.

Alma-Ata has proudly claimed to be the birthplace of the world's apple crops since a century ago, when the great Russian geneticist Nikolai Vavilov marvelled at the wild apple forests during his travels in search of centres of crop diversity. For a long time, scientists believed that the apple was most likely derived from the widespread Eurasian crab apples. Only recently has modern DNA sequencing shown *Malus sieversii* to be the progenitor of the apples we eat every day. Indeed, the fruits, up to 7 cm across, are larger than those of other wild apples and comparable with domestic varieties. Alma-Ata lay close to the Silk Road, a convenient route for apples to spread to Europe and the Mediterranean region, thence to North America. The town remains a centre of apple diversity and trade, and the wild apples themselves are remarkably diverse and yield a range of flavours. But sadly, 90% of the precious wild apple forests were destroyed during the Soviet era and its aftermath, falling victim to the depredations of wood cutters and grazing livestock. China has asked for her portion of the Tian Shan apple forests to be awarded World Heritage Status and it is hoped that Kazakhstan will do the same.

The city of apples has another claim to fame. In 1978, under the auspices of WHO and UNICEF, health experts and policy makers from 134 countries held a seminal world health conference in Alma-Ata, capital of Kazakhstan (then part of the Soviet Union). The resulting Alma-Ata Declaration was the first international resolution to emphasize such need for primary health care for all, which marked a major shift in global public health. And, whereas 'health for all by the year 2000' was never achieved, the declaration did much to focus attention on the problems and inequalities of health provision throughout the world. It directly inspired better primary health care and greatly improved public health in many countries, including Chile, Cuba, Ethiopia, Nepal and Sri Lanka. In 2018 the Global Conference on Primary Health Care was held in Almaty (now Nur-Sultan), which had replaced Alma-Ata (now Almaty) as the capital of Kazakhstan. The Almaty Declaration reaffirmed core aims of the original conference, emphasising disease prevention and health promotion, and taking on board the issues of mental health and the impact of climate change on human health.

What better venue than Alma-Ata, to discuss World Health as apples, notably nutritious and rich in vitamins, fibre and anti-oxidants, have been shown to promote a range of health benefits. It's not for nothing we say, '*An apple a day keeps the doctor away*'!

'THE BIG APPLE' AND ITS NAUGHTY ROOTS

The origin of how New York City became known as 'The Big Apple' has been in dispute for many years. It is a less wholesome story than that of the apple forests of Kazakhstan!

One of the strongest contenders for the city's epithet was the 1937 dance craze, 'The Big Apple' which had become all the rage in Columbia, South Carolina. This was taken to New York by a group of teenagers, who performed the dance in five or six shows a day to packed crowds of 6,500 fans at the Roxy Theater. After the 'Charleston' and later the 'Twist', the 'Big Apple' was the biggest dance craze ever to hit America.

However, New York's Mayor, Ed Koch, always contended that 'Big Apple' was a jazz club name, and entered into a public argument about it with Columbia's Mayor, Patten Williams.

New York City itself has officially disputed both the jazz and dance claim by erecting a plaque at 'Big Apple Corner', at the intersection of West 54th Street and Broadway. This was to honour the horse-racing writer, John Fitzgerald, who brought the term from the stables of New Orleans. In his first column in 1924 for the *New York Morning Telegraph*, Fitzgerald wrote, '*The Big Apple, the dream of every lad that ever threw a leg over a thoroughbred. There's only one Big Apple. That's New York*'.

In fact, however much that New York City may not wish to admit it, it is possible that the origin may be even older, but may also involve throwing legs over thoroughbreds! According to the Society of New York City History, in 1804, a young aristocrat fled the French Revolution and arrived in New York. Evelyn Claudine de Saint-Évremond set up an elegant brothel in fashionable Bond Street. As her friends, admirers and customers insisted on calling her 'Eve', she began describing her beautiful girls as her 'irresistible apples'. Soon, the 'in crowd' was knowingly boasting of '*having had a taste of Eve's apples*'.

By 1870, *The Gentleman's Directory of New York City* asserted touchingly that, 'in freshness, sweetness, beauty and firmness to the touch, New York's 'apples' are superior to any in the New World or, indeed, the Old.' And so New York began to be called the 'Apple Tree', the 'Real Apple' or, worried by its reputation as a centre of vice, by William Jennings Bryan in 1892, the 'Foulest Rotten Apple'.

By 1900, 'Big Apple' or 'The Apple' had passed into general verbal use as a nickname for New York. But in upstate New York, the Apple Marketing Board had started the very first product positioning campaign – with slogans like 'An apple a day, keeps the doctor away' and 'As American as apple pie.' Thus, a new and more wholesome image was to prepare the way for the 'I love New York' tourism campaign for New York state, adorned by an apple symbol.

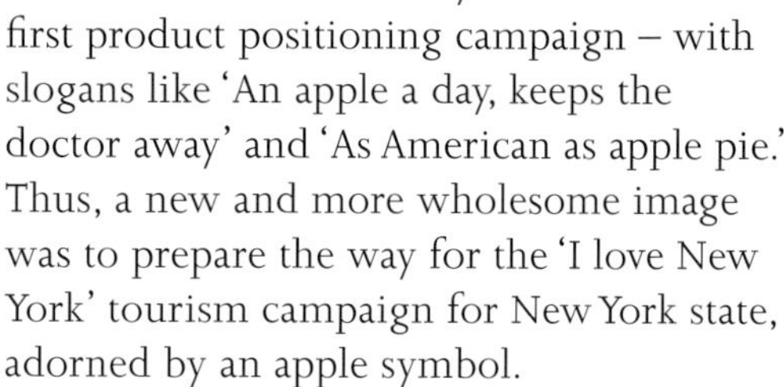

No doubt, the 'Big Apple' controversy between jazz, dance, horse-racing and brothel-owning will continue to entertain the world for years.

But we can be sure it had sadly, unlike Ala-Ata, nothing to do with the Apple tree or its fruits.

IRELAND AND THE SHAMROCK

Green is the colour we associate with Ireland. This small but influential nation of moist climate and green pastures is frequently called 'The Emerald Isle', and the green shamrock symbolises this well. It derives from what botanists call a 'trifoliate', clover-like green leaf. Most countries have a national flower, but Ireland has a national leaf!

The word shamrock (seamróg), comes from the Irish *seamair óg*, meaning 'young clover'. The ancient Druids regarded three as a magical number, and St Patrick, when in the mid-5th century he was converting the Irish to Christianity, adopted the pagan shamrock to demonstrate how its leaves comprise three linked parts – the Holy Trinity of the Father, Son and Holy Spirit. The Catholic religion that he brought from the Roman world has remained a powerful element of Irish life and, like the green shamrock, is associated with national pride and independence from Britain.

So which clover might St Patrick have chosen? Dr Caleb Thelkeld, in the 1726 first book on Irish plants, noted how people wore White Clover (*Trifolium repens*) in their hats on St Patrick's day. He also commented how 'they often commit Excess in Liquor, which is not a right keeping of a Day to the Lord'. How horrified he would be at the boisterous celebrations of modern Paddy's Day!

For a long time, the commonest Irish clover, White Clover, was the Shamrock, sold as such in Ireland for St Patrick's Day on 17th March, recorded by Nathaniel Colgan in his detailed Flora of the County Dublin in 1904. However, by the 1980s when another botanist, E. Charles Nelson, was following up Colgan's enquiries, the majority of the many leafy sprigs of clover sold as Shamrock turned out to be **Lesser Trefoil** (*Trifolium dubium*), though **White Clover** and sometimes the larger **Red Clover** (*Trifolium pratense*) (page 245) were still sold too.

Nowadays, you can buy small packets of Lesser Trefoil seeds labelled as Shamrock all year round in tourist shops; and the Irish Department of Agriculture has made this little yellow-flowered clover of dry grassland and wall-tops the official Shamrock for legal purposes – not least when shamrock is sent out to the many people of Irish descent in America and worldwide. The basic identity problem is that no clovers flower in March in Ireland, but there are plenty of clover leaves around then on lawns and roadsides!

A green plant for Irish people of all political hues

In the turbulent times in Ireland of the late 18th century, both the loyalist militias and the revolutionaries adopted the Shamrock as a symbol of Irishness. The United Irishmen went further and wore green uniforms, and their supporters put green sprigs, including shamrock, in their hats. After the 1800 Act of Union between Britain and Ireland, the shamrock was then incorporated, with the English rose and Scottish thistle, into the Royal Coat of Arms of the United Kingdom, and it grew in popularity. It featured in folksong ('Paddy's Green Shamrock Shore') and sentimental songs, was carved in stone, and appeared widely, along with the harp, as a decorative motif. Irishmen on both sides of the American Civil War had flags with shamrocks waving above them.

Since those times it has become an instantly recognizable symbol of Ireland, whether as an official trademark of the Irish Government, on the banners of the mainly US-based Ancient Order of Hibernians, as the symbol on Aer Lingus planes, or as an emblem of the Irish Guards (here the Duchess of Cambridge is presenting Shamrock on St. Patrick's Day)and the Royal Irish Regiment of the British Army.

HOLLYWOOD AND OTHER HOLLY PLACES

As the centre of the film industry, California's Hollywood is one of the most famous spots on earth. But we can be sure that no **Holly** (*Ilex aquifolium*) or **American Holly** (*Ilex opaca*) trees grew there, instead a mass of **Mexican Nopal** or **'Prickly Pear'** (*Opuntia ficus-indica*)cactus. For the Christmastime tree, with its familiar spiny leaves and red berries, it's just too dry!

The origin of the place name is disputed. The developer H.J. Witley claimed he was inspired to name it after a Chinese workman responded, 'I holly-wood', meaning he was hauling wood. Or maybe it was Harvey and Daieda Wilcox calling it after an Ohio town they knew. Anyway, they created a property development on

It became a film centre when Cecil B. De Mille decided not to film the 1914 silent western 'The Squaw Man', the world's first full-length movie at Flagstaff, Arizona – but got back on the train and opted for an old citrus barn on the corner of what is now Vine Street and Selma Street in Hollywood. It was the start of a massive industry – but nothing at all to do with Holly.

Back across the Atlantic, Holly certainly lent its name to many places in Britain, including villages – Hollingworth in Cheshire, Hollington in Staffordshire, Holmsley and others in the New Forest – and, as Cullin, in Scotland and Ireland, such as Ilnacullin or 'Island of Holly', a sub-tropical garden in Bantry Bay, offshore from Glengariff Wood where Holly and other trees form a last fragment of Atlantic temperate rainforest. Britain, uniquely, has woods purely of Holly. As an evergreen, Holly was both conspicuous and associated with pagan traditions (page 280), while valued for shade, shelter and winter forage for cattle and for garden hedges. John Evelyn, the great champion of trees, wrote admiringly in 1706 of his 400-foot long and nine-foot tall holly hedge, '*glitt'ring with its arm'd and varnish'd leaves*'. Both in Europe and America, the hard, dense pale wood was prized by furniture makers and for whip handles and walking sticks – and it made the bobbins for the 19th-century cotton mills of Lancashire.

When English colonists arrived in the eastern USA, how pleased they must have been to find a native tree so similar to their own Holly. But alas for Hollywood, American Holly occurs no nearer than eastern Texas.

THE LIME TREES OF BERLIN

One of Britain's most ancient native trees is the **Small-leaved Lime** (*Tilia cordata*), present since the end of the Ice Age. During a warm climatic interlude around 4,000 BC it may even have been the commonest tree, declining as the climate cooled. Another species, **Large-leaved Lime** (*Tilia platyphylla*) is native but rarer, and most of the lime trees we see today are a cross between the two. Based on its Anglo-Saxon name 'Linde', lime has given us many place names – like Linwood in Lincolnshire and Lyndhurst in the New Forest. In America it is **Bastwood**, deriving from the bast or inner bark, once a source of durable fibre.

The pale soft wood was a favourite for making musical instruments and of wood carvers. Horace Walpole praised one of the great carvers in lime wood, Grinling Gibbons, (1648–71): '*There is no instance of a man before Gibbons who gave wood the loose and airy lightness of flowers*'.

Surprisingly, it was not the Lime tree that provided the citrus fruits that beat the sailors' scourge of scurvy (page 7) and gave the British the American slang word 'Limey'. These were, confusingly, tropical **Lime fruit** trees (*Citrus aurantiifolia*), part of the large rue and citrus plant family. On the other hand, the flowers of Lime trees, fragrant and humming loudly with bees in June and July, make a delicious herbal tea that is a tonic and gentle sedative.

However, probably the most famous Lime trees are to be found in Berlin. There you will find the grand boulevard called *Unter den Linden*, 'Under the Lime trees', running east from Berlin's City Palace to the Brandenburg Gate. It started as a humble bridle path for the Elector John George of Brandenburg to ride to his hunting grounds,

then the Lime trees were planted in 1647 by the 'Great Elector' Frederick William. The long avenue of Limes was soon regarded as the very heart of the city and Johann Strauss III wrote his waltz *Unter den Linden* in 1900.

However, there was another popular song, written in 1923, and made famous in Germany by Marlene Dietrich before she went to America. Called 'Solang Noch Unter'n Linden', it proved more significant and poignant about the fate of Berlin.

> *'As long as trees still bloom along Unter den Linden*
> *You, my old love, Berlin will always remain Berlin.'*

In the last days of World War II, with the Russians closing in on Berlin, the boulevard was made into a temporary airfield to enable famous test pilot Hanna Reitsch to visit Adolf Hitler, before she flew the last plane out. So all the Lime trees were cut down, and Berliners suddenly remembered the words of the song with foreboding, just before their city was brutally overwhelmed by the vengeful Russians.

Since German re-unification the trees have all been replaced and the avenue is now restored as the most famous display of Lime trees in the world.

ELMS AND AMERICAN TOWNS

The elm tree has always played a special role in American life and history. William Penn signed his treaty with the Delaware Indians to create Pennsylvania under an elm. In 1765, the Boston revolutionaries gathered around an elm to protest against the British Stamp Act. George Washington first drew his sword in 1775 under an elm to start the victorious American Revolution.

Beginning with Philadelphia and Savanna and then the capital, Washington, the deliberate planting of trees soon spread to the streets and parks of cities and towns across the country, spurred by the theory that they made towns healthier. The standard 'plat' of railroad towns show streets called Walnut, Hickory, Oak, Chestnut, Poplar and Ash. But, above all, there was always an Elm Street.

The **American Elm** (*Ulmus americania*) proved the most popular urban tree – fast growing, providing

excellent shade, thriving in poor soil, resistant to urban smog, equally at home in icy winters and hot summers. So familiar was Elm Street that when the evil Freddie Krueger first appeared in 1984 to star in seven 'Nightmare on Elm Street' horror movies, we all knew that he was stalking everyone's small town America.

Sadly, a real nightmare *did* come to Elm Street. In the 1940's, America's elms suddenly started to turn yellow, then brown and, finally, die. Elm logs on railroad cars imported from France to make furniture in Ohio had unfortunately imported something else, a tiny beetle bearing a deadly fungus, *Ceratocystis ulmi*, which we now call Dutch Elm Disease. Forty years later nearly 77 million trees were dead, half of all American elms. Once shady, beautiful avenues had disappeared and parks were bare, a tragic situation also mirrored across Europe.

Botanical researchers have been working for twenty five years to create elm hybrids like 'Valley Forge' and 'New Harmony', which may be resistant to the disease. Gradually the elm may return and 'Elm Street' in thousands of communities may mean something again.

LEBANON AND ITS GREAT CEDARS

The Lebanon is a small eastern Mediterranean country, with three religions. Culturally sophisticated, it was dubbed the 'Switzerland of the East', with Beirut, its capital, called 'the Paris of the Middle East', but it is now threatened by its closeness to Israel and war-torn Syria. In August 2020, Beirut was devastated by a huge explosion of stored ammonium nitrate.

The Lebanese flag bears at its centre a green image of a cedar, the country's national tree. The device dates from the early 20th century but the story of this magnificent tree goes back to ancient Sumeria, where 4,000 years ago it was mentioned in the Epic of Gilmagesh. The biblical Book of Kings tells of how the wealthy and also proverbially wise King Solomon of Israel built a great temple of wood and stone in about 1,000 BC, as well as a royal palace entirely of wood.

Needing the best quality timber, both durable and fragrant, he contracted his ally Hiram, King of Tyre, a Phoenician city north

of Israel: *'Now therefore command thou that they hew me cedar trees out of Lebanon'*. In return, Solomon supplied wheat and olive oil. The trees were not just 'hewn' but then transported to the shores of the Mediterranean and floated in rafts down the coast. Four centuries later, the invading Babylonians destroyed the Temple of Solomon, but great **Cedars of Lebanon** (*Cedrus libani*), survive even today in mountain forests from Lebanon up into southern Turkey. Cedar has the distinction of being the tree most mentioned in the Bible.

These magnificent evergreen coniferous trees, up to 40 metres tall with massive trunks and spreading branches, domed or flattened crowns and upright, barrel-shaped cones up to 12 cm long, are familiar to millions of people far beyond Lebanon, widely planted in parks and gardens and also used for timber – the most stately of all the coniferous trees in cultivation. The oldest living cedar in England, in a rectory garden near Wantage in Oxfordshire, dates from 1646, but planting expanded greatly in the landscaped estates of the 18th century. One was planted by William Kent in the Duke of Buckingham's estate at Stowe (page 286). When Stowe became a school, the boys traditionally showed their courage by climbing to the top of its 130-foot branches – including one of the authors, Donough O'Brien, suitably terrified. (This is now banned by Health and Safety rules.) Only in the mid-19th century was the cedar's special position as the favourite tree for grand estates challenged by the giant conifers then arriving from the New World.

On the moist western flanks of the Lebanon Mountains the cedars survive but in fragmented populations, with the most ancient trees reduced to a few protected groves, the most famous of which is the 'Forest of the Cedars of God' at Bsharri, next to a Maronite Christian monastery, both included in a World Heritage Site since 1998. The trees are revered alike by the three Lebanese faiths – Christian, Moslem and Druze, perhaps summarised best in Psalm 29, *'The righteous flourish like the palm tree and grow like the cedar in Lebanon'*. They were beautifully depicted in the 1861 painting 'The Cedars of Lebanon' by Edward Lear, the landscape artist best known for his Limericks and books of Nonsense. The picture, composed from field sketches in Lebanon and mature trees on a Surrey estate, fortuitously linked the native cedar groves of Lebanon with the trees in English parkland.

From the 1960s the Lebanese government has augmented Bsharri and other cedar reserves by shielding their natural regeneration from fires and goat grazing, and by substantial re-afforestation programme. Cedar of Lebanon remains in the Taurus Mountains of Turkey, where foresters maintain extensive wild and planted stands. Surviving cedars in war-torn Syria, however, remain at much greater threat.

As well as Cedar of Lebanon, other cedar species occur in the mountains of North-western Africa, Cyprus and the Western Himalaya, where **Himalayan Cedar** (*Cedrus deodar*), once used for ship-building and now widely grown elsewhere as an urban tree, forms extensive forests.

Several coniferous trees in North America, notably **Western Red Cedar** (*Thuja plicata*) and Eastern **Red Cedar** (*Juniperus virginiana*), were erroneously named 'cedars' by European immigrants more familiar with the Bible than botany!

NEW ZEALAND AND THE SILVER FERN

Of all the countries that use plants for a national symbol, New Zealanders must use theirs more than any other. The **Silver Fern** (*Cyanthea dealbata*) is a tree fern only found in New Zealand. Its trunk can grow up to ten metres tall, with a dense crown of fronds up to four metres long. The plant gets its name from the luminous silvery colour on the undersides of the leaves. The Maoris called these ferns Ponga and used them to mark paths though the forest in the dark.

New Zealand has two other symbols, the yellow pea-like flower of **Kowhei** (*Sophora tetraptera*) and the famous flightless Kiwi bird. However, Silver Fern now seems to have become attached to almost everything. It first appeared on uniforms of the New Zealand Army in the Second Boer War of 1899–1901 and was then used by the country's Expeditionary Force in both World Wars. All fallen New Zealand soldiers have it carved on their gravestones. In mutual respect, after serving with the New Zealanders at the battle of El Alamein, three British regiments are allowed to wear the revered fern symbol.

In sport, the symbol appears often, starting in 1888 with the touring New Zealand Native Football team. Sometimes the teams attach the fern symbol to their names, as with the All Blacks in rugby, All Whites in football, Black Caps in cricket and Black Sticks in hockey. But the women's teams use both, as with Black Ferns (rugby),

Tall Ferns (basketball), Silver Ferns (netball), Football Ferns (football) and White Ferns (cricket). Along with the country's symbolism in their Olympic team, it is quite hard to get away from silver ferns in New Zealand sport.

The same can be said in commercial life, with the silver fern symbol part of the logo of ice-cream maker New Zealand Natural, a stylised version on KiwiRail trains and a really bold and dramatic use on the fuselages and tailfins of Air New Zealand planes. The design on the aircraft incorporates the traditional Maori *koru* symbol, based on the coiled, crozier-like emerging fronds of the Silver Fern, denoting new life, growth, strength and peace.

For the widespread use of a plant as a symbol, New Zealand's silver fern may even beat Ireland's shamrock!

FREETOWN'S FREEDOM TREE

Large old trees can often be found at the heart of human settlements, providing a meeting place and somewhere for the locals to gather for gossip. Many a Greek village square is dominated by ancient specimens of **Oriental Plane** (*Platanus orientalis*) and an old hollow **Elm** (*Ulmus*) was sometimes a feature of the centre of an English village. London's East End district of Poplar is named after such a tree, and a large and imposing **Black Poplar** (*Populus nigra*) was recorded by woodland ecologist Oliver Rackham forty years ago '*in the midst of railway dereliction*'. A new tree has since been planted there in All Saints' churchyard.

In the middle of Freetown, the capital of Sierra Leone in West Africa, stands an impressive specimen of the **Cotton Tree** or **Kapok** (*Ceiba pentrandra*), said to be five hundred years old and seen as a symbol of freedom from slavery. This tall rainforest tree of the Mallow family (Malvacaceae) is native to Central America and Amazonia and to West and Central Africa, and has been widely introduced in South East Asia, where it is especially grown on Java and in Thailand. It has a trunk up to 60 m tall arising from huge buttress roots and armed with spines, an umbrella-shaped crown of spreading branches and white or pale pink flowers. The stout sausage-like hanging fruits burst open to release seeds and silky hairs that aid dispersal, which are the Java kapok used in stuffing bedding, soft toys and, most important, lifebuoys. It is the lightest of all plant fibres. The tree's American-African distribution perhaps arose by the natural sea transport of the buoyant fruits across the Atlantic.

AM I NOT A MAN AND A BROTHER

Freetown, ironically only twenty miles from the former slave trade station of Bunce

Island, was founded in 1792 as a settlement for black loyalists, former US slaves who had fought for Britain during the American War of Independence and had originally settled in Nova Scotia in Canada. As an advance party cleared the land, the great size of the 'Cotton Tree' attracted them, and the whole group of colonists then gathered beneath its branches to sing hymns and pray. Later the Royal Navy stationed their West Africa Squadron in the large natural harbour of Freetown, a convenient base to enforce the ban on the African slave trade, which, again ironically, the Royal Navy had spent the previous century protecting!

The Cotton Tree, on a roundabout close to the Supreme Court and National Museum, remains a historic symbol and a place of prayer and thanksgiving in the midst of the modern city.

A most welcome sight!

CANADA AND THE MAPLE LEAF

Canada is forever associated with the maple leaf symbol. A red maple leaf is at the centre of the nation's red and white flag and has often adorned the rucksacks of young Canadian travellers, proud to distinguish themselves from the Americans with whom they are all too often confused. It is an emblem of Air Canada, General Motors Canada, the Toronto Maple Leafs ice hockey club and many other businesses and organisations.

Maples, a group of 158 species of mainly deciduous trees or shrubs, most with a characteristic, lobed, palm of the hand-shaped leaf, are by no means unique to Canada. They occur across the temperate Northern Hemisphere from Canada to China; in particular, New England in the USA is famous worldwide for its woods of maple trees and their spectacular display of

yellow, orange and red leaf colours in the fall. Two of the most widespread maples in southern Canada and north-eastern USA are among the most colourful at summer's end, **Sugar Maple** (*Acer saccharum*) and **Red Maple** (*Acer rubrum*). American nature writer Hal Borland praised the Red Maple trees in Connecticut for '*the crimson of their opening buds*' in spring, but more especially: '*when October comes the flame that was like a bed of coals in spring will become a forest fire of leaves, a leaping flame of beauty*'.

Until 1965 Canada lacked a national flag other than the Union Jack of the UK. Many Canadians favoured the Union Jack but French-speaking Canada, especially Quebec, was unhappy with this symbol of the nation that had ended the direct link with France when General James Wolfe defeated the French at Quebec in 1759 during the Seven Years War. In January 1965 after much discussion, Queen Elizabeth, Canada's official Head of State, gave royal consent for a new national flag, flown for the first time on February 15th of that year.

The maple leaf was an obvious symbol as it had long been adopted by both the English and French-speaking communities. It had appeared on coinage and on the badges, and tombstones of Canadian soldiers in the Boer War and two World Wars. Ten species of maple are native to Canada; the stylized 11-point leaf was based on the more usually 23-point leaf of the Sugar Maple but with the vibrant red colour of the Red Maple. Sugar Maple is particularly appropriate as Canada produces 85% of the world's maple syrup, mostly exported to the USA, which itself also produces syrup in New England. For a month or so in early spring the trees are tapped for their rising sap – as much as 30–50 litres from each tree.

Gardeners prefer to grow the smaller maple species from East Asia, notably **Japanese Maple** (*Acer palmatum*), from which over 1,000 cultivars have been selected for their range of dwarf, weeping or spreading growth, and leaf dissection and colour, especially the varied autumn tints. Public gardens on both sides of the Atlantic hold fine Acer collections or 'Aceretums', for example the Arnold Arboretum in Boston, USA, and Wakehurst Arboretum, Westonbirt Arboretum and Windsor Great Park in the UK.

Maples are valued not only for syrup and ornament but also for their fine-grained pale timber used to make furniture, baseball bats and musical instruments – including violins, bassoons and Gibson's iconic Les Paul electric guitars. The flowers are a source of nectar for early-flowering honeybees. Nevertheless, these useful trees are greatly threatened, and research by Botanic Gardens Conservation International has revealed that a fifth of the world's maples are at risk of dying out in the wild, and more than a third face habitat loss through urban sprawl, agricultural expansion or over-harvesting for timber. In China alone, 14 of the 23 endemic maple species sadly face extinction – a terrible toll for such a beautiful tree.

EATING AND DRINKING

Getting it there
Keeping it cool
How to eat it?
Cereals and Civilisation
'Prohibition' and its unintended consequences
Durum wheat and Pasta
Ginger in food and fable
Haricot beans and Henry Heinz
A spice of life
Drink and drugs in battle
Maize - from 'Indian corn' to 'corn on the cob'
Sugar cane, mollasses and rum
Garlic and its strange powers
The Chilli revolution
Cherries, a feast of colour and taste
Rice and Asian Society
Soya, the saviour
Buck's Fizz and its secret
Watercress and its two capitals
Breakfast and cereals
Tomatoes, from curiosity to kitchen staple
Hops and the pleasures of beer
Avocados and their popularity
Peppering things up
Cocktails
Agaves - Mediterranean sunsets to Tequila Sunrises
Rhubarb - edible dock from the East
Bitter Oranges and Marmalade
Mustard and its parable
Oaks and Truffles
Strawberry fields for ever
Quinoa - a new life for the Inca's grain
Grapes and wine
Champagne and celebration

GETTING IT THERE

For most of history, people seldom travelled further than a few miles from their homes. Most food was grown locally and only a few very high value plant products might be taken long distances, for example across deserts by camel or down

the Silk Road. But in Britain and the rest of Europe, to buy food, locally produced and limited by the seasons, people would either grow their own or simply go once or twice a week to market. We can still see many such markets abroad, notably in France and elsewhere in southern Europe, and although the horse-drawn waggons had to travel a little further, London's Covent Garden or Les Halles in Paris were simply larger and more permanent versions of them.

After about 1840, everything changed dramatically with the coming of the railways. Fresh food could now come from hundreds

of miles away in a few hours. Bizarrely, for instance, from the late 19th century each night Yorkshire's 'Rhubarb Triangle' sent a special express train down to London loaded with tons of the pink edible leaf stalks. In Hampshire, a railway was even opened up just to transport watercress, now still operating as the heritage steam 'Watercress Line'.

On a much bigger scale, in North America, railroads transformed the countryside, opening up the land for agriculture, especially of grain in the Mid-West. You can still see hundreds of grain elevators across the prairie and thousands of

big railroad hopper cars sitting waiting in massive yards for harvest time. High-speed refrigerator (reefer) trains thundered across the country to the great railroad hub of Chicago, which became the commodity trading centre of America. Florida, with its warm climate, was opened up for citrus fruit, celebrated with a train and even a song, 'The Orange Blossom Special'.

Improvements to road highways and networks and the invention of refrigerated trucks meant that many crops could be delivered off-season from warm growing centres to colder markets. Every day, trucks leave the massive complexes of polythene

tunnels of southern Spain to drive up through France, cross the Channel and arrive at a special distribution depot in south London, laden with vegetables and fruits that were either unknown in Britain – or once only available, like strawberries, for a few weeks of the year. Nearly half of Holland's tomatoes arrive every day for British supermarkets by ferry on trucks at Harwich.

Ships had always been important for local and coastal trade, and, on long distances, for delivering non-perishable crops like tea and cotton. Indeed, the 'Tea Clippers' were a rather bogus way to

promote speed and freshness (page146). When ships could be cooled, a huge new trade developed all over the world.

Then, of course, came the aeroplane. Once airfreight prices fell and became reasonable, it became possible to fly perishable produce from all sorts of countries like Kenya, Israel, Morocco and South Africa. Today, for instance, fresh flowers from Colombia are flown six thousand miles to the Amsterdam Flower Market every day

in the holds of passenger flights. And now farm and garden produce from the Tropics and temperate southern hemisphere can readily reach markets in the north and thus make all sorts of fruits and vegetables readily available out of season and all year round.

The improvements in transportation have changed the world of eating and cooking. Britain, for instance, now imports 38% of her vegetables and an overwhelming 90% of her fruit.

Whether this is wise or even safe is debatable (page 126), but it is currently a fact of life. It will be interesting to see how this may alter, with climate change, emergence of the post-Coronavirus economy and other factors.

It is always difficult to predict the future, and post-Covid 19, even harder.

KEEPING IT COOL

Tens of thousands of years after we learned to use fire to make things hot, people turned to the opposite challenge, trying to cool things down. It was the Chinese who first flooded fields in winter in order to form ice to use for preserving food. Then the Turks brought their system of storing ice to the borders of Europe – to this day they collect snow in the mountains – and soon any elegant French chateau or smart English mansion had an insulated, often semi-subterranean 'icehouse', supplied by ice from local lakes or even from as far afield as Norway. The railways could swiftly transport both the ice and the produce it cooled. Indeed, that's how from the 1860s onwards the famous British dish of 'fish and chips', became possible.

Pioneered by Frederik 'Ice King' Tudor in America, frozen water from northern lakes was cut into blocks and transported south by steamboat so that 'Southern gentlefolk' could sip their iced mint juleps, even in the height of summer. By 1830, ice was even reaching India and the Far East.

Whole new food industries in fruit, vegetables, meat and fish were created by 180,000 refrigerated railroad cars, cooled by hoppers filled with ice, re-filled at intervals like pit stops. The high-speed 'reefer' trains from California and the West Coast rushed to Chicago and New York, and were given priority even over crack passenger expresses. The possibility of mechanical refrigeration,

rather than relying on expensive and seasonal ice, had been examined by many pioneers. The Americans John Gorrie and Willis Carrier (below) eventually perfected air-conditioning, thus transforming food

production and storage, and of course, its consumption in comfort. Carrier's legacy is a company that is the biggest player in food refrigeration, operating in 180 countries.

A Scotsman, James Harrison, in Australia in 1860 was the pioneer of refrigerated ships for transporting fruit, vegetables and meat long distances. French engineer Charles Tellier developed the first industrial refrigerator in 1856, and twenty years later the first plant to produce ice consistently. That same year the steamship *Frigorifique* trans-

ported mutton from Buenos Aires to Rouen, pioneering the huge trade in Argentinian meat. In 1881 the *Dunedin* brought the first mutton and lamb from the New Zealand pastures to London.

The first refrigerator for consumers, the Monitor Top, was made by General Electric in 1927. It had some early setbacks, not least the horrific habit of killing people with leaking carbon monoxide gas. But once 'freons' – gases containing chlorine and fluorine – were used, it worked very well, although because the Monitor Top initially cost twice as much as a car, only rich people could afford one. But that soon changed, and after World War II, fully 90% of American households had refrigerators. In bankrupt, post-war Britain that figure was only 13% and families had to go to the shops much more often, trying to store their food in cool larders.

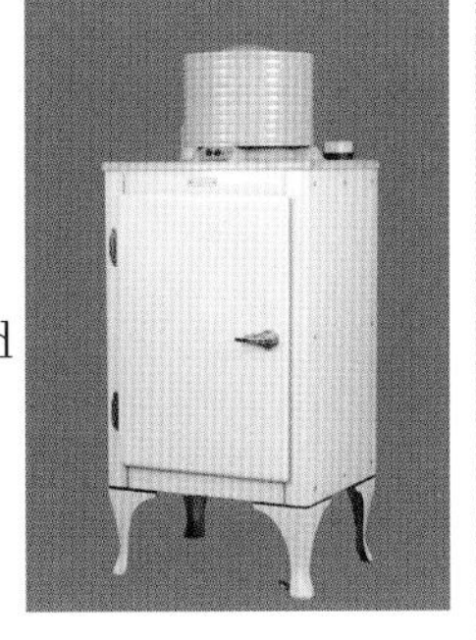

Most 'fridges' had freezer compartments, and working in Canada Clarence Birdseye had discovered from the Inuits how to freeze food quickly, notably peas, which later he did within two hours of picking, preserving the colour and sweetness. Frozen peas are now eaten in preference to traditional tinned or even fresh ones, and Birdseye say we each eat 9,000 of them a year in Britain.

Coupled with transporting food quickly and efficiently, the ability to cool or freeze food transformed the way we cook, present and eat it.

The authors remember only too clearly having to shell peas as children, before insecticides, which prompted Liz Cowley to pen a poem in her cookery comedy book, **Pass the Prosecco, Darling!**

SHELLING PEAS IN CHILDHOOD

Back then, when shelling peas,
it never was much fun,
as maggots lived in pods –
and almost every one.

Disgusting, shelling peas.
It quite revolted me,
with nasty squirming babes
surrounding every pea.

And put peas in your mouth?
Well, rather you than me.
But maybe pods you shelled
were lots less maggoty.

You may be half my age,
and never seen a pod
with maggots curled inside.
Those days have gone, thank God!

HOW TO EAT IT?

When you eat out in an Oriental restaurant, do you enjoy the challenge of using chopsticks? And have you ever wondered when they were first used? You may be surprised that their history goes back five thousand years, starting in China and spreading rapidly to other East Asian countries.

Probably originating from twigs to avoid burning the fingers, they were then made from bamboo, palm fronds and other local woody material. Originally used for cooking, they became fashionable for eating during the Han Dynasty (206 BC–220 AD). They fitted a Chinese tradition that it was barbaric to serve food resembling the original animal, or to carve at the table, so small chopped portions, prepared out of sight, were pre-prepared for chopstick eating.

Our use of the word 'chopsticks' almost certainly derived from English sailors using Chinese Pidgin English, 'chop' meaning 'quick'. Not surprisingly, as this is not far from the Chinese kuàizi, meaning 'quick bamboo'. We still say 'Chop Chop' to make people hurry up.

For eating more liquid food, simple spoons were developed as far back as the Stone Age, hollowed out from bits of wood. Indeed, our word 'spoon' comes from the Anglo-Saxon word 'spon', meaning a splinter or piece of wood.

Knives at the table always suffered from their perceived dual role, eating and fighting. Cardinal Richelieu, the Chief Minister to Louis XIII, also began to dislike the way people at Court stabbed their chunks of food and later picked their teeth with the points of their daggers. He therefore ordered his kitchen staff to round off all the knife blades, which soon became the fashion. But it would, of course, make the need for something to fix or lift the food – resembling a fork – ever more important.

Forks originated in Greece, some made with wood, soon of metal, and were first used in the kitchen with two 'tines', or prongs. They had spread to the Middle East by the 7th century and then to Constantinople and the Byzantine Empire. The name we use today comes from Italy and the Latin '*furca*'. Curiously, forks seem to have come up against a rather cranky resistance. In the 11th century, when the Doge of Venice married a Greek princess, she brought forks to Court and amazingly created a scandal. Forks were regarded as a heretical affectation and, when she died, her demise incredibly, was thought of as a justly deserved divine punishment!

Four hundred years later, when the traveller and writer Thomas Coryate brought forks from Italy, he encountered

the same resistance in England. He was mocked as effeminate and called 'Furcifer', or fork-bearer. Once again, it was the church that seemed to hate forks, the clergy claiming that only human fingers were 'worthy of touching God's food', and, as in Italy, preaching that those using a fork would die of God's displeasure! However, once again the use of forks became fashionable and spread downwards through society.

So, to eat plants or any other food, when people are not struggling with chopsticks, most of them are using knives, forks and spoons.

But from what to eat them?

In hot climates, the earliest form of platters, or plates, were large leaves or halves of gourds while in cooler countries, wooden platters were used. Food was placed in the middle and people helped themselves.

Today we use the word 'trencherman' for someone with a large appetite. It comes from the word 'trencher', an early form of plate for individual use. Trenchers were sometimes made of wood, but more popularly of coarse bread, left to harden and then carved to shape. Once they had been used and soaked with food, they were thrown out – to be eaten by the poor or the dogs. Trenchers made of wood could at least be re-used, but there could be hygiene problems.

It was certainly a very good thing that clay, china and porcelain would eventually take over.

CEREALS AND CIVILIZATION

Imagine the constant anxiety of a woman desperately hoping her man has found something for the family to eat from a plant or tree – or has perhaps been able to kill some animal for food.

A precarious life indeed, and not so long ago. Luckily it was about to change. Plants were to be domesticated – perhaps the most significant step in the development of civilization. The move from hunter-gathering to settled agriculture and arable farming hugely expanded food production and led to a major increase in the human population. Above all, it propelled the growth of all community life; trade, transport, towns and culture – what we now call 'civilisation'.

About ten thousand years ago, not long after the last Ice Age, people in South-west Asia began to cultivate plants deliberately rather than just gather them from the wild. The 'Fertile Crescent' of plant domestication centred on the wide plains of the Tigris and Euphrates valleys and extended in a broad arc from Kurdistan and the Persian Gulf to Palestine and Egypt. The extensive cultivation of crops as a staple food source enabled the rise of the civilizations of Sumeria and Egypt, and spread to the Indus Valley. Not long after, rice was being domesticated in China (page 197).

The key plants in this game-changing 'Neolithic Agricultural Revolution' in the Middle East were a group of cereals – grasses with starch-rich grains – which these early farmers not only grew but selected for desirable characteristics and, by both accident and design, bred into newer, improved varieties. Gradually familiar staples emerged from populations of wild ancestors, the sort of annual grasses we would now call weeds. The most important of these cereals was **Wheat** or **Bread Wheat** (*Triticum aestivum*), which is today the world's largest and most widespread source of food. Wheat is extraordinarily variable, with countless old and local versions, and has a complex family tree that involves crosses between several wild and cultivated species of both wheats and the related **Goat Grasses** (*Aegilops*). Not until the 'Green Revolution' was there to be much improvement to this crop, although it has come at the cost of the loss to cultivation of potentially useful wheat races or varieties. Fortunately, many have at least been stored as seed in gene banks.

About 95% of the world's wheat crop is Bread Wheat. This evolved later than the other wheats, probably following crossing around 6,000 BC with a wild goat grass from just outside the region, but would gradually replace them. Several of the most ancient wheats are still cultivated, notably the hard-grained **Durum Wheat** (*Triticum turgidum*) used to make semolina, pasta and the couscous of North Africa and the Levant. An older crop, regarded by some botanists as a subspecies of Durum, **Emmer Wheat** (*Triticum dicoccum*) was the main wheat that spread with Neolithic agriculture through Europe and the Mediterranean region, where it persists today in remote and mountainous parts such as the Abruzzo Mountains of Italy. **Spelt** (*Triticum spelta*), another plant with hard grains and suited to poorer soils, was largely replaced by modern wheats during the 20th century but has now seen a revival of interest in popular artisanal bread. **Einkorn** (*Triticum monococcum*), now rare but once widely

cultivated in northern Europe, may also have a brighter future. High in protein and low in gluten, to which many people are intolerant, it grows in the poorest soils and even those that are salty – all invaluable attributes for crop breeders. Emmer, Spelt and Einkorn together contribute the old Italian grain dish farro. One of our friends spotted the following notice outside a shop in Castallucio, a hill village in Umbria famous for its lentils and traditional farming: '*Chi mangia farro, non la gisogno del medico!*' ('Whoever eats farro does not need a doctor')!

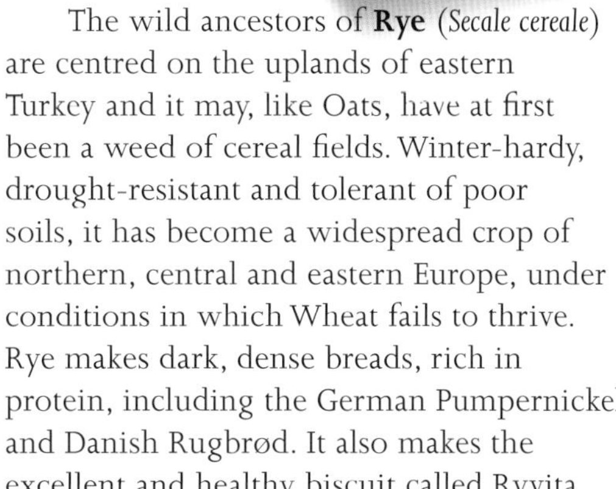

Along with the early wheats, **Barley** (*Hordeum vulgare*) was domesticated from the closely related wild barley species, and having spread widely with Neolithic agriculture, became the major grain crop of Antiquity. It is hardy and gives a good yield on poor, dry and salty soils, but Bread Wheat was increasingly prized for its better flavour and suitability for making bread, not least modern industrial bread. Indeed, wheat has come to be almost synonymous with 'bread'. But Barley long provided the poor man's bread – and that of the Roman legionary and other soldiers – as well as animal feed and was also, from the earliest times in Egypt and elsewhere, favoured for brewing beer.

Other cereals emerged later. **Oats** (*Avena sativa*) were probably a secondary crop derived from the wild oats that are widespread in and around the Mediterranean region and infest crops as weeds to the present day. It was not widely grown as a crop until about 1000 BC and found its niche in the cooler, wetter parts of Europe. Oats are a high-energy cereal that feeds both horses and their masters, with oatcakes and porridge the last relics of a basic diet that sustained Europe's peasantry for centuries.

The wild ancestors of **Rye** (*Secale cereale*) are centred on the uplands of eastern Turkey and it may, like Oats, have at first been a weed of cereal fields. Winter-hardy, drought-resistant and tolerant of poor soils, it has become a widespread crop of northern, central and eastern Europe, under conditions in which Wheat fails to thrive. Rye makes dark, dense breads, rich in protein, including the German Pumpernickel and Danish Rugbrød. It also makes the excellent and healthy biscuit called Ryvita.

Rye is also used as animal feed and the tall stems provide thatch. In the United States it is made into whiskey. However, a serious disadvantage is that the grains are susceptible to infestation by Ergot fungus, which used to inflict outbreaks of serious illness, on rye-growing rural communities, ergotism or the so-called 'St Anthony's Fire', an unpleasant combination of blood vessel constriction, convulsions, hallucination and even death (page 44).

It is difficult to overstate how much these cultivated cereals influenced the growth and survival of human communities, from the great cities of the Middle East and the Mediterranean lands to farms and crofts from Italy and Central Europe to Scotland, Scandinavia and Russia.

They were indeed the building blocks of civilization.

Barley, Beer and Marmite

Beer made from both Emmer Wheat and Barley was being brewed in Egypt and Mesopotamia from at least 3,000 BC. The process remains substantially the same today. Barley grains are soaked, and when they sprout, the food store of starch they contain converts into a sugar, maltose. The grains are then heated to kill them, milled and soaked in hot water to make a mash, which is filtered and boiled with hops or other plants as flavouring and preservative, the resulting 'wort' being fermented by yeast.

A by-product of brewing beer, marketed since 1902, is the savoury, dark brown spread Marmite. Yeast extract with added salt, vegetable flavourings and spices, it is a characteristically British food, which people claim either to love or hate. Indeed, 'Marmite' has passed into the English language to symbolize something or somebody (often a politician) that divides opinion. It is rich in B vitamins and has been used both to supplement army rations and to treat malnutrition. Marmite is now a trademark of Unilever, but similar products exist elsewhere, including Vegemite in Australia, another iconic product.

'PROHIBITION' AND ITS UNINTENDED CONSEQUENCES

Plant-based products have created extended episodes of extreme and brutal violence twice in the recent past. One of them is still with us – the drug wars in the Americas. These are definitely the result of evil intent. Not only do drugs kill tens of thousands of addicts in the United States, but also thousands more – the producers and traffickers – who die violently in the fierce competition to bring the drugs to a $70 billion market. Last year, the death toll in Mexico was nearly 20,000.

Two plants, **Opium Poppy** (*Papaver somniferum*), yielding heroin and morphine, and **Cannabis** or **Hemp** (*Cannabis sativa*) cause enough problems, but nowadays cocaine is the worst offender. In Colombia, which processes its own **Coca** (*Erythroxiglon coca*) leaves and those of Peru and Bolivia, about 400,000 have died. And in New York City, a third of all homicides are related to 'crack' cocaine (page 74).

By contrast, the previous epidemic of violence, in the early 20th century, was created by mistake, born out of good intentions. This was 'Prohibition' and its attempt to reduce the consumption in the United States of alcoholic drinks.

All such drinks are, of course, made

from plants: **grapes** provide wine, brandy, port and sherry. Beer comes from **barley** and **hops**, whiskey from **barley, corn, rye** and **wheat**, gin from various grains and **juniper** berries and vodka from **sorghum, rice, corn, rye**, **wheat** and **potatoes.**

The movement to prohibit alcohol had been active for a century, and the American Temperance Society was formed in 1826. Women had always been the driving force and since 1873 the Woman's Christian Temperance Union had sought to 'transform

Some might prefer liquor!

by Divine grace those who are enslaved by alcohol'. Four years later, a judge had declared that 'idleness, disorder, pauperism and crime are traceable to this evil'.

So there was, in fact, considerable public support in 1918, first for the temporary Prohibition Act, designed to save grain for the war effort after the United States entered the First World War. Then, in 1920,

Congressman Andrew Volstead (left) brought in the Volstead Act and 'Prohibition', which barred the production and sale of alcoholic drink – but not everywhere its possession. It did not apply to neighbouring countries, which swiftly moved into the smuggling business.

The Prince of Wales regaled his father King George V with a song he had heard in a Canadian border town:

'Four and twenty Yankees, feeling rather dry
Went across the border to get a drink of rye.
When the rye was opened, the Yanks began to sing
'God bless America, but God save the King!'

In reality, Prohibition bore down mostly on the poor. Both President Woodrow Wilson and then his successor Warren Harding kept their own large liquor supplies, and the rich could get their drink from the thousands of 'speakeasies' and from bootleggers.

But the biggest effect was on crime. The mobsters like 'Lucky' Luciano, Meyer Lansky and Al Capone quickly turned from prostitution and gambling to supplying what the public actually wanted – drink. And they competed fiercely, hundreds dying in shoot-outs like 'The Valentine's Day Massacre' in Chicago. Al Capone (right) even had his Chicago bootlegging rival, Dion O'Banion, gunned down when clipping chrysanthemums in his flower shop – not what you usually expect in such an establishment!

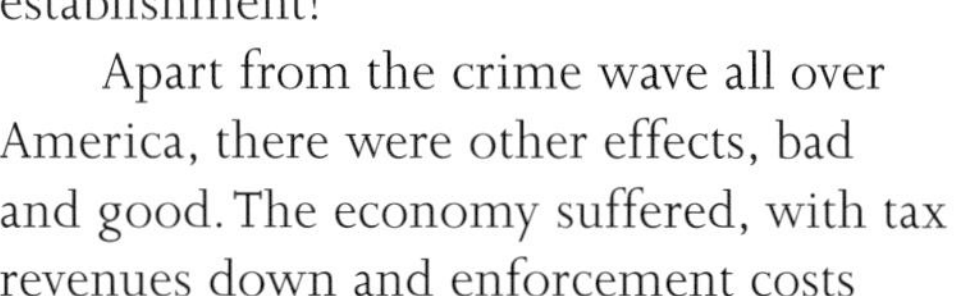

Apart from the crime wave all over America, there were other effects, bad and good. The economy suffered, with tax revenues down and enforcement costs

TUESDAY, NOV

"ARCH CRIMINAL" OF CHICAGO SLAIN IN HIS FLOWER SHOP

Dead Gunman and Gangster Responsible for 25 Murders, Police Chief Says.

(BY THE ASSOCIATED PRESS.)

CHICAGO, November 11—Gang rivalry, beer runners, feuds, gamb-

"I don't doubt that O'Bannion was responsible for at least 25 murders in this city," he said.

Often under suspicion and questioned, O'Bannion never was tried for murder. Occasionally when he was named in connection with a killing he would appear voluntarily.

"Why, I'm a florist," he would say. "If I've ever been in the booze racket, I'm out now."

A theory that possibly twenty-

spiralling. Women started drinking unashamedly in public. Beefed-up cars used as 'moonshine runners' led to the amazingly fast and dangerous NASCAR saloon car motor racing. Racial integration started in the jazz bands of the speakeasies, and the gambling city of Las Vegas was created, financed by bootlegging profits.

Then America tired of its well-meaning experiment and Prohibition was repealed in 1933. Plant products could return to providing the raw materials for drink, legally.

Winston Churchill, half-American himself, stated that Prohibition was 'an affront to the whole history of mankind.' But, of course, knowing his splendid drink consumption, he would have had to say that, wouldn't he?

DURUM WHEAT AND PASTA

It's hard to think of Italy and its food without thinking of pasta. Contrary to what Richard Dimbleby solemnly told us on his BBC Panorama programme on April Fools Day, 1957 (page 381), spaghetti clearly doesn't grow on trees!

Rather, as with all pasta, it's made from **Macaroni Wheat** or **Durum Wheat** (*Triticum durum*), a hard-grained cereal, perfect for making pasta. It provides, too, the bulgur wheat of dishes such as tabbouleh in the Levant and the couscous of the Maghreb countries of North-west Africa. On the other hand, pizzas, pastry and bread tend to be made from **Common Wheat** or **Bread Wheat** (*Triticum aestivum*), about 90% of the global wheat crop; 600 million tons of which are grown annually, across 500 million acres and which comprise one of the world's staple sources of food, second only to rice.

Pasta is first mentioned in the Jewish texts of the Talmud in the 5th century AD., dried pasta being easily portable and cooked with boiling water. It may have been the Berbers who brought the long, thin form to Sicily in the 12th century, soon to become popular throughout Italy. The resulting spaghetti, soon to be the symbol of Italian cooking, could be made with milled flour (semolina) and water into dough and then cut by hand or by simple pasta-extruding machines. In Italy it is often served with a tomato sauce containing herbs like oregano and basil, olive oil, ham or salami and vegetables.

For foreigners, especially the British, it may come as a shock to discover that the Italians do not favour the UK's favourite – minced beef 'Spaghetti Bolognese'. They don't

think Bolognese sauce suits this particular pasta, preferring it served as Carbonara or Amatriciana – and reserving Bolognese sauce for Tagliatelli. Indeed, Italian pasta experts point out that the many types and over a hundred shapes of pasta, often associated with particular regions, are designed go best with specific kinds of sauce, because the sauces adhere better to the pasta and thus transmit their taste.

To serve lovers of Italian food and the tens of thousands of Italian restaurants worldwide, gone for the most part are housewives' rolling pins and little extruding machines. Now, huge companies like Barilla operate great halls of amazing, sophisticated production lines pouring out the various types of pasta. While Italians still enjoy their pasta at home, 65% of production goes off to 120 countries.

Cheap, nutritious, tasty, easy to prepare, versatile – pasta has conquered the planet! Nor need it be associated, as sometimes in the past, with putting on weight. Iconic Italian actress Sophia Loren, a great lover of pasta, alluded to her famously voluptuous curves with the quip: 'Everything you see I owe to spaghetti'.

GINGER IN FOOD AND FABLE

How many readers remember being horrified to hear the famous but unsettling childhood story of 'The Gingerbread Man' – about a childless old woman making gingerbread into the shape of a little figure and baking him in the oven? The poor fellow then manages to leap out and successfully scurries away, singing triumphantly, '*Run, run as fast as you can! You can't catch me, I'm the gingerbread man!*' Unfortunately, as you may recall, the tale ends with him being caught and devoured, not by the cook and her husband, but by a hungry passing fox, with the doomed and tragic little gingerbread man uttering his last pathetic words, '*I'm quarter gone...I'm half gone...I'm three quarters gone... I'M ALL GONE!*'

This old fable inspired a classic 20th century Irish novel, J.P. Donleavy's *The Ginger Man*, an anarchic romp through bohemian life in post-World War II Dublin. But the

story was almost enough to put one of the authors of this book – Liz Cowley – off ginger-made products for life, and certainly why she never made gingerbread cookies for her daughter! However, like many people, she is a fan of other ginger products – ginger cake, ginger beer, ginger wine and ginger biscuits, not to mention chocolate-coated ginger, to name but a few.

Curiously, the theme of 'runaway' foods is found all over the world. The Russians have 'The Pancake', the Germans 'The Big, Fat Pancake' and also *Der fortgelaufen Eierkuchen*, or 'The Runaway Pancake'. Hungarians preferred 'The Little Dumpling', the Americans 'Johnny-cake' and the Scots' The Wee Bannock' – a flat wheat biscuit. There's even 'The Runaway Tortilla', 'The Runaway Ice Cake', 'Little Brown Egg', the 'Stinky Cheese Man' and the 'Cookie Run'.

Broadway even staged in 1905 'The Gingerbread Man', a musical, which then toured America for four years. Its hero was dubbed 'John Dough', another name for gingerbread and a grisly reference to 'John Doe', what American police traditionally call an un-named person or corpse.

Ginger (*Zingiber officinale*) itself is among the very earliest recorded spices to be cultivated in India, still the world's largest producer. Probably first domesticated among the islands of S.E. Asia, it is unknown as a wild plant. Its historical appeal is of no surprise, such is the enjoyable and distinctive flavour of its stout underground stems or rhizomes – which contain the spice, can be easily divided and transported, take root and grow easily. A 5th century Chinese traveller even reported ginger being grown in pots on ocean-going Chinese ships to prevent scurvy (page 7). It is pleasing to know that production today is still very much a family business, done by both male and female farmers, with everyone pitching in on the numerous family farms. Ginger is also produced by China, Indonesia, Thailand, Nigeria and Jamaica.

Like many other spices, ginger is a medicinal plant, used in Ayurvedic medicine since at least 2,000 BC and remaining a safe and popular herbal remedy. It has anti-inflammatory properties, settles the stomach, aids digestion and reduces wind.

Which countries most like Ginger in their food? Not surprisingly, those in which it is grown! In India, it is particularly popular for making gravies, but also widely used for all kinds of meat and vegetarian dishes, in curries and also, surprisingly, in tea and coffee.

Ginger, curiously, has also passed into our language as a verb, as in to 'ginger up' something, making it more exciting, or to handle a bit 'gingerly' something we are unsure of. And, of course, it's a common nickname for someone with red hair!

Elsewhere in the world, countries have their own favourite recipes. Ginger is an ancient and important ingredient in Chinese cookery and was reputedly a favourite of the philosopher Confucius (557–479 BC). Burma uses it widely in cooking and in salads; Thailand has its popular garlic and ginger paste; Indonesia includes it in a range of local recipes; in Malaysia it is particularly enjoyed in soups, while in the Caribbean it spices up the traditional 'Sorrel' drink, made with the red petals of **Roselle** (*Hibiscus sabdariffa*).

In the West, we more associate ginger with sweet drinks and food – ginger ale, beer and wine, gingerbread, ginger snaps and biscuits, and, in Yorkshire and Lancashire, parkin. The following recipes from Prue Leith's excellent book 'Leith's Simple Cookery' may tempt us to be more adventurous!

Some Prue Leith Ginger recipes
Ginger and apple chutney, Ginger and apricot jam, Pak Choi steamed with Ginger, Ginger and celery soup, Chicken breasts with Ginger, Ginger in crab filo tartlets, Ginger and date biscuits, Honey and Ginger sauce, Ginger, honey and lime sauce, Ginger and mascarpone cream, Ginger and orange cookies, Ginger and orange stir-fried prawns, Ginger and orange tiramisu, Ginger syrup, Gingernut puddings, Ginger and apricot glaze.

HARICOT BEANS AND HENRY HEINZ

Who doesn't like baked beans? And who hasn't heard of Heinz, who've been producing them ever since 1896? Perhaps surprisingly, in Britain they first arrived as a luxury in Fortnum & Mason, an upmarket store associated with rather more sophisticated fare. Success followed for Henry Heinz and his beans becoming a staple food as part of the traditional 'full English breakfast'. Colourful, nutritious, healthy, simple to prepare, edible hot or cold, delicious on buttered toast, popular with both adults and children – keeping the family 'full of beans' was now deliciously simple!

Official recognition arrived with Britain's Ministry of Food recommending Heinz Baked Beans as an essential food during wartime rationing in 1941.

Iconic further success came with the

brilliant 1967 slogan BEANZ MEANZ HEINZ, created by Maurice (Mo) Drake, becoming one of the best-known advertising slogans of all time in Britain. Indeed, so enduringly popular did the brand become that there was a pop-up 'Heinz Beanz Museum' in Covent Garden in 2019 and a permanent 'Baked Bean Museum of Excellence' in Port Talbot in Wales.

But what exactly *are* the beans? They are **Haricot Beans** (*Phaseolus vulgaris*), or Common

Beans, popular in central America long before Europeans arrived to settle, plunder and kill with their unfamiliar diseases. The three staple Mesoamerican crops were Haricot Beans, Squash and Maize, called 'The Three Sisters'. The Native Americans mixed beans, maple syrup and bear fat in earthenware pots placed in underground 'bean pits', heated with hot rocks to cook slowly.

The British colonists of New England adopted the dish, partly because it resembled pease porridge, substituting sugar for the maple syrup and bacon or ham for the bear fat. They soon substituted molasses for sugar to avoid British sugar taxes, and Boston became so popular for its baked beans that it became known as 'Beantown'.

Nowadays, the British use tomato sauce, while American tins contain bacon, ham, brown sugar and onions and people eat baked beans with barbecue and picnic food.

Whatever their slight differences, cans of baked beans would be regarded as a food essential on both sides of the Atlantic.

One of the authors, Liz Cowley, has a special reason for remembering Heinz with fondness. Back in the 1960s, she wrote a successful advertising campaign for Heinz Baby Foods, picturing a delighted new Mum in a maternity ward hugging her new-born child, with the headline 'A mother is born', and lots of tips for new mums. Before that, no baby food advertisement had ever shown a delighted new mother and this really struck a chord.

She still remembers with awe a tour of the bean factory in Wigan and the miraculous machines testing every single bean for quality. It's the biggest baked bean factory in the world and now makes and fills 2,000 cans a minute, three million in a day.

Full of beans? We certainly are!

THE SPICE OF LIFE

Today we mostly think of spices as little more than delicious additions to our food.

But it's no exaggeration to claim that spices were once one of the great influences on our world – in finance, politics, culture, exploration and even war and peace. Spices, in their day, were as important to world trade and politics as gold, oil or computing were to later become later.

Spices were the reason why the Queen of Sheba urgently visited King Solomon in 950 BC. She was desperate that her kingdom, Sheba (now Yemen), should not be cut out of the spice trade. While Egypt was the first ancient civilisation to use spices extensively (not least to mummify bodies), the new power, Rome, soon took over and made the port of Alexandria a spice hub. More than 60 spices were used by the Romans for food or medicine.

In the Dark Ages, there was something of a hiatus. Then the huge value of spices from the east began to influence Mediterranean politics, with Venice and Genoa becoming rich and powerful. The Crusades further opened the eyes of the West to spices, and indeed the 4th Crusade was cynically planned to capture Constantinople to help the spice trade. Spices meant wealth, and wealth meant culture. Indeed, the Renaissance was financed by spices.

When, in the 15th century, the Turks blocked the spice routes from the East, it created a huge change. Countries now looked West across the Atlantic and what became the New World. Spain and Portugal, and then Holland, France and England began to dominate world trade. In 1493, Pope Alexander VI divided the world up between Spain and Portugal and then, the next year, altered the line so as to give Brazil to Portugal. Five years later Portugal's explorer Vasco da Gama sailed round the tip of Africa and reached Calicut in India. (To have a useful place to stop on the way back, the Portuguese were casually to colonise Mozambique!). The Dutch and Portuguese fought a Spice War. Then, the Dutch from Indonesia and the British from India also embarked on bitter and violent rivalry and even their own murderous Spice Wars.

Extraordinary and long-lasting decisions were made over the perceived value of spices. The Dutch decided to give up New Amsterdam (New York) preferring to keep their apparently more valuable tiny **Nutmeg** island of Run (page 132). France, in 1763, gave up all of Canada and half of America to keep her spice and sugar islands in the Caribbean.

As Robert Carrier says in the Foreword to his famous book, *Great dishes of the world*: *'Spices were the measure by which wealth was counted in the West, so coveted were they. So coveted, in fact, that Columbus died disgraced for only having found gold in America and not the precious spices that he had promised.'*

Nowadays, of course, spices do not start wars and crises, and are luckily just an essential part of worldwide cooking.

What kitchen doesn't have some, if not all, of the following on its shelves?

Allspice
Black mustard seed
Black pepper Caraway
Cardamon
Chilli
Cinnamon
Cloves
Coriander seed
Cumin
Dill
Fenugreek
Ginger powder
Mace
Nutmeg
Root ginger
Saffron
Sage
Sesame seeds
Turmeric
White pepper

DRINK AND DRUGS IN BATTLE

We've all seen the pervasive influence of plants in the production of alcohol. Warfare has been no exception to this influence. Throughout history, of all the stresses of life, going into battle must be one of the worst. The threat of being killed, or maybe worse, badly wounded, would drive anyone to drink.

And indeed it did. Most of us are familiar with the phrase 'Dutch Courage', but may not realize that it came from the calming effect of 'genever' (page 46) for soldiers fighting in the Netherlands in the Thirty Years War.

Faced by the prospect of battle, the armies of many nations have officially sanctioned alcohol to steady their men. The French Foreign Legion may have been an extreme example. As one legionnaire said, 'We drink to forget – but we seldom forget to drink.' Indeed, they turned to the local drink of wherever they were fighting – absinthe and pastis, cheap rum or tafia, fig liqueur in North Africa, the fierce rice spirit 'choum-choum' in Tonkin and Annam, 'agua ardiente' in Mexico, fortified wines laced with quinine (page 17) and the rough red wine known as 'pinard', the defining drink of the French army, of which they were doled out half a litre a day in the horrifying trenches of World War 1.

When Napoleon invaded Russia in 1812, he took 530,000 men. But he also took 28 million bottles of wine and 2 million of brandy! The French even employed women called '*viavandiers*' to dispense brandy during battle, to those wounded - or not.

Some men apparently joined their armed forces mainly to have access to drink. The Duke of Wellington once remarked '*English soldiers are fellows who have all enlisted for drink.*' In his successful storming of Badajoz in 1812, several British soldiers actually drowned in vats of wine. Such was the level of drunkenness, that only hanging some men from a public gallows stopped it.

Winston Churchill once referred to life in the Royal Navy as '*Rum, sodomy and the lash*'. He was clearly alluding to the drink ration issued every day to the sailors. This had originally been of beer, no less that a gallon or eight pints a day! But under pressure from West Indian sugar cane planters, it was changed to rum, a daily half pint, mixed with water as 'grog', named in 1740 after Admiral Vernon's silk and wool cloak, called 'grogram'. This generous helping was, probably sensibly,

reduced to one-eighth of a pint, a half-gill or 'tot', and mixed with lemon and lime juice to reduce scurvy (page7).

Many battles have been lost because of drink. It is said that the citizens of Troy went off to drink rather than guard that strange Wooden Horse. In 1560, Magawa Yoshimoto failed in his attempt to take the Japanese capital Kyoto because his huge force of 35,000 chose to get drunk and then lost to the tiny, but sober, force of Oda Nobunaga. Ten years later, the Ottoman Sultan Selim II, famously known as 'the Sot', lost to a Christian fleet the critical naval battle of Lepanto. In 1836, after celebrating his victory at the Alamo, Mexican General Santa Anna was snoozing after lunch, probably having had one too many, when he was surprised and beaten by Sam Houston's Americans at San Jacinto. During the American Civil War, in the second Battle of Murfreesboro or Stones River in 1863, the Confederates lost their advantage because General Cheatham fell drunkenly off his horse. And, at the Siege of Petersburg in 1864, the Union General James Ledlie did not lead his men to stop them

being slaughtered at the site of a detonated mine in 'The Crater', but was found in a shelter clutching a bottle of rum. On D-Day in 1944, Major Hans Schmidt was drinking with his girlfriend when a mile away British gliders swooped to capture the vital bridges he was meant to be guarding. The list must be endless.

However, a bit of drink may be no bad thing in war. The big three winning World War II leaders, Roosevelt, Churchill and Stalin, all enjoyed more than a few drinks, and the losers, Hitler, Tojo and Mussolini were all teetotal.

Drugs in battle

Muslims are forbidden to drink alcohol, so they have turned to other drugs for strength in battle. Colonel Ronnie Waring, a friend of co-author Donough O'Brien, was advising the Portuguese Army in Angola, and wrote: *In one ambush, a terrorist rushed out of the elephant grass and with a machete chopped the head of the Portuguese soldier next to me clean off. The soldier had started firing his sub-machine gun as soon as he saw the terrorist running towards him and I could actually see the 9mm bullets hitting him, but they seemed to have no effect whatever. He rushed across the track and into the grass. Later, we searched and found the body with 18 bullets in him. He had been so high on bhang that he had not felt a thing.* (Bhang is unrefined hashish, from the Cannabis plant (page11). One war plagued with plant-based drugs was Vietnam. In 1971, 51% of US soldiers had smoked marijuana, 31% had used psychedelics like LSD and 25% were addicted to heroin. In Afghanistan, producing 90% of the world's opium, American soldiers' drug use has actually been less serious, but several have died of overdoses.

MAIZE, FROM 'INDIAN CORN' TO 'CORN ON THE COB'

Most of us enjoy eating popcorn, tinned sweetcorn, 'corn on the cob' and perhaps polenta, or use cornflour as a thickening agent. It's easy to forget that maize or corn, the plant from which these foods derive, is a major traded commodity, has fed populations for thousands of years, and helped to build America long before Europeans arrived.

Ancient civilizations have all depended on efficient agriculture and domestication of nutritious food crops.

In the Americas, from Chile to southern Canada, native peoples with a variety of cultures and lifestyles cultivated maize. This high-yielding crop enabled them to develop highly organized communities, culminating in the construction of huge earth mounds at Cahokia, Illinois (a city that in 1,200 was larger than London), and elsewhere around the Mississippi, and the impressive stone cities and pyramids of the Andes and Central America. Maize is represented in native American artefacts and embedded in folklore.

A robust, single-stemmed annual grass, **Maize** or, in north America, **Corn** (*Zea mays*), can grow up to 5 metres or more tall. At the top of the stem is a branched 'tassle' of small male flowers, and lower down the stem, sheathed by leaves and topped by a bunch of long styles or 'silks', are the 1–3 female flowers which ripen and are harvested as multi-grained corn cobs. The archaeological and genetic evidence indicate that Maize was probably domesticated in the valleys of the Mexican highlands before 6,000 BC, bred from a smaller wild grass with tiny naked cobs, now regarded as a Maize subspecies, **Teosinte** (*Zea mays* subspecies *parviglumis*). Because Maize is a 'C4 plant', with an enhanced capacity to fix carbon during photosynthesis under hot and dry conditions, it has an advantage over the other main cereal crops.

Maize is the most important crop to come to Europe from the Americas in what Alfred W. Crosby described as the 'Columbian Exchange' of plants, animals and diseases. (See Haricot Beans, page 181). As he wrote:

'If maize were the only gift the American Indian ever presented to the world, he would deserve undying gratitude, for it has become one of the most important of all foods for men and their livestock.'

Columbus first encountered it in 1492 in the Caribbean, and, when in 1620 the Pilgrim Fathers arrived in New England, they soon learned to survive on what they called

'Indian Corn'. Columbus took the plant to Spain where its value was greatly appreciated and later introductions of hardier stock from North America enabled it to be grown more widely in Europe. By the mid-16th century, it was already being grown in Germany, the Ottoman Empire, Italy and West Africa. It was reported from England in 1546, but did not become a crop there much before the 1970s.

Probably through the agency of Portuguese mariners and traders, Maize soon spread through Africa and on to Asia, including China, where it usefully complemented rice and other existing crops. Now cultivated worldwide, maize is a plant of rapid growth, genetic diversity and broad climatic tolerance, which has made it a widespread staple food for people and livestock and the largest global crop – over a billion tons per annum. Only wheat and rice are more important. The USA grows more than half the global crop, in the 'Corn Belt' from South Dakota and Kansas to Ohio and Kentucky.

In Africa, because it had a higher yield than the native grains, **Finger Millet** (*Eleusine coracana*) and **Sorghum** (*Sorghum bicolor*), Maize became a major source of nutrition, which led to a progressive expansion of the human population. It remains an important food, especially in South Africa, where it is known as known as 'mealies', and continues to dominate the continent's agriculture. On a more depressing note, Maize was cheap sustenance for the African slaves, and the population increase that it brought about may even have contributed to competition for resources and subsequent expansion of the slave trade.

The several variants of Maize have different uses: hard 'dent' corn, mostly fed to animals either directly or as silage, harder 'flint' corn for poultry food, flour corn with soft starchy grains, popcorn with hard kernels that swell and burst on heating, and sweetcorn, which has sugar rather than starch in the kernels, so is eaten as a vegetable and is the version we grow in gardens. Over 3,000 years ago, ingenious Meso-Americans discovered that if the grains are soaked and cooked with lime or ash, this both helps to remove the husk and increases the supply of vitamin B3 or niacin to the body. Deficiency of this vitamin causes pellagra, marked by dermatitis and other symptoms, which occurs in parts of Africa and India and was once prevalent among poor sharecroppers of the US southern states.

Maize as a staple food also lacks a couple of essential amino acids, but this can be remedied by combining it with beans.

The range of foods to which Maize contributes is remarkable. Ground, it can be cooked into bread, tortilla pancakes or chips, hominy, porridge (sometimes fermented) and, in Italy and Romania, polenta. And in the USA and Britain, cornflakes are a triumph of food marketing and presentation (page 204). Maize oil, which is poly-unsaturated, is widely used in cooking, while maize starch is a common thickener of processed foods and is hydrolysed into the ubiquitous sweetener, corn syrup, as well as industrial starch in adhesives and cosmetics. Maize is also fermented to make beer and other alcoholic drinks, notably American whiskey or bourbon, and for alcohol biofuel.

Maize is indeed a wonderful gift to the Old World from the native Americans, who for centuries the Europeans treated so ignorantly and cruelly.

The tale of Hiawatha, Mondamin and Maize

In his day, Henry Wadsworth Longfellow (1807–82) was one of the most popular US poets, widely admired in Europe as well as in North America. His epic poem 'The Song of Hiawatha', very loosely based on Ojibwe legends, tells how Hiawatha, a warrior, hunter and visionary, brought maize and other gifts to his people. In one episode, Hiawatha wrestles for three days with Mondamin, a native American maize god, who appears in the form of a youth dressed in green and yellow with green plumes in his golden hair.
On the fourth day Mondamin dies of the struggle, having instructed that he be buried in soft earth open to the rain and sun. Hiawatha tends the grave of his former antagonist until green feathers start to shoot up:

'And before the summer ended
Stood the Maize in all its beauty,
With its shining robes about it
And its long, soft, golden tresses'

In a nod to Longfellow's fame, Mondamin later lent his name to a popular German brand of corn starch products, now part of Unilever. What a strange legacy!

SUGAR CANE, MOLASSES AND RUM

There are, sadly, too many countries founded on the monstrous practice of importing human slaves from Africa – Brazil, Venezuela, Mexico, Colombia, Cuba, Jamaica and numerous other smaller islands. And crucially, of course, the southern states of America.

Another country was founded on the only slightly less unpleasant concept of being Great Britain's huge prison – Australia. And one drink was to play a powerful if different role in the development of all these countries – rum.

The spread of rum basically followed that of the giant grass **Sugar Cane** (*Saccharum officinarum*) from South-east Asia. Rum, made

by the fermentation and distillation of sugar cane juice, molasses, is first mentioned in Indian writings of the 7th century, but in Malay culture it goes back much further, called brum. Marco Polo encountered it in Iran, calling it '*a very good wine of sugar* '. In the Americas and the Caribbean, rum was produced from the molasses of the universally grown sugar cane and in 1651 someone in Barbados wrote about '*Rumbullion or Kill-Divil.*' Sugar production, from cane, became one of the great drivers of slavery (page 48). Brazil, for instance, used 4.9 million imported African slaves, even surpassing America. Rum itself became a method of payment, with one slave famously being bought for four gallons of rum and a piece of cloth.

Rum also influenced the political events that led up to the Declaration of American Independence, because, amazingly, rum accounted for 80% of New England's exports. Indeed, English attempts to tax molasses with the Molasses Act and then the Sugar Act of 1764 were maybe as financially annoying to the colonists and as crucial to the American Revolution as Lord North's stupid and pointless Tea Tax that triggered, nine years later, the 'Boston Tea Party' (page133). Although George Washington still insisted on rum at his inauguration!

In the Caribbean. pirates traded in

smuggled (rum-running) and fought over rum. But a more respectable maritime connection also started there in 1665, when the Royal Navy, having captured Jamaica from Spain, changed its traditional daily ration for sailors from brandy to rum. This was diluted with water and called 'grog', from which we get the word 'groggy'. It was only as late as 1970 that the Navy stopped giving out a daily 'tot of grog'.

In Australia, rum would play a dramatic and startling role. Again, because of lack of coinage, it was used as a payment system.

And huge amounts of 'Bombay Rum' barrels were shipped from India and floated ashore secretly and illegally in New South Wales, adding to public drunkenness – and also defying the Governor's orders that ships should be searched. That Governor was none other than the infamous William Bligh(right), who had caused the notorious Mutiny on the Bounty in 1789. Cast adrift with 18 others, he resourcefully and almost miraculously survived the 3,500-mile perilous voyage in a small, open boat and gone on to quite a distinguished naval career, both in battle and as a coastal surveyor, serving under Lord Nelson and eventually rising to Rear-Admiral.

Less fortunate than Bligh's party were the over a thousand plants of **Breadfruit** (*Artocarpus altilis*), a staple crop in Polynesia which the Bounty was conveying from Tahiti to the Caribbean as food for slaves. The mutineers threw them all overboard. Bligh repeated this botanical mission in 1793 and today the large starchy fruits – tasting somewhere between bread and potatoes – remain popular in Puerto Rico and elsewhere.

Despite his abilities, all his life the tactless, short-tempered Bligh seems to have been rather better at making enemies than friends. When, as Governor, he tried to crack down on both corruption and on rum smuggling, he was deposed by 400 armed men of the New South Wales Corps with fixed bayonets and a marching band. It became known as the 'Rum Rebellion'. He was effectively imprisoned in Tasmania until a new Governor arrived after two years.

Thus, rum played a significant role in slavery, the American Revolution, the piracy of the Caribbean, the Royal Navy's rations, and a country's full-scale rebellion. So it could be argued that among popular alcoholic beverages, rum from sugar cane was the most influential one of all time.

Rum appears in a great many variations – Cachaça, Charanda, Clairin, Marmajuana, Tafia, Arguardiente, Spook, Tuzemak, Rum-verschnitt, Pitorro Moonshine.
And it is mixed to make many exotic drinks – not just Rum Punches, Daiquiri, Cuba Libre and Pina Colada, but Dark 'N' Stormy, Painkiller, Hurricane, Gunfire, and Ti' Punch – as well as cakes, sauces and even ice creams.

GARLIC AND ITS STRANGE AND IMPRESSIVE POWERS

Love it or hate it, garlic certainly has a huge legion of fans – and some strange and impressive powers – going back thousands of years. The bulbs of **Garlic** (*Allium sativum*) were found scattered in the tomb of the Pharoah Tutenkhamun from 1346 BC, reflecting their importance to ancient Egyptian culture. When workers on the Cheops pyramids threatened to down tools, they were bought off by the Pharoah with a fortune in garlic. A century later, when Moses led the Hebrews to freedom out of Egypt, these former slaves complained, rather ungratefully, about missing the foods they had grown used to there – especially garlic. Both the Greeks and Romans ate garlic for strength in athletics and battle, and other races, oddly, considered it an aphrodisiac. Furthermore, a whole set of legends arose about its ability to ward off evil (see Panel).

Today, garlic is mainly used to flavour food and in herbal medicine. It is an easily grown bulb in the onion and leek family or Alliaceae, with a cluster of 'cloves' enclosed in a papery envelope. Curiously, nearly all of the thirty million tons consumed annually comes from China – although it is widely grown in Europe and the United States. Indeed, so ancient is the cultivation of Garlic that it is not known as a wild plant, but may have originated in southern Central Asia.

We mostly associate garlic with its sharp taste and strong smell, created by sulphur compounds released when its cells are chopped or crushed. It is thought to have evolved such a pungent odour to deter plant-eating animals, clearly not realizing that humans would actually enjoy it. Plants, unfortunately for them, do make mistakes! The downside of eating garlic is the fact that its smell is carried to the lungs and expelled in the breath and excreted through the skin – and unfortunately lasts a long time. However, that has not stopped it from being a favourite in kitchens all over the world, a basic flavouring for all kinds of dishes and an essential addition to oils, sauces, dips and garlic bread. Furthermore, it remains a central ingredient in Jewish cookery, just as it was in biblical times, and the Jews probably helped to spread garlic through eastern Europe. Both the Spanish Inquisition and the Nazis regarded the smell of garlic they associated with Jews as yet another excuse to denigrate them.

Garlic has also been used for thousands of years for medicinal purposes. Sanskrit records show its use about 5,000 years ago, and it has been utilized for at least 3,000 years in Chinese medicine. The Egyptians, Babylonians, Greeks, and Romans all used garlic for healing, and today herbalists employ garlic to alleviate a wide variety of illnesses including high cholesterol, colds and other respiratory ailments, ringworm and intestinal worms, and liver, gallbladder, and digestive problems. Moreover, scientific papers suggest that garlic may be effective in preventing heart disease and cancer. During World War 1, the Russian army used garlic as an anti-bacterial to treat wounds, as did the British, who added garlic juice to dressings made from **Bog Moss** (see page 9). Although Alexander Fleming's discovery of penicillin in 1928 largely replaced garlic at home, the Red Army physicians relied so heavily on garlic that it even became known as the 'Russian Penicillin'.

All in all, it seems that this small smelly bulb has had a great deal of influence!

Garlic against evil

In Islamic writings, the Prophet Mohammed attributed garlic to Satan when he was cast out of the Garden of Eden. Where the Devil's left foot touched the earth, garlic plants sprang up, while his right footprint generated onions.

Garlic was placed by the ancient Greeks on piles of stones at cross-roads, as a supper for Hecate – the Goddess of the wilderness and childbirth - and for protection from demons. The garlic was supposed to confuse the evil spirits and cause them to lose their way. European folklore gives garlic the ability to ward off the 'evil eye'. In the Carpathians especially, it represented a powerful weapon against devils, werewolves and vampires. To ward off vampires, garlic was worn on one's person, hung in windows and over beds, or rubbed on chimneys and keyholes. And, in a practice dating back to ancient Greece, midwives hung garlic cloves in birthing rooms to keep the evil spirits away.

In one part of Korea, eating 20 cloves of garlic and some Korean mugwort for 20 days was reported to transform a bear into a woman. (How you persuade a bear to stick to this diet – and what kind of woman you end up with – is not explained!)

THE CHILLI REVOLUTION

Of course, not everybody likes spicy food. But many of us do, and some take it to extremes, positively rejoicing in hot pungent flavours that seem to burn the mouth and can actually sting sensitive skin or irritate the eyes. But despite centuries of lucrative trade in spices, until Western European navigators reached the Old World the most pungent spice that any cook had to hand was **Black Pepper** (page 210).

Then from 1492, when Columbus sailed to the New World, everything changed. Among so many other valuable edible plants, Europeans now encountered peppers and, perhaps more significant, their small cousins the chillies. These had been cultivated in Central and South America since perhaps before 5,000 BC. Seeds of these members of the potato and tomato family or Solanaceae, completely unrelated to the small-fruited, vine-like Black Pepper, came to Europe from Columbus's first voyage. **Sweet Pepper, Ball Pepper** or **Chilli** (*Capsicum annuum*), a variable species with mild or sometimes pungent, fleshy fruits – hollow, hanging red, green, yellow, orange or purple berries – has since become a staple of southern European and Mediterranean cuisine, enjoyed raw, pickled, grilled or stuffed and served in colourful vegetable stews such as the French ratatouille, sometimes called *ratatouille Niçoise* in honour of its origins in Provence, Italian *peperonata* and the Basque or Spanish *piperrada*. Paprika, often dried or powdered, is the smaller, thinner-fleshed, sweeter or more pungent cherry pepper or, in Hungary and elsewhere, a long, pointed pepper. These variants of the Sweet Pepper flavour goulash and other Hungarian dishes and (as *pimiento*) much Spanish food, as well as being the familiar red stuffing of prepared canned or bottled olives. Cayenne pepper is another hot red variant of Sweet Pepper.

Yet another pungent pepper, perhaps not botanically distinct from Sweet Pepper, is the extremely hot group of **Scotch Bonnet** and **Habanero** (*Capsicum chinense*) chilli peppers, the latter named after Havana in Cuba. Other species are still grown in Peru and elsewhere in South America.

Even more influential on the global diet has been the similar, smaller but in general much hotter true **Chilli** (*Capsicum frutescens*), a small shrub with upright, usually narrowly conical fruits but with hundreds of varieties, and now prized worldwide for their heat and flavour. It has been said that that no other flavouring has so profoundly advanced traditional cooking, on so large a scale. Within a few years of the 'discovery' of America, the Spanish, and more so, the Portuguese, had taken chillies around the world to become firmly established as an essential ingredient of African, Indian and S.E. Asian cuisine, which now have their own special varieties through selection and cross breeding. Later, Portuguese mariners took them to eat on long sea voyages, spreading some of the varieties ever further. They created recipes too, like that for fiery vindaloo, today a staple extra hot dish of British curry-houses, which they took to their colony in Goa, from where it spread into India. Without chillies it would never have existed.

Chillies took a while to feature in the British diet, although in the USA, where they are native, or at least long-established in the south, they were always an ingredient of many Mexican and Tex-Mex dishes. In recent years they have become almost a craze, and the world's hottest chillies – once associated with Assam and Bangladesh – are now bred and grown in England.

And chillies are not just good to eat but also good for health, containing carotenoids (hence the bright colours), iron and a package of vitamins, notably Vitamin C. The pungent heat derives from capsaicin, a chemical with anti-inflammatory properties that appears to provide natural pain relief for arthritis and other complaints. Few plants can do so much to enliven even the dullest food.

Tabasco sauce

S.E. Asian cuisine has many chilli sauces and pastes or sambals. The simplest is *sambal oelek*, which combines hot chilli, salt and vinegar, the same combination that is the basis of the famous Tabasco sauce. This high-quality condiment is still made by the McIlhenny Company on Avery Island in the southern US state of Louisiana, from where it originated in 1868, although its special variety of Chilli (var. *tabasco*), hailing from the Mexican state of the same name, is now also grown in South America. The chillies are hand-picked, mashed, salted with local salt and aged for up to three years, after which vinegar is added and the sauce is bottled. A family business, the McIlhenny Company is one of few US companies to hold a royal warrant to supply Queen Elizabeth in the UK.

CHERRIES, A FEAST OF COLOUR AND TASTE

Cherries permeate human lives in many small but pervasive ways. Not only are they a popular summer fruit, often more expensive than many others and generally seen as a treat, but their colour too, the 'red as cherries' of song writers, has immediate impact. Take, for instance, 'Cherries in the Snow', which reads like a shock headline in a horticultural magazine. It is in fact the evocative name of a red nail varnish that first appeared in 1932, helping to launch the Revlon company.

Revlon is credited with pioneering perfectly colour-matched nails and lips – and in 1953 launched the 'Cherries in the Snow' lipstick, with the gently flirtatious strapline: *'Who else but Revlon understands you as you* <u>*really*</u> *are…a trifle shy, but oh-so-warm … and just a little reckless, deep inside … as strange and unexpected as cherries in the snow.'* Both nail varnish and lipstick remain a cosmetic classic, not least because of a well-chosen name.

So, what is it about cherries? Maybe the reason for their image and appeal is that they are an icon of summer and properly in season for a shorter period even than asparagus. They are delicate fruits irresistible to foraging birds, and do not travel well, bruising easily. But, hard to resist eaten raw, they look wonderful in the supermarket or

on a roadside stall. Their saving grace is that they preserve well, both the flavour and the red colour. Cherry pies are just one facet of a delicious and versatile fruit, widely used to create or enhance juices, pies, cakes, ice-cream and chocolates, and to flavour vodkas, brandies and liqueurs. Truly, at times life *can* be that proverbial 'bowl of cherries'!

Although we talk about fruits or lips, even shoes or waistcoats, being cherry-red, the cherry fruits, themselves, borne in small clusters, vary greatly in colour from the predominant red, and also in size and sweetness. The **Sweet Cherry** (*Prunus avium*), the early summer favourite, is a tall tree native to Europe and SW Asia, from where the larger Sweet Cherry of cultivation arose. Wild cherry trees with small, rather sour fruits are called **Gean** or **Mazzard**. A smaller tree, with fruits that underpin the canned cherry industry, the **Sour Cherry** (*Prunus cerasus*), of which the most famous variety is **Morello Cherry,** is a native of Anatolia and the Caucasus. Cultivated cherries have been widespread since the 1st century BC, when the cultured Roman general Lucullus is said to have returned home from campaigning in the east, bringing with him much treasure, not least cultivated Sweet Cherry plants from Cerasus, which gives us the word 'cherry' or '*cerise*' in French. On the Black Sea coast, now the Turkish port of Giresun, Cerasus is still a centre of cherry growing – with Turkey the main world cherry exporter.

Henry VIII, who seems to have loved fruit, is credited with introducing cherries to Kent from Flanders, although they would have almost certainly been grown in Britain in Roman and monastic gardens. They reached North America in the 1600s via Brooklyn in New York, then the Dutch colony of New Amsterdam (page 132). Ever since, cherry pie has remained a US kitchen staple and a mainstay of the diner – where Agent Dale Cooper of the 1990s cult TV series 'Twin Peaks' habitually enjoyed a slice with his coffee.

It is not just the fruit that gives colour. Furniture makers, both antique and contemporary, have long favoured the fine-grained, reddish-brown heartwood of the cherry tree, comparable in appearance with tropical mahogany when polished. The pale pink blossom too is much-loved, although that so admired by the Japanese (page 152) belongs to one of the many related ornamental cherry species.

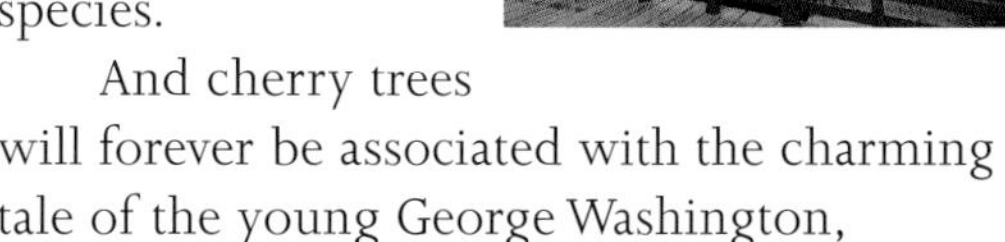

And cherry trees will forever be associated with the charming tale of the young George Washington, confessing to hacking at his father's cherry tree with an axe, '*Father, I cannot tell a lie.*' An enduring myth, it may just have been flattery from an admiring biographer – but is a good moral story nevertheless!

RICE AND ASIAN SOCIETY

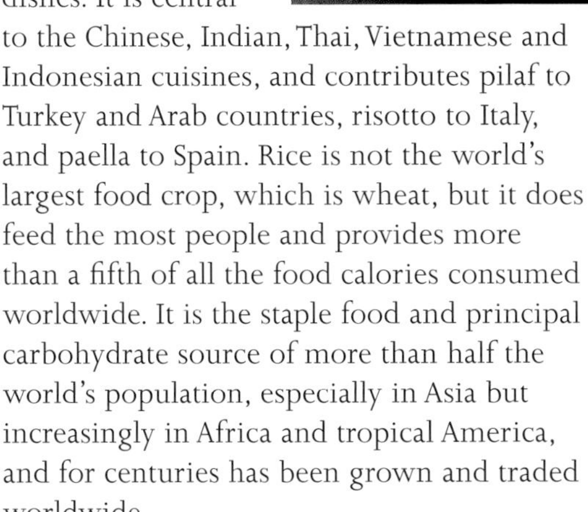

Most of us eat rice, but millions more depend on it and eat it every day, which is why rice is an essential part of so many national dishes. It is central to the Chinese, Indian, Thai, Vietnamese and Indonesian cuisines, and contributes pilaf to Turkey and Arab countries, risotto to Italy, and paella to Spain. Rice is not the world's largest food crop, which is wheat, but it does feed the most people and provides more than a fifth of all the food calories consumed worldwide. It is the staple food and principal carbohydrate source of more than half the world's population, especially in Asia but increasingly in Africa and tropical America, and for centuries has been grown and traded worldwide.

The robust annual semi-aquatic grass, **Asian Rice** (*Oryza sativa*), is a crop of tropical regions of high rainfall. Unlike most cereals, it can be grown repeatedly on the same ground and can yield more than one crop each year, so readily feeds large human populations. Rice was first domesticated around 6,000 BC or earlier in the basin of the Yangtse River in China, and with **Millet** (*Panicum miliaceum*) and **Soya** (*Glycine max*, page 200) was the economic basis of the growth of cities from 2,000 BC. By then it had spread to India, hence long-grained rice is called variety *indica*, and was cultivated by the farmers of the advanced Indus Valley civilization from at least 2,300 BC. Rice cultivation later spread to the Philippines, Indonesia, Indo-China and elsewhere while Northern China, Korea and Japan grow the short-grained variety *japonica*, adapted to more temperate climates.

Rice reached Europe following the Asian campaigns of Alexander the Great, but did not become established until the Arabs took it to Spain a millennium later. It was not until the 17th century that it was grown in northern Italy. Rice arrived in the Americas in the 15th century with the Spanish and Portuguese in Mexico and Brazil respectively, and reached North America in 1694. Like cotton and sugar, it was first grown in the southern states using the labour of African slaves, who themselves introduced irrigation and threshing techniques learned from cultivating rice in their native West Africa. There, from about 1,500 BC, **African Rice** (*Oryza glaberrima*), was being grown in the Niger delta but is today more or less displaced by plentiful quantities of Chinese Rice.

The predominant rice in the Carolinas was indeed an African Rice cultivar known as 'Carolina Gold'. After the American Civil War and the freeing of the slaves, most US rice cultivation moved to the Mississippi basin, where it remains a major crop. California too produces a substantial rice crop, mostly of the *japonica* variety. Quite distinct, **American Wild Rice** (*Zizania aquatica*), an aquatic grass with long dark grains rich in protein and B vitamins, has long been harvested by the native Americans, but is now grown commercially as a niche or luxury product.

This wide distribution of rice in cultivation has led to selection and evolution of some 40,000 cultivars, with a range of grain types adapted to local climate and growing conditions and associated with different culinary usage. For example, Indian cuisine is associated with long-grained, fragrant Basmati rice and long- or medium-grained mild-flavoured Patna rice, Thai cuisine with long-grained fragrant jasmine rice and Japanese with short-grained sticky rice, made into sushi and other dishes. Unlike other cereal grains, rice lacks gluten and is indispensable for those with gluten intolerance. Brown, unhusked rice, although healthy, is rarely seen outside the West.

Apart from its influence on what all of us eat, rice has undoubtedly helped to create and mould the civilizations and teeming populations of Asia. Mostly grown in flooded paddy fields, even on terraced mountain-sides, which suppresses weeds and pests in the growing crop, rice is associated with low labour costs and high labour input. It is very much a crop of interdependence, with farming communities co-ordinating both large-scale irrigation and the hard work of the villagers who harvest the crop by hand. There is an old Chinese proverb: *'Don't depend on heaven for food, but on your own two hands carrying the load.'*

This community-based rural rice civilization even seems to have influenced the development of the civic, social and political discipline in Chinese society, and

that of other societies in East Asia, with their stricter social norms and less tolerance of non-conformity by comparison with the wheat-dependent West. Fascinating research by Professor Thomas Talhelm of the University of Chicago's Booth School of Business not only supports this hypothesis but also compares and contrasts the social differences that exist between the rice-growing south of China and the less conformist colder wheat- and millet-growing country to the north of the Yangtse.

In China from early on, extensive rice cultivation may too have been a factor in the establishment of an authoritarian, bureaucratic élite who ruled from cities. Hence the Chinese have maintained a civil service for three thousand years. And from 605 until as late as 1905 these administrators or 'mandarins' (from a Portuguese word for them) were selected on the basis of a rigorous imperial examination and were as much scholars as public officials. Only in the 20th century, with the fall of the last Emperors, were they replaced by modern civil servants. Since the triumph of Chinese Communism in 1949 most of the population have effectively been public servants!

Rice, Spice and Sylhet

It is claimed that Chicken Tikka Masala is the UK's national dish – either in a restaurant or takeaway. And most people in Britain would say they love such 'Indian food'.

But the strange thing is that this cuisine, although it embraces a range of dishes from right across the Indian sub-continent, is not Indian at all, but from Bangladesh, and what is more, largely from one city – Sylhet.

In the 1940s, Sylhetis arrived in London and began setting up restaurants. They had left the city of Sylhet, on the right bank of the Surma River in the north-eastern division of Bangladesh. An essential part of their cuisine, which is varied and flavoured with a range of plant spices, is Ala Bhat or Atop rice, a traditional rice variety. Short-grained, rather sticky and glutinous, it fortuitously contains more selenium and zinc, and less arsenic, than other types of Bangladeshi rice.

More and more Sylhetis set up in Britain, but perhaps a lack of confidence – or maybe a nod to 'British India' – encouraged them to allow the British to call their food and restaurants 'Indian'. In fact, 90% of UK Indian restaurants are Bangladeshi and nearly all of them Sylheti!.

It was no less than Britain's former Foreign Secretary, Robin Cook, who in 2001 called the Sylheti dish Chicken Tikka Masala 'Britain's national dish' – although it doesn't even exist back in Bangladesh. And food historian Lizzie Collingham, in her book *Curry: A biography*, claimed that Sylheti cooks had '*converted unadventurous British palates to a new flavour spectrum*.'

Not bad for a place most people have never heard of or couldn't place on the map!

SOYA, THE SAVIOUR

Conservationists often rail against soya because it's cultivated on a huge scale to feed cattle. Yet it is a vegetarian's dream, as an acre of soya cultivation can yield 20 times the protein that beef cattle produce per acre. The problem is the manner in which soya is grown and utilized.

There is nothing at all intrinsically bad about **Soya Bean** or **Soybean** (*Glycine max*), a branched, upright reddish-hairy annual plant with white or lilac flowers and hanging pods that contain 2–3 seeds. One of the many nutritious bean species in the Fabaceae, a plant family which does much to feed humans as well as animals, it is one of the world's staple food crops, the fifth largest by yield – over 335 tonnes per annum – only exceeded by maize, rice, wheat and potatoes.

Soya has been described as 'meat without bones'. The seeds yield 35–50% of protein and 20% or more of oil, and contain no less than 22 health-promoting amino acids, including nine regarded as essential for human nutrition, together with B Vitamins, isoflavones, all with anti-oxidant, anti-inflammatory and plant oestrogen properties, and the fatty substance lecithin, which can help to emulsify and eliminate cholesterol. The Soya Bean is therefore a veritable cocktail of food and health!

In various forms it is, with rice, a mainstay of the diet of East Asia, whence it originated. Soya Beans were cultivated in northern China from at least 1000 BC, then spread through the region. They only arrived in Europe in the early 1700s – although soy sauce from fermented soya was already being imported by the Dutch, to be served not only in the better London taverns but also at sumptuous banquets at the court of France's Louis XIV. In the 19th century Soya was grown on a small scale in France, Italy and elsewhere, but it was still for the most part regarded as a botanical curiosity.

As a food commodity, in the early 20th century large quantities of soya beans came into America and Britain from Manchuria – which had a surplus after the end of the 1904-5 Russo-Japanese War when soya had fed both armies – to be milled for oil, supplementing shortages of cotton seed. In the USA, the new oil soon competed with corn and peanut oil and replaced linseed in paint. The residue or 'cake' from pressing it fed livestock. When cultivated, it proved to be a versatile crop, supplying silage for cattle, forage for hogs and green manure on arable land.

US soya production gradually increased and harvesting became mechanized. But, although the plant had been introduced as early as 1770 by the ever-inventive Benjamin

Franklin, domestic cultivation and export of soya did not really take off until the 1940s. Today America grows three quarters of the world crop, mainly for the oil, which has many uses including as a biofuel. As well as the demand for cattle feed, the rise in vegetarianism and a more cosmopolitan approach to eating has boosted production. Soya milk is processed into soya milk and cheese, and easily digested soya milk has become almost mainstream. Soya is also widely added to bulk out meat and bakery products.

The present influence of soya on Western cuisine and the names we give to soya products have been led by Japan. There the beans are fermented and made into miso paste, which most Japanese people eat every day, especially as a bowl of miso soup for breakfast. They also eat cooked immature bean pods or edamame. Tofu or bean curd is widely eaten in Japan, China and Korea. Tempeh, a similar, lightly fermented bean curd is popular in Indonesia. Soy sauce, a fermented product traditionally used to preserve food over winter, is an essential condiment in all East Asian cuisines.

Soya, for all its usefulness, has sadly become a notorious plant villain. It is now a major crop in South America, especially in Argentina and Brazil. It is here that soya has proved to be most destructive, being grown both in tropical rainforest areas previously cleared for cattle ranching and in Earth's most biologically rich savannahs, the Cerrado region of the Brazilian highlands. This type of habitat, rich in endemic animals and plants, is now reduced to a fifth of its former extent. The region supports 70% of Brazil's cattle rearing and, with the addition of phosphorus and lime to soils and the use of specially bred tropical Soya Bean varieties, the industrial-scale farming that has made Brazil into the world's largest exporter of soya for cattle feed.

Genetically Modified Soyas

Apart from habitat destruction, another controversial issue concerns the Soya Beans which are genetically modified for herbicide and pesticide resistance. GM crops, of which Soya is one of the most important commercially, have been widely opposed on environmental grounds, because of the effect on animal species higher up the food chain, the danger of creating resistant 'super weeds' and the effect of crossing into populations of wild crop relatives and ancient cultivars. GM crops are not permitted to be grown in the European Union (in fact relatively little Soya is grown in Europe, except in the south-east) but are now well established in many countries, especially China and the USA. The defenders of GM technology argue that it will lead to larger yields and reduction in pesticide use. The jury is still out, but it may be significant that most recent advances in crop improvement have involved crossing with old varieties and crop relatives, and gene editing, rather than controversial insertion of 'outside' genetic material.

BUCK'S FIZZ AND ITS SECRET

Only one of London's 'gentlemen's clubs' has achieved worldwide fame. To be sure, there are many people in Britain who have at least heard of White's or Boodle's or the Turf Club. But only Buck's can claim more - and all because of a pop group named after a drink.

Buck's is the youngest of such clubs, created just after the First World War. Captain Herbert Buckmaster of the Royal Horse Guards sat in a shell-blasted dugout on the Western Front and resolved, if he survived, to create a small, intimate club. In 1919, 'Buck' and his friends bought the lease of a house on the corner of Old Burlington Street and Clifford Street in Mayfair. At the beginning it had a distinct military base. Three brothers were founder members, of whom two had won Victoria Crosses for gallantry, and the third a Distinguished Service Order (twice) and a Distinguished Service Cross. He was cynically known as the coward of the family!

One of the 'characters' of Buck's was John Loder. In 1916, he was the young officer who accepted Padraic Pearse's surrender after the Dublin Easter Rising. Pearse was so impressed by John's kindness that he handed him his cap badge and other mementoes 'in case he was executed' – which he was. John became a heart-throb actor in the thirties and was married many times, one bride being Hollywood's Hedy Lamarr (pictured right)

But it was not 'Buck' and his elegant friends who were to make 'Buck's' famous. It was McGarry, the barman who created a memorable and refreshing drink for them. 'Buck's Fizz' is another good botanical concoction: made from champagne, orange juice, just a touch of grenadine (mostly juice of **Pomegranate**, *Punica granata*) – and something else kept secret.

Even with 'Buck's Fizz' a staple drink at Ascot and Henley, the club's name would be confined to upper-crust Britain until a pop group was put together expressly to try to win the Eurovision Song Contest of 1981.

Mike Nolan, Bobby Gee, Cheryl Baker and Jay Aston of 'Buck's Fizz' duly won with the song 'Making Your Mind Up'. 'Bucks Fizz' went on to be one of the most successful groups of the 1980s with 20 more hit singles, including 'The Land of Make Believe' and 'My Camera Never Lies'.

Not many of the fans probably knew about Captain Buckmaster and his club in Mayfair. Not many 'Buck's Fizz' drinkers do either. And don't think that grenadine is the only magic ingredient to add to champagne and orange juice. At Buck's Club they insist there's something extra but won't tell you what! Probably another plant product?

WATERCRESS AND ITS TWO CAPITALS

Watercress beds are a feature of the chalk stream districts of southern England. But Alresford in Hampshire, from where Liz Cowley's family hails, claims to be 'The Watercress Capital of the World'. It turns out that there are two of them!

Watercress (*Nasturtium officinale*), a white-

flowered member of the cabbage family or Brassicaceae, can claim to be one of the oldest leaf vegetables eaten by humans. With a pleasant mustardy flavour, it is a healthy food, low in calories and rich in vitamins A, K, B2 and B6, together with calcium and manganese. Widespread as a wild plant of wet places, watercress was popular in earlier times as a readily available green which would help to stave off scurvy and other ailments of wintertime. Today it remains especially popular in Britain and Portugal.

It is grown in slightly alkaline water beds, often near the springs that are the headwaters of the pure chalk stream water.

For Alresford to get its watercress to the London market and beyond, the railway built in 1865 turned out to be vital to preserve the cress's freshness. Today this is celebrated by 'The Watercress Line', a

heritage steam railway run by enthusiasts – on which you can travel in style and dine splendidly. An annual 'Watercress Festival' attracts 15,000 visitors.

In Alabama in the United States you can find the same mild climate and water quality as Hampshire. A young entrepreneur, Frank Dennis, had been marketing watercress since 1874, but the farms that supplied him in Pennsylvania, Maryland and Virginia, all suffered from harsh climates that limited production.

But then he discovered the perfect climate – in Madison County, Alabama. There, as in Alresford, he grew the watercress in shallow ponds and then it was sent off in ice-filled barrels to New York, Chicago and New Orleans. Once again, railways made this possible, with rapid and efficient rail links vital to deliver to the cities what was considered a 'Southern treat'.

Which of these two little rural communities can really be called 'The Watercress Capital of the World' might depend on your point of view!

CEREALS AND BREAKFAST

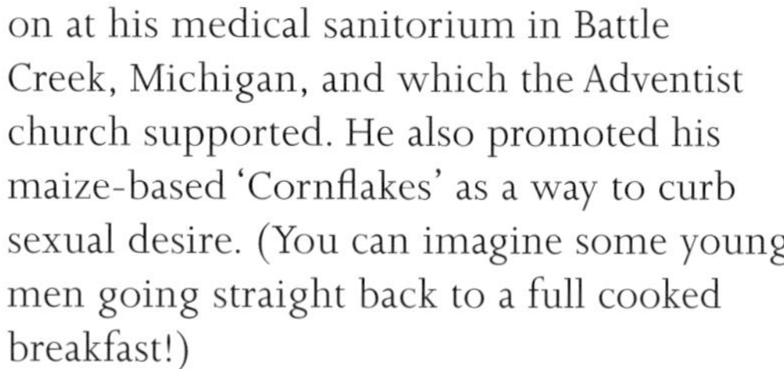

The great writer Somerset Maugham once said, 'To eat well in England, you should have breakfast three times a day'. Assuming he was not just being rude about the English ability to cook any other decent meals, there is no doubt that a lavish 'Full English Breakfast' is a fine one, consisting of eggs, bacon, sausages, tomatoes, mushrooms, baked beans, and maybe black pudding and toast!

All over the world, people enjoy their breakfasts in their own style. The French, of course, simply prefer a croissant and a cup of coffee, the Central and Eastern Europeans various kinds of cheese and ham. And a Greek friend just has a tiny 'Turkish' coffee and a cigarette!

But in Britain and America, what hard-pressed mother didn't welcome a ready-to-eat and healthy breakfast dish, with no need to cook and little clearing up? This was provided by cereal grains and came from America. The first pioneer was Ferdinand Schumacher in 1854 with a hand oats grinder in Ohio. We now know his company as Quaker Oats, soon to be huge and producing 200 food products – eventually bought by PepsiCo.

Next came two brothers, John and William Kellogg. And, with them, cereals were part of a religious movement. The Seventh-Day Adventist Church believed that Saturday should be the Sabbath and that Jesus would return. They also believed in a very healthy diet – and a vegetarian one, which Dr John Harvey Kelly insisted on at his medical sanitorium in Battle Creek, Michigan, and which the Adventist church supported. He also promoted his maize-based 'Cornflakes' as a way to curb sexual desire. (You can imagine some young men going straight back to a full cooked breakfast!)

One of Kellogg's patients was Charles W. Post, who, impressed by the brothers' efforts, decided to go into the food business and produced 'Grape-Nuts". Curiously, these contained neither grapes nor nuts, but still made him a fortune. His company later acquired Jell-O, Bakers's Chocolate, Maxwell House coffee and Birdseye frozen foods, eventually to become General Foods and later part of Kraft. Because of Kellogg and Post, the town of Battle Creek,Michigan, is called the 'Cereal Capital of the World.'

General Mills entered the market in 1924 and worked on rolled wheat flakes, eventually becoming 'Wheaties', famous for sponsoring sporting heroes. It was also the first company to start targeting children with increased sugar and products like 'Rice Krispies'.

While many parts of the United Kingdom, especially rather chilly Scotland, like to heat up their cereals as 'porridge', in Western countries cold cereals for breakfast have continued to be no less than a huge financial success. But perhaps change is in the air. UK millennials are apparently avoiding breakfast cereals, and it is said a third have never eaten them!

TOMATOES, FROM COLOURFUL CURIOSITY TO KITCHEN STAPLE

Sitting in a café or restaurant in Greece or Italy, it's an amusing distraction to imagine a similar establishment in ancient Athens, Rome or Constantinople. The bread, olives, oil and wine might not have been too different, but the food would decidedly contain a poorer range of ingredients and seem dull to a modern palate. Pasta dishes and so many Greek, Turkish and Levantine specialities such as moussaka, stewed beans and okra owe their colour and flavour to many things – but not least to the tomato or to tomato sauce or paste.

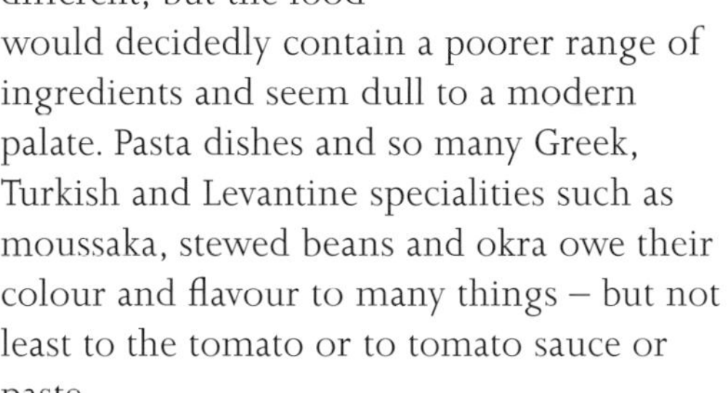

The **Tomato** (*Lycoperscon esculentum*) is a member of the Solanaceae, a plant family which contains both crops such as **Potato** (page 102) and poisonous plants. It probably originated on the slopes of the Andes from Ecuador to northern Chile and later spread to Central America. There it was domesticated by the Mayans and the Aztecs, who called it *xitomatl*, a name that in a modified form has stuck – and passed into the world's languages. A sprawling vine, grown as an annual, which has been bred from a wild variety with tiny yellow or red berries, the Tomato now exists as hundreds of varieties, with fruits of assorted sizes and shapes selected for eating raw or cooked, and for drying, canning, juicing and making into paste.

Tomatoes have not fed great populations, as have rice and other cereals and grains, but like **Chillies** (page 193) they have revolutionized cookery worldwide. Above all, it is the Mediterranean region where their impact has been the greatest and a native or visitor unfamiliar with their Latin American origin might assume that they were indigenous. Hernán Cortés himself (pictured) may have introduced Tomato seeds to Europe shortly after his 1521 conquest of Mexico. The Spanish not only took them to Europe but also spread them around the world, including to the Philippines, whence they reached China and the rest of South-east Asia. They remain central to the cuisine of Spain, where Buñol in Valencia province even holds an annual Tomatina festival.

In 1544 an Italian botanist noted the arrival of the Tomato in Italy and four years later it was recorded that a basket of them had been sent from the estate of Cosimo de Medici, Duke of Tuscany, probably just to provide a table decoration. For, as a food, the Tomato took a while to catch on. It was merely a garden ornamental and curiosity, which in Italy became *pomo d'ora* or 'golden apple', alluding to the yellow fruit of an early introduced variety, and in France *pomme d'or*, but later *pomme d'amour* or 'love apple', as the fruit was regarded rather oddly as an aphrodisiac. In England, John Gerard, author

of the famous 1597 *Herbal*, recorded that tomatoes were eaten in France and Spain but he regarded them, as did most commentators of the time, as poisonous. John Parkinson, botanist to Charles I, wrote disparagingly in 1629 of their '*pale reddish colour, or somewhat deeper … full of a slimie juice and a waterie pulp*'. Seventy years later John Evelyn included pickled tomatoes in *Acetaria*, his book of salads, and they gradually established themselves over the next century.

It was not until the 19th century that Tomatoes were grown on any large scale, especially in southern Italy and the USA, where they had arrived in South Carolina from the Caribbean as early as 1710. In the 19th century the Americans were the first to can them and to market tomato ketchup commercially. By the end of the century English market gardeners were cultivating them under glass in Kent, Sussex and the Lee Valley north of London. Today they are grown worldwide, with China, India, California and Florida in the USA, and Turkey being the main producers.

The best feature of Tomatoes is that they are good for you: a source of fibre, vitamins A, C and K, potassium and the red carotene pigment lycopene, an antioxidant which has been linked to a lowering of the risk of heart and circulatory disorders, especially when cooked. But a raw Tomato is hard to beat. In his classic 1973 book of hippie vegetarian recipes, *Tassajara Cooking*, Edward Espe Brown celebrates the pleasure of a ripe fresh tomato, '*plump, warm with summer sun, fleshy … juices rushing out flooding the mouth with uncommon succulence*'. Nearly half a century on, his joyful endorsement remains a timeless tribute to a vegetable that for five hundred years has served the world's cooks as one of their most versatile ingredients.

Tomato Ketchup

No burger restaurant, diner, hot dog stall, greasy spoon café, shop selling pies, fried chicken or fish and chips, or other food outlet of the sort that that drives doctors and nutritionists to despair, lacks dispensers or sachets of this essential accompaniment. Ketchup is almost a symbol of Western popular culture and its all-pervasive spread. And most of us love it, not least singer-songwriter Ed Sheeran, who even has the Heinz Ketchup logo tattooed on his left arm! The origin of the name is disputed but probably derives from a Malay word, *kecap*, for a sauce of pickled fish and spices that came originally from China. A British version, with onions and mushrooms, evolved in the 18th century, spreading to America, which took this flavoursome new sauce to its heart. They added tomatoes by the 1820s and in 1876 Heinz launched the 'catsup' that became their ubiquitous condiment, Heinz Tomato Ketchup. Today it commands 60% of the US and 80% of the UK market share.

Along with tomato-rich Heinz Baked Beans, this iconic ketchup could be said to be the greatest of the many influences that the humble Tomato has had on our lives!

HOPS AND THE PLEASURES OF BEER

Beer has become a universally popular drink. Indeed, it could be said that few plant products give so much enjoyment to so many people as do the papery cone-like hops that flavour and preserve beer. And yet the plant from which they derive harbours a guilty secret: it is in the same small family of Cannabaceae, along with the much-demonised Hemp or Cannabis (page 90). One is smoked, usually illegally, the other is drunk in the most respectable circles.

That said, nobody has ever accused the **Hop** or **Hops** (*Humulus lupulus*) of having any hallucinatory effects! Native in damp woods,

it's a rough-hairy climbing or scrambling plant with deeply lobed leaves and – like Hemp – separate male and female, wind-pollinated greenish flowers. In cultivation, female plants grow up a framework of poles, wires and strings. Hops are the fruit clusters of the female flowers. Their bitter resins and aromatic essential oils enhance the flavour of the malted barley (page 175) in the beer and their useful anti-bacterial properties help to prevent the beer from going sour.

Although the ancient Egyptians brewed and drank beer, using ingredients other than hops, which are indigenous to northern and central Europe, it was only in the Middle Ages that hops became associated with brewing. Several other bitter-flavoured plants had previously been used (Panel). An early written reference to brewing beer with hops comes from 9th century France, and a passage in a 12th century medical work by mystic and polymath Hildegard of Bingen (1098–1179) suggests that by then hops were an essential ingredient in German beer. Later German beer quality was protected by the *Reinheitsgebot* or 'purity degree', a Bavarian law of 1516, whereby beer had to contain only water, barley, hops and yeast. This was to prevent adulteration by a range of sometimes toxic additives, and originally also to protect wheat and rye supplies for bread making. In 1871 Bavaria insisted, as a condition of joining Bismarck's unified Germany, that the law passed into national legislation, where it remains to this day – even though Germany now produces more than 5,000 different beers.

German immigrants took their brewing techniques and standards over to America, but the industry was devastated after the First World War by the years of Prohibition (page 176). Only in 1979 was home brewing in the USA again permitted by law, and recent years have seen the rise there of micro-breweries and craft beers.

In England, beer is a national institution but hops as a crop are said to have arrived there only in 1526, from Artois in Flanders. As one version of an old saying goes:

'Turkeys, carps, piccarel [pike], hops, and beer
Brought into England all in one year.'

Beer brewed with hops had in fact been imported from Flanders for at least a century and continental brewers were already established in England, certainly in some coastal towns. Hops were initially grown around Maidstone in Kent, and the county remains the centre of English hop growing, now largely confined to parts of the South-east and Worcestershire in the West Midlands. The late summer hop harvest, now mechanized, was formerly labour-intensive and until the early 1960s attracted thousands of casual labourers, especially poorer Londoners, for an annual working holiday. As in the folk song 'Hopping down in Kent':

'Now hopping's just beginning,
We've got some time to spend.
We've only come down hopping
To earn a quid if we can.'

It was tough work but there seems to have been jollity and relaxation too, as adults and children briefly escaped the slums of London's East End. The writer George Orwell, who himself had a go at hop picking, remarked in '*A Clergyman's Daughter*'

(1935), how '*the Cockneys rather enjoyed the trip to the country, in spite of the bad pay and in spite of the discomfort.*' Singer-songwriter David Essex, from East London, also picked hops in his youth.

Commercial brewing now often involves industrially extracted hop essences, but traditional hops and hop gardens happily survive in Kent. Faversham-based brewery Shepherd Neame still uses the old local hop variety 'East Kent Goldings' in its range of 'Spitfire' beers, and craft beers as well have given hop growing a new lease of life. So 'Cheers', or, as they say in Dublin, 'A Pint of Plain's your only Man'!

Some plants other than hops that traditionally flavoured beer

Yarrow (*Achillea millefolium***)**
Mugwort (*Artemisia vulgaris***)**
Heather (*Calluna vulgaris***)**
Ground Ivy or **Alehoof (***Glechoma hederacea***)**
Juniper (*Juniperus communis***)** berries
Bogbean (*Menyanthes trifoliata***)**
Sweet Gale (*Myrica gale***)**
Wood Sage (*Teucrium scorodonium*)

AVOCADOS AND THEIR POPULARITY

Doctors constantly tell us to cut down our intake of animal fat, butter and cheese, but one cultivated tropical plant yields its own healthy vegetable 'butter'. **Avocado** (*Persea americana*), is an evergreen tree and a member of the Laurel family, up to 20 metres tall, with an open, spreading crown, smooth grey bark and stalked, drooping leaves. Tiny yellowish-green flowers in conspicuous branched clusters towards the ends of green twigs give rise to the pear-like fruits up to 15 cm or more long, with their familiar soft-leathery green skin, apple-green flesh and single stout, egg-shaped seed. To the foodie the avocado is heaven, to the botanist it is but a huge berry!

Originally from south-central Mexico and Guatemala, avocados were long cultivated and spread by native people in Central America and south through Colombia and Ecuador to Peru. Introduced into Spain in 1601, by the mid-18th century they had soon spread to the Pacific and to the USA. Now grown on a major commercial scale in many frost-free, warmer areas of the world, they grow best on lime-poor soils. The fruits vary in size, shape, skin colour and texture. For a long time they were cultivated on a small scale and in gardens. However, one of the most nutritious of all edible plants, these buttery fruits provide a perfect food: low in sugar but rich in protein, fibre, anti-oxidants, vitamins and potassium, and contain up to a third of their weight in oil, a third of which is mono-saturated. The name is a conversation piece – a nice pun, being ostensibly the Spanish word for advocate, *abogado*, but in fact a corruption of *ahuacatl*, an Aztec word for testicle that alludes to the shape and size of the seed! The Aztec word *ahuacamolli* (avocado soup or sauce) lends its name to the popular dip, guacamole.

In Britain, it was only in the 1960s, promoted by Fanny Cradock (right) and an early generation of TV chefs, that avocados took off as a must-have food, then usually served with prawns, but today presented in all manner of dishes and styles. Esteemed by an increasingly vegetarian or vegan younger generation, especially for their subtle taste, pleasant yielding flesh and attractive colour, since the millennium they have become increasingly popular, even as a substitute for breakfast eggs on toast.

Such is the insatiable demand in the UK, USA and elsewhere that the world crop of some six million tonnes is expanding and even proving a source of social and ecological problems. Michoacán state in west-central Mexico produces nearly a third of this, although Peru, Colombia and Indonesia have become major suppliers. In Mexico, ruthless and vicious drug cartels demand protection money from growers and have themselves started to move into the lucrative avocado industry in a big way, clearing hillsides of often biodiversity-rich forest and establishing plantations.

Of course, unlike cocaine and marihuana, avocados are an entirely legal product, but the ecological issues can be the same.

Another problem of increased demand for avocados is water. Apart from in regions like Peru which have a constant moist humid climate, the crop requires irrigation for much of the year. This is especially true of California – Avocado is the official fruit of the state of California – already short of water through droughts and over-extraction for agriculture, but supplying no less than 95% of the avocados grown in the USA.

As with other plants, popularity can lead to ecological and social problems.

This substantial fruit and its huge seed may represent adaptations to being eaten by large, now extinct, mammals such as giant ground sloths and elephant-like mastodons. The seeds would have passed right through the gut, as probably did the huge seeds or 'conkers' of horse chestnuts, which were probably dispersed by elephants in prehistoric times.

PEPPERING THINGS UP

What household or restaurant doesn't have a pot of peppercorns or a pepper grinder handy? **Black Pepper** (*Piper nigrum*) is the global favourite among spices, now grown throughout Earth's tropical regions and exported worldwide. Botanically distinct from the bell and chilli peppers, Black Pepper is a climbing vine, bearing numerous long clusters of miniature grape-like fruits , the peppercorns, that are harvested before they ripen. It comes originally from the Western Ghats mountain range of Kerala state, in SW India, which is a centre of rich wild plant and crop diversity.

Its history of use goes back a surprisingly long way – to at least 2,000 BC in India, from where it went east to Indonesia and west to Egypt. Indeed, peppercorns, curiously, were even found

inserted into the nostrils of the Pharoah, Ramases the Great, who was mummified in 1213 BC.

The Romans took to pepper in a big way, re-exporting it from their trading hub of Alexandria, although one commentator seemed less than impressed. The Roman natural history writer Pliny the Elder said disparagingly, '*Pepper has nothing in it that can be recommended, its only desirable quality being a certain pungency. Yet it is for this we bring it all the way from India!*' That may have been because he knew it was often adulterated with cheaper juniper berries. In fact, Rome itself was saved from being sacked by the Visigoths in 408, with a bribe of gold, silver and 3,000 pounds of pepper. They returned in 410 and sacked the city anyway.

With Rome's decline, the Arab caliphates became the dominant traders in pepper, and indeed everything else. In order to shroud pepper's source in mystery and to justify the ratcheted-up price, they spread the rather ridiculous story that the trees in India were '*guarded by snakes that had to be driven away by fire, turning the white corns to black*'. In reality, 'White Pepper' is merely Black Pepper with the outer layer removed.

In Europe, by the 10th century, pepper had become highly prized. Indeed, the English King Ethelred the Unready ordered German spice traders to give him 'ten pounds of pepper' as a condition of trading. In his classic *Great dishes of the world*, Robert Carrier observed: '*Some of Europe's greatest families were founded on the peppercorn. Medieval spice merchants became very rich, for a pound of pepper would buy a sheep, a pound of cloves would buy a cow, and a sack of pepper would buy a man.*' He adds that 'at one time pepper was so expensive that it was sold by the individual peppercorn'. To buy just one peppercorn? Unimaginable – but at least, from when it was used as a symbol of tenancy, it has left us the expression 'peppercorn rent'!

At such prices, great trading centres like Genoa and Venice were underpinned by pepper, as were the international trading empires of first the Portuguese, then the Dutch and eventually the British. Wars were fought and whole countries, indeed entire continents, were discovered by European explorers trying to source and trade pepper. By the time the Dutch displaced the Portuguese from Indonesia, pepper was too widespread for them to dominate its trade, as they did with **Quinine** (page 17). Amazingly, the biggest exporter is now Vietnam, war-torn just a generation ago, to the tune each year of 150,000 tons and a billion dollars!

What is it about pepper? In the old days, to make decaying or over-salted food edible? To spice up rather monotonous ingredients? Our need to kick up the flavour of dishes or challenge the tastebuds? Or even its mildly anti-bacterial and other medicinal properties? Whatever it was, once discovered, it was and remains a roaring success.

The truth is that pepper (just like salt) makes our food more interesting in a trice – even if we don't quite know why! Clearly, it just tickles the tastebuds!

Most of us may probably never have drunk a 'cocktail' – nor ever attended a genuine 'cocktail party' in the true sense. And most of us would probably assume that cocktails were invented in America. The first cocktail party was said to have been organized in 1917 by a hostess in St Louis, Missouri in 1917, and the idea caught on rapidly.

In fact, they were first mentioned in Britain as far back as 1798, inspired by 'punches'; bowls of spirits, fruit juices and flavours, and served in punch houses. The name itself probably came from the French '*coquetier*', an egg-cup-shaped measure.

Cocktails – one of the more imaginative uses of plants in drinks, are not only reliant on plant-based liquors like gin, whisky, vodka and rum, but also on a variety of ingredients like sugar, lime, lemon, mint, tomato juice, cranberry juice, pomegranate juice, Cointreau (made from sweet and bitter orange peel) and Angostura Bitters (a secret recipe, but containing orange, vanilla, cloves, juniper, cinnamon and gentian).

The success of cocktails was totally dependent on the availability of ice, pioneered by the American pioneer Frederic 'Ice King' Tudor, who by 1830, was even shipping ice from ponds in New England to India and the Far East.

While real 'cocktail parties', which blossomed in the 'Roaring 20s' and the Jazz Age, died out in the austerity and rationing of the Second World War, recent years have seen something of a revival for cocktails in bars in London and America.

A recent survey of the 50 most popular cocktails listed, at number 14, 'Bloody Mary' (vodka and tomato juice) – although so unfamiliar are some younger, modern barmen with such drinks that, on the train to Edinburgh, when one of the authors asked for a Bloody Mary, she was soundly reprimanded, 'Madam, we don't allow swearing on this train!'

The Top Ten of today's most popular cocktails includes the 'Manhattan', 'Margarita', 'Whiskey Sour', 'Dry Martini' (page 47), 'Daiquiri', 'Negroni' and, at the top, 'Old Fashioned'. And you can't beat a straightforward 'Gin and Tonic'.

That said, cocktail parties or receptions these days tend to be dominated by red and white wine of variable quality, orange juice and sparkling mineral water. And, if you're lucky, Champagne, or at least Prosecco or maybe Cava from Spain.

AGAVES – MEDITERRANEAN SUNSETS TO TEQUILA SUNRISES

Rosettes of large spear-like agave leaves are a familiar sight in the deserts of the southern USA and Mexico. Providing vital water storage, the tough fleshy leaves are usually toothed along the edges and have a fearsome spine at the tip. Once agaves were classified among the lilies, but botanists now place them in the Asparagus family (Asparagaceae), with the similar yuccas and various garden bulbs. Agaves are perennials that may take years to come into flower, producing a tall central stem, and most die after flowering. Or at least the main shoot does, to be replaced by younger suckers that grow up around the original rosette of leaves.

Popular ornamental plants for hot dry climates, one agave in particular, **American Agave** or **Century Plant** (*Agave americana*), is often photographed silhouetted against the orange sunset of a Mediterranean seascape, its huge flowering stem leaning picturesquely at a drunken angle. The leaves are fibrous and those of another species, **Sisal** (*Agave sisalana*), originally from Yucatán in southern Mexico, has long been used to make ropes, agricultural binder twine and coarse fabrics in Mexico and in Brazil, the Caribbean, East Africa, South Asia and elsewhere. Sisal has largely been replaced by other fibres but still has local, minor and specialist uses, from mats and rugs to buffing cloths and even scratching posts for pet cats!

In a bizarre footnote to history, Neville Chamberlain, the British Prime Minister at the start of the Second World War, began his career by setting up an unsuccessful sisal plantation in the Bahamas. Perhaps he was just as bad at growing things as he was appeasing dictators!

But it is an alcoholic drink for which agave is most famous. The ancient, national drink of Mexico, pulque or agave beer, a vitamin-rich milky beverage, is made from the fermented sap of American Agave and other species. The introduction of distillation by the Spanish conquistadores then enabled the production of brandy-like mescal (different to the hallucinatory drug mescaline, derived from **Peyote** (*Lophophora williamsii*), a spineless cactus of the same region). The most famous of these agave brandies is tequila, made from **Blue Agave** (*Agave tequilana*). The main cultivation district and distillation centre lies around the town of Tequila in Mexico's Jalisco state, and the volcanic landscape there, from which

300 million agave plants are harvested annually, is now a UNESCO World Heritage Site. Skilled labourers continue to tend and harvest the plants mostly by hand, cutting off the sharp-pointed leaves and selecting the fleshy core for processing and fermentation.

Tequila is drunk by tradition with lime juice and salt around the rim of the glass. Tequila Sunrise, immortalized in an Eagles song and made with orange juice, ice and grenadine, is an easier tipple, if just a bit 1970s. Another tequila tradition is mythical. The infamous mescal worm in the bottle, actually the larva of a moth (*Comadia redtenbacheri*) that feeds on agaves, is never permitted in authentic tequilas but is added to other mescal brands, more as a gimmick than a necessity!

Santé!

RHUBARB: EDIBLE DOCK FROM THE EAST

We eat few members of the dock family (Polygonaceae), which are better known as weeds. Nevertheless, one is a familiar food, bottled or canned, or fresh in spring and early summer. Old-fashioned private schools, in Britain especially, included a number of mildly laxative ingredients in the regular and often monotonous diet of their students: dried dates, figs, prunes and, undoubtedly more popular, rhubarb in pies, tarts or crumbles. This pale pink to greenish dessert is no fruit but the edible leaf stalks of **Rhubarb** (*Rheum* x *hybridum*), a garden cross between two or more wild species native to the mountains and upland steppes of Asia, from the Himalayas and Siberia to eastern Turkey. Cold- and frost-tolerant, all form large perennial clumps of stout rootstocks with crowns of long-stalked leaves, from among which huge cream flower clusters arise in summer.

Long before school dinners, rhubarb was a precious commodity imported from faraway Siberia and NW China, its sour yellow to reddish rootstock a gentle laxative that was also astringent and thus helped to bind after promoting ease of passage. First recorded as a medicinal product, *da huang* or great yellow, in China in 2,700 BC, the dried roots arrived in classical Greece and Rome from Asia via caravans along what became the Silk Road and, it seems, the River Volga, which flows into the Caspian Sea.

The name 'rhubarb' derives from the Greek *rha* – the same as the Volga's ancient Scythian name, Rha – and *barbaron*, i.e. 'rha of the barbarians'. We perhaps allude to this when we say 'rhubarb' if we think someone is talking nonsense – the ancient Greeks would have said they were talking the language of barbarians!

During the medieval period (when

Marco Polo may have been the first westerner to spot it in the field) the root again reached Europe but was affordable only by the rich – rhubarb purged Henry VIII during his final illness. For hundreds of years purging remained one of few remedies available to doctors, and from the 17th century rhubarb became a widespread and important laxative, especially in Britain, a nation famously concerned about its bowels. By the late 18th century huge quantities, some sixty tons of the dried root in 1768–69, were arriving in London. In Russia its economic value was such that it was for a long time a strictly regulated and enforced state monopoly.

Until the end of the 18th century it was the root that was prized; but in 1808 a nurseryman sent five bundles of the leaf-stalks to Covent Garden fruit and vegetable market. Only three sold but he persevered, he and others grew more, and rhubarb gradually became accepted as a food. After 1817, when some crowns were accidentally buried in soil at London's Chelsea Physic Garden (page 291), the appeal of tender, forced early rhubarb increased its popularity. Sugar (page 48) had by then come down in price and the public rapidly developed a taste for these sweetened stalks. So too in the USA, where rhubarb became 'Pie Plant'.

Unfortunately, the large heart-shaped leaves themselves *do* contain toxic quantities of oxalic acid, and for a while in World War I, official advice that the leaves should be cooked as well as the stalks reputedly led to a number of deaths.

How sad that the warnings were sometimes thought to be 'rhubarb', in other words, rubbish.

Rhubarb in England relies today mostly on an early crop from January to April, forced in warm dark sheds. The 'Rhubarb Triangle' of west Yorkshire arose over a century ago via a combination of factors: a cool wet climate and clay soil for rhubarb growth, plentiful coal to heat the sheds, waste wool 'shoddy' for fertilizer and railway links to the south of England, along which a fast night train took the crop to market. Its heyday was the 1930s. Today the 'Rhubarb Express' trains are gone with only a dozen growers left, but its time may come again. In 2010 the EU awarded Rhubarb the status of Protected Designation of Origin. Still widespread in gardens and on allotments, it is now seen as a healthy food, championed by celebrity chefs and widely prized at a time of year when fresh fruits are not available.
Far from Yorkshire, rhubarb became a major crop in the USA, particularly in Washington

state and the Pacific North-west, and in Michigan around Detroit, where the small town of Utica once styled itself 'Rhubarb Capital of the World'. It is, alas, unloved in France and Italy but remains popular in Germany and, introduced by German colonists, parts of Transylvania in Romania. Elsewhere it joins green herbs and spices in more savoury dishes; in Kurdistan added to lentils and in Poland cooked with potatoes. And it is now praised as a 'botanical' flavouring in gin. But to the English, not least those from Yorkshire, rhubarb will always be served sweet with custard, a sauce the French appropriately call *crème anglaise*.

BITTER ORANGES AND MARMALADE

Why do we eat marmalade at breakfast and not later in the day? Because the Scots taught us! And they were right to do so – a perfect breakfast spread on toast, with a pleasing 'wake-up' tang.

While we take the name 'marmalade' from the Portuguese *marmelo* or quince, and while it can also be made from lemon, lime, grapefruit, mandarin and other citrus fruits, the favourite ingredient to emerge was **Bitter Oranges** or **Seville oranges** (*Citrus aurantium*), made distinctive by having both the thick peel and juice included. Most Seville Oranges come to Britain from Spain and are on sale only in January and February.

The quince version has a long history, as **Quinces** (*Cydonia oblonga*), native to SW Asia, go right back to ancient Mesopotamia, then the Greeks and Romans, later becoming fashionable in Tudor times. The quince was certainly regarded as fit for kings. Henry VIII was delighted to receive a box from a Mr Hull of Exeter to give to Anne Boleyn who adored it. This was almost certainly *marmalada*, a solid quince paste imported from Portugal, still popular there and now called *membrillo* in Spain.

It was a Scottish mother and her son with a small confectionery shop in Dundee who were to change everything. In 1797, James Keiller happened to buy some Seville oranges from a Spanish ship that had been delayed by storms and were no longer fresh. Janet Keiller boiled the bitter oranges with sugar, added bits of the peel and extra water and created what we today call 'marmalade', now more liquid rather than a paste and perfect for spreading on bread, or better, toast. A breakfast treat was born, and starting in Scotland and spreading to England, it was at breakfast that it would best be enjoyed.

The Keiller family began to realize that marmalade was the product that most deserved their concentration. They started producing it in the Channel Islands (temporarily, to avoid sugar taxes), then

London and finally returned to Dundee. Soon their 'Dundee Marmalade' was not only a favourite in Britain, but was exported, especially successfully to British Empire countries like Australia, New Zealand, South Africa and India.

Janet Keiller has another connection with plants: one of her descendants is Monty Don, BBC television's gardening guru, another of whose ancestors is Scottish botanist George Don (1798–1856), born at the time when the Keillers were first producing marmalade, and whose father and younger brother were also botanists.

A children's favourite character, 'Paddington Bear', who features in more than twenty books by the late Michael Bond, always packed marmalade sandwiches wherever he went. It's said that marmalade sales increased when the first 'Paddington' film was released in 2014.

The Keiller company is now owned by Robertsons of Paisley, another Scottish company, whose Golden Shred marmalade, created in 1874, must be one of the most successful and long-lasting brands in the world's food industry.

MUSTARD AND ITS PARABLE

How many adults don't like mustard, even in a hot dog, or don't see it as an essential in the larder? Probably none, or very few! Perhaps surprisingly for such a piquant condiment, mustard is among the world's favourites – enjoyed right across Northern and Southern Europe, the Mediterranean, Asia, the Americas and Africa. Adding to its widespread popularity is its sheer versatility – consumed with all kinds of hot and cold meat dishes, especially beef, burgers, sausages and ham; as an easy way to spice up soups, gravies, dressings, sauces, glazes and marinades, and furthermore, inexpensive and widely available. In the UK, Colman's Mustard, founded in 1814, is a household name.

Annual or biennial plants from the Mediterranean region and SW Asia, there are numerous species of mustard. All have edible leaves, some produce an edible oil, and three in particular produce the seeds crushed to produce the familiar yellow condiment. These three are the spicy and piquant **Black Mustard** (*Brassica nigra*), the less piquant **Brown Mustard** (*Brassica juncea*) and the not as piquant but a touch more bitter **White Mustard** (*Sinapsis alba*). The last two are the commonest blend in table mustard, Black Mustard being harder to harvest commercially. What is it that produces their characteristic flavour? When the seeds are

crushed in water, the enzyme myrosinase splits glucoside molecules to release pungent mustard oils.

In the ancient world, mustard was first thought of as a medicinal plant, with Pythagoras lauding it as an excellent remedy for scorpion stings, and Hippocrates claiming several cures. In AD 78, Pliny the Elder in his *Natural History* extolled it as '*extremely beneficial for the health*'. We probably have the Romans to thank for mustard's role as the condiment we know so well today when they began blending unfermented grape juice – 'must' – with ground-up mustard seeds to create *mustum ardens*, which means 'burning must'. In 812, Charlemagne included mustards among the plants to be grown on farms in his empire.

By the 13th century, Dijon in southern France had established a strong lead in mustard production, and incredibly there are reliable written accounts of guests at a gala dinner getting through 320 litres of mustard in just one sitting! (Impressive, even though French mustard is milder than English.) But how much did they actually eat? One of the curious things about mustard is that people often do not consume all they put on the side of their plates. Indeed, it is said that the mustard that was *not* finished made Sir Jeremiah Colman (1859–1942), Britain's great mustard producer, rich and famous, together with his hometown of Norwich. Unilever, the parent company of Colman's Mustard, has now moved its main production to Burton-on-Trent and Germany, but mustard is still grown and milled near Norwich.

When did mustard first become popular in Britain? Perhaps in around 1390 when *The Forme of Cury* (with one 'r', meaning 'to cook') was written by King Richard's Master Cook, extolling mustard balls made with flour and cinnamon. The town of Tewkesbury soon became famous for such edible balls, which blended Mustard seeds and the ground root of the related **Horse-radish** (*Armoracia rusticana*), even mentioned in Shakespeare's play *King Henry the Fourth* (Part II) – with the fat knight Sir John Falstaff saying of a friend, '*his wit's as thick as Tewkesbury Mustard*'. Mustard was particularly handy as a home-grown spice rather than one brought at huge expense from the East (see page 183).

Mustard's great advantage is its versatility, giving us whole-grain mustard, honey mustard, sweet and hot pepper mustard, a range of fruit mustards and even mustards made with alcohol.

Which one 'cuts the mustard' with you?

Jesus's parable of the Mustard Seed

Jesus used the example of how mustard starts as a tiny seed which can grow into 'a tree' to encourage his followers that the coming Kingdom of Heaven would grow from small beginnings. In the Gospel of Matthew 13: 31–32 (repeated by Mark and Luke), Jesus is probably referring in his parable to **Black Mustard** (*Brassica nigra*), as this plant can form small thickets and grow two metres or more tall, with far-spreading branches.

'He set another parable before them, saying 'The Kingdom of Heaven is like a grain of mustard, which a man took, and sowed in his field, which indeed is smaller than all the seeds. But when it is grown, it is greater than the herbs, and becomes a tree, so the birds of the air come and lodge in its branches.'

OAKS AND TRUFFLES

In parts of southern France, you can see groves with rows of newly planted little oak trees. The trees will be useless for ten years, but after that there will be something growing on their roots that will be valuable – truffles.

These small fields are a reminder of the *champs truffiers* which in 1890 covered no less than 200,000 acres in France, benefitting from mulberry plantations (page 140) made useless by silkworm diseases and vineyards utterly ruined by Phylloxera bugs (page 114).

Truffles are the underground fruits of a type of fungus, first noticed by the Romans but reaching their greatest cooking fame from the Renaissance to the 19th century. What had been dug up by peasants using the smelling ability of pigs and dogs became a delicacy and one so expensive that it '*graced the tables of only great nobles and kept women.*' The famous gastronome Jean Anthelme Brillat-Savarin (1755–1826) called truffles '*the diamond of the kitchen*', and Alexandre Dumas of Three Musketeers fame said, it was '*the holy of holies for the gourmet*'.

Around 1709, truffles began to be cultivated, because the link had been noted between them, loose soils over limestone rocks and the roots of **Oak Trees** (*Quercus robur* and other *Quercus* species). It takes many years for the truffle fungus, which lives in symbiosis or state of mutual benefit (*mycorrhiza*) on the roots of trees, to develop, and the planted groves have to be carefully protected from soil contamination by other fungi and now with electric fences stopping the ravages of wild pigs, costing as much as 10,000 euros a hectare.

Such high production costs ensure that truffles remain a luxury for cooks and restaurants. Cultivation has improved and they are now being cultivated in Australia (Tasmania), New Zealand and the United States. They are also gathered from the wild in France, Italy and Spain, in woods of oak, hazel and other trees. The most prized, and therefore most expensive, truffles are the **White Truffle** (*Tuber magnatum*) and **Black** or **Périgord Truffle** (*Tuber melanosporum*).

The smell and flavour of fresh truffles is intense, pungent and musky. They need to be served raw or lightly cooked by slicing them extra-thin or shaving them over warm or hot dishes such as pasta, risotto, mashed and dauphinoise potatoes or scrambled eggs. Small pieces of truffle can also be infused in olive oil, and just a few drops will enhance these dishes, patés, sauces and salads.

But you still have to dig deep into your pocket to afford to eat them!

STRAWBERRY FIELDS FOREVER

Strawberries are ever popular in both Europe and North America. What on earth would Wimbledon's Lawn Tennis Championship be without copious servings of strawberries and cream? Yet only three centuries ago, this handsome, sweet-tasting and delicious red fruit did not exist. But its wild American ancestors certainly did.

In 1711 France's King Louis XIV, sent the military engineer and polymath Amedée-François Frézier on an intelligence gathering expedition to Peru and Chile. Fighting the British, Austrians and others in the War of Spanish Succession, Louis was worried about the declining French influence in South America. Frézier was impressed by the large strawberries sold in markets in the port of Concepción in Chile. Returning to France, he brought some live plants back, one of which he gave to a colleague in Brest in Brittany, and another he passed to botanist Antoine de Jussieu at the Jardin du Roi in Paris. Because the fruits were not fertile, for propagation de Jussieu instead grew on the plantlets produced at the end of the plant's long runners.

Chilean Strawberries (*Fragaria chiloensis*), native from the Andes and right up to the Pacific North-west of America, had been long grown by native people in Chile, who had bred variants with larger fruits. In 1764 Antoine Nicolas Duchesne, a botanist with a keen eye for variation in plants, established a 'national collection' of strawberries for Louis XV at Versailles. He produced fruits by crossing Chilean strawberries with European wild ones, but due to several intrinsic genetic differences, still no fertile seed.

However, luckily the strawberry growers of Brest had been busy cultivating plants from the original Chilean plant, alongside European wild strawberries and also **Virginia Strawberry** (*Fragaria virginiana*), from eastern North America. Crosses between the Chilean and Virginian Strawberries, close relatives that had never met in the wild, yielded vigorous plants with large fragrant fruits, which Duchesne named *Fragaria ananassa* or 'Pineapple Strawberry' – thus our old friend the **Garden Strawberry**.

Further crossing and selection have much improved this popular tasty fruit, and the global crop now exceeds some 9 million tons, with 40% grown in China.

The original Chilean Strawberry is still grown by local people in Chile, a small but precious resource for plant breeders.

By a nice coincidence, the surname of Amédée-François Frézier, who first brought us the Chilean strawberry, is believed to derive from *Fraisier*, French for strawberry plant. The Scottish clan, Fraser, is a branch of the same family.

QUINOA – A NEW LIFE FOR THE INCAS' GRAIN

Every so often a new food enters public consciousness but may not become established. One that *has* done so and indeed taken off in recent years – with the growing interest in plant-based diets – is **Quinoa** (*Chenopodium quinoa*), which, like the potato, is a staple food of the Andes. A member of the beetroot and spinach family (Amaranthaceae), it is a robust annual up to 250 centimetres tall with dense leafy clusters of tiny flowers that produce many, yellow to reddish fruiting masses containing lens-shaped dark brown or black seeds. This ancient food crop was developed in the Andean Highlands in pre-Colombian times, around 4,000 BC, probably selected from a native weedy ancestor in the Lake Titicaca region.

Ancient civilizations grew up wherever there was a centre of diversity of crop plant relatives, especially cereals and other grain staples: wheat, barley and oats in the Middle East, rice in Asia, corn (maize) in Central America. In the Andes, rather than a cereal the grain was quinoa, a crop that was a mainstay of Inca civilization, and one the Incas regarded as sacred and named 'the mother grain'. After Francisco Pizarro overthrew the Inca Empire in 1532–33, the Spanish replaced the gods of the Incas and disrupted traditional agriculture, planting European cereals and even destroying quinoa in the fields and in stores. Farmers were sent to work in the silver mines. Like the Incas themselves, quinoa cultivation retreated into the high mountains and, even though it has persisted until today among subsistence farmers, it was gradually dying out by the 1970s. Since then it has seen a major revival and is now an increasingly popular healthy 'superfood'.

Quinoa has many plus points. It is cold and drought-tolerant, growing up to 4,000 metres (13,000 feet) in the mountains, where few other crops thrive. Nor does it suffer from the fungal rust diseases that plague cereals and has a higher protein content, as well as yielding the important amino acid, lycine. The nutritious seeds can be bitter and need to be separated from their coverings before cooking, either as they are or as flour. The high protein, fibre and mineral content of the seeds, together with B vitamins and amino acids makes quinoa a valuable addition to a mixed, vegetarian or vegan diet. In addition, it is gluten-free and even regarded by Jews as kosher. Grown in the USA and other countries, but rarely in the UK except to provide cover and food for pheasants, large amounts are imported from Peru and Bolivia, who together produce the great bulk of the world crop. Unfortunately, the high demand and price, ten times that

of wheat, for this local crop turned global commodity has made it unaffordable to local Andean people, many of whom are desperately poor. A 2016 study found that many farming families (not least the women) were making more money, but at the same time these subsistence farmers who had traditionally relied on this nourishing food as a staple rather than a cash crop for sale and export, were themselves switching to an unhealthy western diet. Efforts are now being made to distribute quinoa more widely and ensure that poorer people have access to it and are aware of its nutritional significance. The high consumption of quinoa, like avocados, in the wealthy West is another nice example of fashion and social trends having unintended consequences.

Too little remains of the once mighty Inca civilization that gave us the ubiquitous potato, but their sacred grain is another physical as well as a less tangible link.

Similar grain species are cultivated and eaten in South and Central America but not on the same scale. **Goosefoot** or **Fat Hen** (*Chenopodium album*) and a complex of closely related species, similar to but usually much smaller than Quinoa, are common farm and garden weeds in Europe and North America. Once grown both for the spinach-like leaves and the seeds, they feature prominently in archaeological remains in Britain and elsewhere but much less so after the Middle Ages. They are still cultivated or at least foraged in the Himalayas and even in southern Europe, and one member of this group, **Tree Spinach** (*Chenopodium giganteum*), is beginning to attract attention as a fast-growing leaf vegetable.
All, like Quinoa, are extremely healthy.

GRAPES AND WINE

When we travel in Europe, especially in the south and west, we see endless vistas of vineyards. For thousands of years these well-ordered plantations of grape vines have been a powerhouse of the rural economy, with agriculture in the Mediterranean region from earliest times dependent upon three staple crops – grapes, olives and cereals.

Grapes are a versatile, nutritious fruit – eaten fresh or dried, or fermented into wine, which can itself be distilled into brandy or fermented into acetic acid, better known as the preservative and condiment, vinegar (from the French *vin aigre* or 'sour

wine'). Vineyards with rows of grape vines are an essential element of the landscapes of the Mediterranean and much of the rest of Europe.

Although associated with dry sunny hillsides, **Grape Vine** (*Vitis vinifera*) was probably once a wild plant of damp woods, ravines and along rivers and streams in the Caucasus, Black Sea region and SE Europe. It is the only European member of the Vitaceae, a family of some 800 tropical or warm temperate species, most of them vines. Grape Vine is a woody plant with long tough stems, and branched tendrils enabling it to scramble and climb, or be trained along wires. Tiny scented green flowers in spring give rise to the familiar dense bunches of berries of various colours, which contain 'pips' or are seedless and ripen in late summer.

Above all, grapes are cultivated for making wine, one of the most widespread and enjoyed of human pleasures. 'A meal without wine is like a day without sunshine' is often quoted, although nobody can quite remember who first said it – but almost certainly a Frenchman! The first evidence of grape cultivation is wine jars found in Georgia that date from as early as 6,000 BC. Grapes were established in Mesopotamia and Egypt by 4,000 BC and feature prominently in the Bible, including in the parables of Jesus, who grew up in a village and would therefore have been familiar with vineyards. Wine was a part of Jewish religious ritual before Christianity and Holy Communion.

Wine drinking was a widespread pastime in Antiquity, even if drunkenness was discouraged and regarded with disdain. Indeed, Alexander the Great (pictured)and Mark Antony were noted drinkers. To modify the effects of alcohol, the ancient Greeks diluted their wine with water, while the Romans combined drinking with feasting. Throughout the ancient world wine was an important part of trade, and grapes feature prominently in art and on coins, as well as in myth and legend. Many ancient shipwrecks have been found full of terracotta amphorae, the tall two-handled jars in which wine travelled.

The Phoenicians, Greeks and Romans spread vine cultivation around the Mediterranean and far into Europe north to Germany and Britain. Two millennia later, in the colonial era, the Spanish and British would take vines worldwide, especially to California, South America, South Africa, Australia and New Zealand.

These markets matured and are now booming, not only in volume, but in quality. Australia pioneered many innovations – irrigating their vines (unlike the French), cooling their vineyard buildings, inventing the bag-in-box and asking a French company to create the screw-cap. Californian wines are highly respected worldwide and the authors' friend Josh Jensen's 'Calera' beat several top French Burgundies in a memorable blind tasting in Paris. Malbec from Argentina is now thought the world's best, and Argentina is the world's 5th largest producer,

However, Chile is even more highly regarded. It has a very varied climate, from hot coastal plains to the highest (3,500

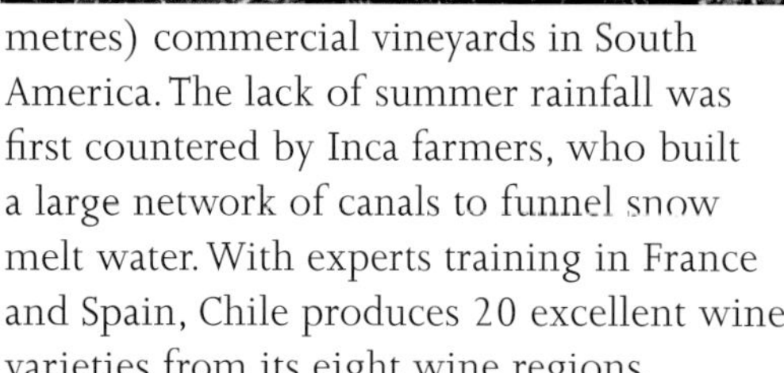

metres) commercial vineyards in South America. The lack of summer rainfall was first countered by Inca farmers, who built a large network of canals to funnel snow melt water. With experts training in France and Spain, Chile produces 20 excellent wine varieties from its eight wine regions.

South Africa with its well-balanced climate is also a major player. With apartheid gone, there are now 600 wineries, its Chenin blanc grapes being the most popular. The small berried Muscat grapes are allowed to shrivel on the vine and produce a sweet wine that became very popular in the 18th century, so much so that Napoleon, in exile on St Helena, ordered deliveries of it to cheer him up!

Three surprising new players have recently entered the scene, although 'new' can hardly be applied to China, which had a thriving wine industry in the 2nd century. It now boasts 1.5 million acres of vineyards and its enthusiasm for drinking Chateau Lafite and other Bordeaux wines has vastly increased their prices!

Japan's wine industry also goes back a long way, to the 8th century when Buddhist missionaries started it – 185 wineries now thrive, despite challenging climate conditions, including typhoons. The Japanese are also wine investors, owning French vineyards like Chateau Lagrange.

And then there is Britain. With a warming climate, British still white wines and sparkling wines are now becoming highly respected. With an eye to the future, Champagne houses are now buying into England.

So wine is a huge industry, and today's global grape crop is over 70 million tons, yielding 70 trillion gallons of wine.

However, it is wise to watch out for threats. During the mid-19th century, North American vines introduced to Europe brought with them Phylloxera (*Daktulosphaira vitifoliae*), a sap-sucking bug to which the native Grape Vines were highly susceptible (page34). Today's vines were saved by being grafted on to phylloxera-resistant American rootstocks.

Wine production, as old as grape cultivation, is made possible by the high natural sugar content of the grapes, the yeasts naturally present on the skins that bring about fermentation, and the tannins and pigments present in the pips and skins, adding variety to the products of fermentation. Distillation (boiling and condensing the wine) produces brandy, which can also be added to fortify wines such as sherry (over page top right), port and Madeira or, with added herbs or 'botanicals', vermouth. The residue after pressing the grapes may be distilled to make spirits such as marc in France or grappa in Italy and the aniseed flavoured ouzo aperitif of Greece and Cyprus, or the often slightly stronger raki (arak) of Turkey and the Levant.

Little is wasted. Crushed vine seeds yield a quality culinary oil high in vitamin E and polyunsaturated fatty acids; and vine leaves, stuffed with rice, minced meat, nuts and herbs, feature prominently in Near and Middle Eastern cookery.

Along with wine grapes, sweet dessert grapes, which contain up to 25% sugar and are rich in potassium, fibre, vitamin C and B vitamins, are a major Mediterranean product, particularly in parts of Spain and Italy. Dried grapes – raisins, currants and seedless sultanas – are a more significant commercial commodity, which before sugar (page 48) was widely available, were prized for their sweetness. 'Currant' (in the USA, 'Zante currant'), a product mentioned by Pliny in his *Natural History* of 77 AD, is a corruption of Corinth, the ancient and modern Greek city once famous for its export.

Grapes, in all their variations and uses, have proved to be one of the most important, and pleasurable plants of all.

BARLEY AND HOPS, DUBLIN'S WORLD-BEATING DARK BLEND

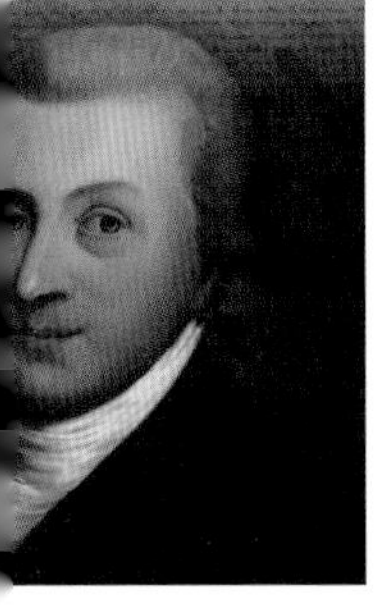

Beer has been one of the most enduring influences that plants have had on human society. Beers come and go but perhaps the most famous of all beers, which are basically barley and hops, has survived for just two and a half centuries. Neither a bitter nor a lager, those usual stalwarts of bars and pubs, but a dark, full-bodied Irish stout with a creamy white head – Guinness.

A household name, even among those who claim not to touch it, Guinness is ubiquitous worldwide and is drunk in the

most unlikely places. It is as much a symbol of Irish identity as the harp and Shamrock (page 157) and drinking Guinness is an essential part of the great St Patrick's Day Parades of New York and Chicago, let alone those in

Ireland itself.

In 1752, Arthur Guinness (pictured), aged seventeen, was bequeathed £100 by his godfather, the Archbishop of Cashel, and he founded a brewery in Leixlip, near Dublin. Seven years later he moved into the city, to a four-acre site at St James's Gate by the River Liffey, signing the longest lease in history, 9,000 years, for the princely sum of £45 a year.

Initially, he brewed dark 'porter' beer, well-known in England. But soon his own blend of roasted barley, hops, brewers' yeast and isinglass finings (made from dried air bladders of fish), made Guinness a huge success. The roasting of the barley, at a precise temperature, and perhaps a special strain of yeast, gave it the distinctive taste we still know today.

When the first barrels of Guinness went to England, its popularity grew amongst all classes, enjoyed from the lowliest pub right up to No. 10, Downing Street itself, for even Prime Minister Benjamin Disraeli developed a special taste for it. 'Black Velvet', Guinness with champagne, was invented in 1861, somewhat strangely honouring the death of Prince Albert, beloved husband of Disraeli's friend Queen Victoria.

Barley (*Hordeum vulgare*), the main ingredient of beer (page 207), is itself an emblem of Irish nationhood and freedom. Following the 1798 Rebellion against British rule, barley grains were sown to denote the unmarked mass graves of the defeated Irish rebels. The growth of the barley, their basic provision and field ration, symbolized springtime regeneration, and Ireland's unwillingness to submit. The popular 19th-century ballad 'The Wind that shakes the Barley' tells of a young man torn between his lover and his wish to join the fight. More than a hundred and fifty years later, the song is widely performed by traditional and contemporary folk and rock artists.

Meanwhile Guinness grew into one of the most famous brands in the world. Clever advertising made it into a true marketing phenomenon, because it played on people's belief that it was good for their health. Hence the iconic 'Guinness is good for You' advertising (see panel). British advertising agencies ever since have won awards for their Guinness advertisements. In 2000, 'Surfer', featuring white horses in the sea, was voted the best British TV commercial of all time.

How pleased those disappointed patriots of 1798 would have been to see Ireland's charismatic, barley-based drink take on and conquer both Britain and the world!

In 1923, young 'Bobby' Bevan, the uncle of author Donough O'Brien, joined the London advertising agency S.H. Benson. His first task was to find out why their new client, an Irish stout called Guinness, sold so well without owning pubs, as most breweries did. The answer – people thought it was good for their health. The dramatic result was the iconic 'Guinness is Good for You' advertising slogans. The first advertisements, written by Bevan and the novelist Dorothy L. Sayers, and illustrated by John Gilroy, implied some health advantages which could not be claimed today. The illustrations were witty, with zoo animals including the toucan that became ever associated with the brand, and Dorothy Sayers even included Bobby Bevan as 'Mr Ingleby' in her 1933 thriller Murder Must Advertise.

CHAMPAGNE AND CELEBRATION

The night they invented champagne – you may remember that rousing song from the musical *My Fair Lady*. However, to create the magical wine that the whole world drinks in celebration took rather longer, of course, than just one night!

Since Roman times, Champagne's chalky region in France had been producing excellent red wines, so good that the Emperor Domitian, in 92 AD, decreed the vineyards should be uprooted to eliminate competition with Italy's wine producers. That same year he did the same for Malbec in Cahors, and his proposed double vineyard vandalism led to his assassination by his Praetorian Guards, helped, rather typically for Rome, by his wife!

By the seventeenth century, the wines of Champagne rivalled those of Burgundy, and because of their monastic connections, were used for the sacrament, at the royal table, for coronations in the cathedral at Reims and to celebrate treaties.

However, there was a problem. The cool climate caused the fermentation to 'pause'. When warmer weather returned, carbon dioxide gas was produced. The gas, in the future to be so valuable, was then considered a mysterious and dangerous nuisance. The cellar men wore iron masks to avoid flying glass from the exploding bottles of what they called 'the Devil's wine' or 'the crazy wine'.

Dom Pérignon was appointed cellar master at Hautvillers in 1668, and he made it his mission, as he wrote to the elders of Epernay, to 'make the best wines in the world'. He succeeded, vastly improving what were all still red wines, called 'the eye of the partridge, and 'clairet'. But he also did his best to stop the secondary fermentation in the casks and bottles.

Curiously, it was an Englishman who first pointed out how this nuisance gas could be harnessed to *deliberately* create a sparkling wine. Christopher Merrett was a distinguished physician, amateur botanist and scientist who had produced one of the first lists of the flora, fauna and minerals of England and the first comprehensive list of British birds.

Merrett was fascinated by glass and glass bottles, in whose manufacture Britain now led the world. In December 1662, six years before Dom Pérignon arrived at Hautvillers, Merrett presented a paper to fellow distinguished members of the Royal Society, then the world centre for scientific learning. It was called *Some observations concerning the ordering of wines*, in which he advocated adding sugar and molasses to stimulate a second fermentation in strong bottles to create a sparkling white wine. He was effectively describing what would become the *Méthode Champenoise* as we now know it. As a French monk, Dom Pérignon, almost certainly never got to read many Royal Society papers. But by trial and error, after thirty years he did produce a sparkling wine, at first rose-tinted, using bottles with thick glass and indented bases of the 'English type' from the Argonne and corks which could cushion gas pressure.

Then the English played a role in helping to create demand for this wine, and by complete accident. Welcomed to England by Charles II, the French exile, Charles de Saint-Evremond, had already made still wine from Champagne popular in English high society. Some wine that he had ordered was shipped in casks and underwent a second fermentation in the warm weather during

the voyage. Bottled with cork stoppers, the wine retained its lively sparkle. Soon it was all the rage in London. And this popularity soon spread to France. When the Duke of Orleans, the Regent of France, started serving it to his aristocratic guests, it became a craze in Paris. His son, Chevalier Jean-Philippe d'Orleans, was made Abbot of Hautvillers and the link with the French royal family became ever stronger. Indeed, Louis XIV liked sparkling Champagne so much that he was ordered to desist by his doctor. The winemakers of Champagne realized that the new sparkling wine was their future, and they gave up the struggle to avoid those bubbl and used them to perfect the product.

Champagne has since successfully created an image niche as a drink for royalty and the rich – although it is main consumed by many others. It has cleverly positioned itself with women for romant celebrations like engagements, weddings and christenings. There is no other drink so strongly associated with celebration ar (literally) sparkling occasions. Of the 31 wine-producing villages in Champagne, three have names splendidly redolent of drinking a little too much – Bouzy, Dizy Rilly!

Dom Pérignon's statue looks out at Epernay. In 1936, 'Dom Pérignon' was launched by Moët & Chandon as the first *cuvée de prestige* and is now probably the mo famous and iconic champagne brand. An just recently, a plaque to honour a deserv Christopher Merrett has gone up in his village of Winchcombe.

PLANTS AND SOCIETIES

PLANTS AND PLEASURES

Just as plants have been vital for us in sustenance, health, industry, culture and, sadly, warfare, so they have in our very simplest pleasures.

Which of us never enjoyed climbing a tree, testing courage and skill, or the pleasure of waving triumphantly to our parents from the top? Who didn't like playing hide and seek in the woods? And who didn't long for a tree house in the garden? And what children now wouldn't love one, and bemoan the fact that they live in a high-rise flat?

There are now over thirty companies in Europe and America that market tree houses in various sizes and styles, such is the demand for the 'high life', and 'tree house holidays' are becoming ever more popular. Even Prince Charles has one in his garden!

Of course, tree houses were not always for relaxed pleasure. They were first created for protection from animals and it was only 40,000 years ago that most humans dared to come down from them. But now it's the pleasure of being 'above it all'.

And how many of us used to play 'Poohsticks', a game created by A.A. Milne for his son Christopher Robin and then featured in his book *The House at Pooh Corner?* You may remember the rules. Two of you drop sticks on the upstream side of a bridge, then run across and see whose stick first appears on the other side. The Milnes' bridge still exists, Posingford Bridge in the Ashdown Forest in Sussex, restored with the help of Disney. Since 1984, there has even been a World Poohsticks Competition. Because of the crowds, it is now held near Oxford and governed by strict rules and usually featuring **White Willow** (*Salix alba*) sticks.

And what little girl or boy hasn't held a buttercup under their friends' chins, to see 'how much they like butter'? It has now been discovered that the yellow glow is because the numerous species of **Buttercup** (*Ranunculus* species) have evolved a unique petal structure with a layer of starch crystals that makes the yellow especially shiny-bright, attracting insect pollinators. It also reflects ultra-violet rays, making it a beacon for bees.

Which of us didn't make a chain out of **Daisies** (*Bellis perennis*), or play 'Conkers' with the fruits of **Horse Chestnut** (*Aesculus hippocastanum*) or use Ash or Hazel to make swords or bows and arrows? The list of

pleasures from plants is endless, and becomes even longer in adult life.

For adults, gardening is now the biggest hobby in the world, with millions of us participating and millions more visiting flower shows like Chelsea or Hampton Court, botanical gardens and show gardens and their equivalents all over the world.

Cooking is probably the next biggest hobby involving plants, having gone from a necessity to a real pleasure and with celebrity chefs, starting with Fanny Cradock and 1960s chefs introducing television audiences to the **Avocado** (*Persea americana*) and many other plants we had never heard of. (page 209).

The tools of participant sports used to be provided by plants, although technology has created many changes. Golf clubs for centuries were made from dense, shock-resistant **Hickory** (*Carya*), but are now steel. Tennis racquets were made from **Ash** and **Beech**, but are now much lighter, having gone from steel to graphite. Baseball bats are made from **Maple**, **Ash**, **Hickory** and **Bamboo**, although titanium and aluminium are now used. In ice hockey, traditional **Willow** and **Ash** have been replaced with carbon fibre, fibreglass and aluminium, although wood is still used, but laminated. Needless to say, all kinds of woods are used in marine sports, for the hulls of boats and yachts, for oars and paddles and specialist woods for masts, although some of them are being replaced by metals and plastics.

One piece of sporting equipment that has remained the same is the cricket bat.Its white willow wood is even called **Cricket Bat Willow** (*Salix alba* var. *caerulea*). It is light, very tough and shock-resistant, avoiding denting and splintering when hitting balls at high speed. Bats require raw **Linseed** oil and, when newly purchased, hours of 'knocking in', with an old cricket ball or rubber mallet, which compresses the fibres to resist damage.

Rubber (*Ficus elastica*) has provided the material for many of the products used in sports. It was first brought to Europe in 1582 by Hernan Cortés, who had seen Aztecs playing their game Ulama and, with a bouncing ball, amazed the court of Spain's King Charles V, an astonishing sight at the time. In sport, rubber provides the basis for balls of all kinds – for cricket , soccer, polo, squash, baseball, basketball, golf, rugby, waterpolo – the list is endless. Then there are handles, shoes, playing surfaces and, of course, the tyres, hoses and gaskets in racing cars.

As with nearly all other aspects of our lives, plants are vital components in our pleasures, hobbies and sports, although we probably don't think about it, simply taking them for granted.

BLACKBERRIES AND THE MIND OF A CHILD

Who would have thought that blackberry picking can teach us so much about children's personalities – and, indeed, the way they may go on to behave as adults?

A great lesson in life

Watching kids pick blackberries –
illuminating, always true.
Just hand each one a bag or bowl
and then watch out for what they do.
Some will pick and never eat one,
while others eat half those they pick,
or end up eating all of them
until they cough up purple sick.

Watching them and how they pick
is almost most enlightening.
It shows how different they are.
I've always found it interesting.
You notice who's competitive
and other children who are not –
all kinds of tiny little things
that show the characters they've got.

Some work like demons picking them
while others don't, and soon lose heart –
miffed to see the quicker pickers.
The children can be poles apart.
You spot dissenters – also true,
the ones who quickly go on strike
and hide behind a blackberry bush
and find the whole darned thing a hike.
You notice who gets into it
or out of it in minutes flat,
staring round at other children –
you very often notice that.
You spot the future freelancers –
the ones who strike out on their own
and do not like to work in teams
and maybe won't when fully grown.

You soon hear the faint-hearted ones
who give up at the first small scratch,
and moan and groan to see their blood –
the first to give up, leave the patch.
You spot the ones who carry on,
determined to achieve their goal –
regardless of a nick or two –
until they've filled a brimming bowl.

You also notice bossy kids
who nick the gathered fruit of others,
while claiming why they have the right –
'Mum cooks better than your mothers'.
You see the more adventurous
who work at greater distances
or higher up into the bush,
however dangerous that is.

You watch the most competitive,
and others, quite the opposite,
disliking the whole exercise
and longing to get out of it.
So many little clues are there
about their personalities.
A fascinating exercise
is watching kids pick blackberries!

Liz Cowley

BLACKBERRIES

One of the most widespread of wild plants, with its tangle of arched prickly stems and clusters of white or pinkish flowers and black fruits, **Blackberry** or **Bramble** (*Rubus fruticosus*) is familiar to all. Each autumn, along woodland edges and in scrub and hedges, the heads of black, fleshy one-seeded fruitlets feed birds and mammals – and provide a delicious bountiful harvest for people, especially children, although in our more affluent times perhaps not so much as in the past. Both the fruits and the leaves make herbal tea, and the roots and leaves yield dyes. Blackberries are rich in fibre, antioxidants and Vitamins C and K. But this useful plant is also an invasive weed of woods, gardens and waste places. In Australia, to where it was unwisely introduced in the 1840s for hedging and fruit, it has become a serious pest of grazing land – eaten not by small hedgerow birds but by emus, spread about in their droppings.

Botanists divide Bramble into more than four hundred similar 'micro-species', many rare or local in distribution, which vary in the size, taste and texture of the fruits as well as more mundane attributes such as the size and density of the sharp prickles. So, if you have a favourite special blackberry patch, your choice may well reflect the science!

FLOWER ARRANGING AND CONSTANCE SPRY

How many people do you know who became famous nationwide for flower arranging?

Perhaps, like the authors, only one name springs readily to mind – that of Constance Spry, talented enough to warrant a blue English Heritage plaque on her London house for her exquisite and thoroughly unconventional arrangements, and to play a leading role in floristry displays at royal weddings and events.

Her crowning achievements were all the more remarkable given the early tragedies in her life – both her brothers killed in action in the First World War, with her mother so traumatized that she was unable to speak for two years and a miserable and violent first marriage from which she had to flee.

A tenacious survivor, she became a headmistress in a London school, teaching cookery and dress-making – and only later flower-arranging, where her greatest skills as a true original were to emerge. Her attitude to flower arranging was as unconventional as her life. She moved from the stiff and formal, using all sorts of strange plants to enhance and support her flower designs: fruit, weeds, vegetables and grasses. She then placed them in all sorts of unconventional containers, and was known to raid people's attics to find them! Here is her startling advice to other designers:

ENGLISH HERITAGE
CONSTANCE SPRY
1886-1960
Designer in Flowers
worked here
1934-1960

'Do whatever you please. Follow your own star. Be original if you want to be and don't if you don't want to be. Just be natural and gay and light-hearted and pretty and simple and overflowing and general and baroque and bare and austere and stylized and wild and daring and

conservative. And learn and learn and learn. Open your mind to every form of beauty.'

Fame was soon to follow when she turned from teaching to run her first flower shop, and one of her first assignments was to create flower arrangements for a well-known jewellery store window nearby, which was so dramatic that it drew crowds and caused a traffic jam! People had never seen anything like it, and it was obvious that she was truly shaking things up – a true original.

Unsurprisingly, her flower shop thrived, as did her flower-arranging academy, with its six-month courses, and her clients became increasingly prestigious – and even royal. Indeed, the Royal Family commissioned her to provide and supervise all the flowers for the 1953 coronation of Queen Elizabeth, the highest possible honour for anyone in her field.

Sadly, she was never given the official Royal Appointment to the Royal Family. The reason is not hard to find. She had provided the flowers for the controversial wedding in France of (ex) King Edward VIII and Wallis Simpson.

This did not stop Constance providing the flowers for the wedding of Princess Margaret, nor the amazing display of 'The Hanging Gardens of Babylon' for the Shah of Persia – let alone providing the flowers for Covent Garden Opera and countless commercial companies and lavish social events.

Her shop, 'Flower Decoration', turned into an entire domestic science school while Constance turned to writing, eventually producing no less than twelve books. Not only an inspired flower-arranger, she was a talented cook and author of cookery books. Not many people could claim to provide all the flowers at a coronation in the morning, but then also the dish the royal guests ate that evening – 'Coronation Chicken' – but she did just that.

She toured all over the world, and her tours to Australia and America were a particular success.

Roses were one of her favourite flowers, and her collection at her house at Winkfield, near Windsor, was famous. Indeed, David Austin created a beautiful pink rose for her, which he called 'Constance Spry'.

Her great influence remains to this day. In fact, the London Flower School thinks it so important that they run a course called 'Two days inspired by Constance Spry'.

Tragically, this genius with flowers died in her seventies falling down in her house, but still with the wit to quip as she lay there, 'Someone else can arrange this!'

PIPES AND PERCEPTIONS

These days we rarely see people smoking a wooden pipe. But it was a common enough sight until the 1960s, with the smokers (nearly all of them men) probably thinking that their pipe smoking gave them added gravitas. This was particularly true at office meetings, which could soon become a fug of smoke, and it was considered most discourteous for others to flap the fumes away!.

Liz Cowley, one of the authors, clearly

remembers a colleague at an advertising presentation to try and win, ironically, the Zip firelighter account, tapping out his pipe into a wastepaper basket that he had not realized was full of paper. Unsurprisingly, it immediately caught fire and when he surreptitiously tried to stamp it out, it erupted in flames and he emerged from behind the table with a blazing shoe. Unsurprisingly, the account went elsewhere!

Pipe smoking is the oldest form of smoking. In 1586, Sir Walter Raleigh brought back tobacco to be smoked, of course, in pipes, and they were part of rituals all over the world – not least those of Native American tribes smoking **Tobacco** (*Nicotiana rustica*) in their 'Pipes of Peace'.

Pipe smoking and its rituals were

always associated with being serious, contemplative, grave, measured and thoughtful – sometimes also an excuse for gathering thoughts in a key discussion. Indeed, the famous poet William Cowper sums it up perfectly.

'The pipe with solemn interposing puff
Makes half a sentence at a time enough.
The dozing stages drop the drowsy strain,
Then pause, and puff, and speak, and pause again.'

For twenty years, pipes have had the same public smoking restrictions as cigarettes, but these days have a tiny following in Britain – probably only 2% of men, but surprisingly 25% in Sweden.

Pipes can be made from many types of robust wood including **Boxwood**, **Cherry**, **Elderberry**, **Maple**, **Plum**,**Walnut and White Ash**. But the most popular is the hard root of the **Briar** (*Erica arborea*) , often two hundred years old. It has to be carefully 'broken in', with a form of seasoning that prepares the bowl of the pipe for frequent use, creating a hard protective layer with the splendid name of 'dottle'.

Even though pipe smoking is now far less common, we still tell people to pay attention by saying 'Put that in your pipe and smoke it!'.

But even that expression is now increasingly rare – indeed, as rare as seeing anyone nowadays smoking a pipe!

WOOD AND JIGSAW PUZZLES

Writing this book during the Covid-19 crisis, the authors noticed an increasing interest in jigsaw puzzles, with friends asking if we had any they could borrow. This sudden interest is confirmed by Wentworth, Britain's biggest jigsaw maker maker, who recently reported a huge spike in sales as 'locked-down' people fought off boredom.

It's interesting that there was a similar huge increase during the 1930s Great Depression. Do such puzzles cheer us up? People certainly seem to enjoy the challenge of puzzling things out, and if we're older, there's the added advantage of keeping our brains active. It's also a cheap way to have fun.

Curiously, the jigsaw puzzle was never made with a jigsaw, but with a fretsaw, so the name is strange, although the appeal is not. Puzzles can keep us absorbed for days on end depending on their size and complexity, ranging from a mere 300 pieces up to forty thousand, with smaller and easier ones for children.

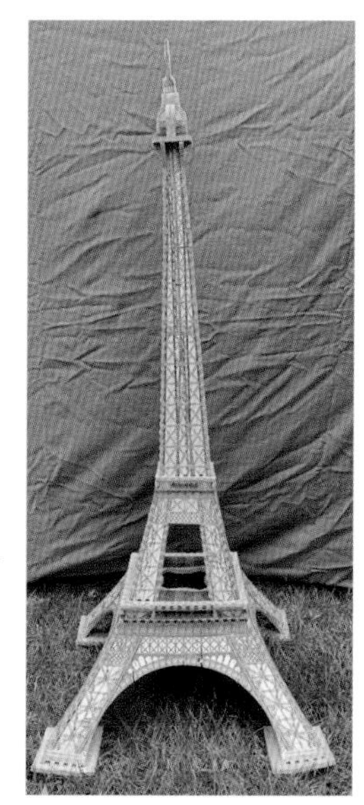

Who gave us the jigsaw puzzle? They have been popular since the 1760s when John Spilbury, a London mapmaker and engraver, began to make them from thin panels of **Mahogany** (*Swietenia macrophylla*) from South and Central America, and **Cedar of Lebanon** (*Cedrus libani*) (see page 161), then widely used as furniture veneers. Early puzzle themes for teaching children were world maps, called 'dissected maps' – and first used by royalty, for the children of King George III. And, for many years, puzzles remained an educational aid rather than a pastime for adults. Puzzle enthusiasts say that their favourite was 'English Counties', including the County of Rutland, whose pieces were often lost due to its minature size.

While wood, mostly plywood, has continued as the basis for puzzles, cardboard has also been used since the late 1800s, and this really took off at the beginning of the Second World War when wood was in short supply. Today they are mostly of paperboard, with **Birch** (*Betula*) and other types of plywood used for a quality product. These have to be cut out with hydraulic presses exerting an amazing 700 tons of force. Modern innovations also include laser-cutting, 3-dimensional puzzles, like the Eiffel Tower (illustrated) and computer versions.

For those of enjoying quite simple puzzles, it's astonishing to discover that the largest on sale is made by the Czech company, Martin, with no less than 52,000 pieces. And the most expensive was sold for $27,000 in aid of The Golden Retriever Foundation. Goodness, lucky dogs!

But for sheer size, there is the

largest puzzle at 58,435 square feet, well over an acre, assembled by 777 enthusiasts with 21,600 pieces in Hong Kong's old airport building.

And we have to admire Vietnam, which holds the Guinness World Record figure for a 552,232 piece puzzle made in 2011.

Wentworth are famous for their unique 'whimsy' pieces cut in shapes like weapons, animals, birds and plants.Innovative jocular twists are boxes with no guiding pictures and even puzzles called 'WASGIJ', ('jigsaw' backwards), where you must use your imagination and the clues provided to piece together not what you see on the box, but what the people on the box see!

VINES AND BUNGEE JUMPING

One of the most alarming days of the author Liz Cowley's life was when her headstrong teenage daughter phoned from Zimbabwe in her gap year to announce that she was to 'bungee jump' from the Victoria Falls Bridge on the Zambezi river the next day. The desperate search for costly insurance against the possible risks of anything from eyesight damage, whiplash and a broken neck to a stroke quickly followed. Thankfully, there was nothing but a triumphant call of success!

This spectacular, if terrifying, sport started centuries ago in the South Pacific on Pentecost, one of the islands of the archipelago of Vanuatu. It's said that a local woman on the island was being treated cruelly by her husband and that each time she ran away, he found and punished her. She then had the idea of climbing the tallest tree on the island, a banyan, probably a **Small-leaved Fig** (*Ficus obliqua*), and tying a thick tropical vine around each ankle. With her husband in hot pursuit, she jumped from the top of the tree and the attached

vine saved her. Then, taunted by her for cowardice, he jumped himself and fell to his death. (Not only a brutal fellow, but seemingly stupid!)

'Vine-jumping' – from a 30-metre wooden tower, lashed together with vines, on to a bed of turned soil – became a ritual on the island for young men, demonstrating bravery and manhood and also thought to be a way of warding off evil spirits. The ritual was considered vital, too, to create a good harvest of **Yam** (*Dioscorea*) tubers and continues to this day. It has become a tourist attraction – but only locals can dive – and is carefully monitored to protect cultural identity.

This spectacle was observed in the 1970s by Alan John Hackett from New Zealand, and then taken up by the Oxford University Dangerous Sports Club and a new sport, 'Bungee or Bungy jumping', was born. Hackett jumped from many iconic places like the Eiffel Tower and has gone on to create a very successful 'World Home of Bungy' business in New Zealand.

Certainly not a pleasure for the faint-hearted!

COFFEE, CAFÉS AND COFFEE HOUSES

Did you have a cup of coffee, perhaps two, this morning? You're one of billions if you did. Coffee is one of the most influential of all drinks, consumed worldwide and with many millions involved in its production. But through modern history, its powerful influence may be even stronger, not in itself, but because of where it has been drunk.

Coffee comes from the beans, actually the seeds of a cherry-like fruit, of two tropical evergreen shrubs; **Arabian Coffee** (*Caffea arabica*) and **Robusta Coffee** (*Caffea canephora*) from Africa, in the family Rubiaceae (which also includes **Goose-grass**!. There are many stories of how humans (and animals) were stimulated by eating the berries, and even that the great Prophet Mohammed had introduced it to replace the (forbidden) wine of Islam.

Coffee as a drink spread up from Yemen to Mecca and Medina, then to Cairo, Damascus, Baghdad and Constantinople. Curiously, it was briefly banned in parts of the Islamic world and by the Catholic Church because of its perceived stimulant effects. But its popularity was inexorable: it was traded up from Malta and Venice, and given a boost when sacks of coffee beans were captured from the Turks after their defeat at Vienna in 1683 (page 80).

Soon it was *where* it was drunk, rather

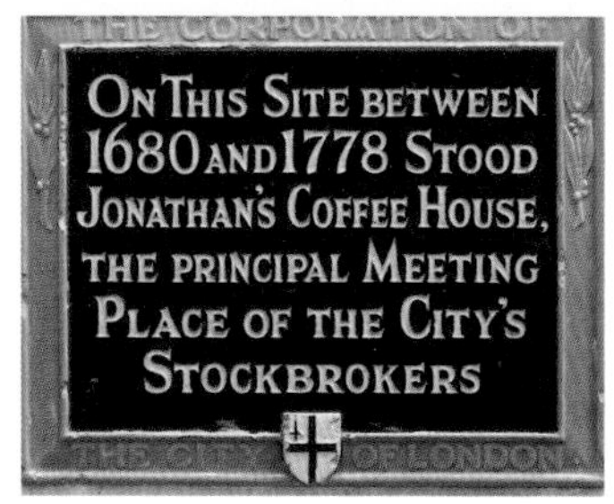

than the drink itself, that became the big influence. By the 18th century there were 3,000 coffee houses in England; centres of conversation on politics, religion and trade. While most praised coffee's qualities, women seemed to think it had one bad effect:

'The excessive Use of that Newfangled Abominable, Heathenish Liquor called COFFEE has Eunucht our Husbands and Crippled our more kind Gallants that they are become as Impotent as Age.'

In Germany, there were no such worries. The Great Elector, Frederick William of Brandenburg, drank it and the composer Johann Sebastian Bach (pictured), clearly an early addict, included it in a 'Coffee Cantata' in 1735:

'Coffee, coffee, I've got to have it,
And if someone wants to perk me up,
Oh, just give me a cup of coffee!'

As the consumption of coffee spread and grew, so did its production and, as so often is the case, there arose a dark side – slavery.

The French plantations relied on brutal slavery, and in Haiti this led to an equally brutal revolt. Brazil, which by 1832 came to dominate worldwide coffee production, imported more African slaves – four million – to tend the coffee and sugar plantations, than did America.

America itself would become one of the biggest markets for coffee, as 'patriotic' citizens turned away from tea after the Boston Tea Party (page 133).

What of the places where people met to drink coffee? They have given the world an everyday word, via French, for that universal institution, the *café*. In the late 1950s and early 1960s, parents in Britain worried about their children gathering in disreputable 'coffee bars', merely slightly upbeat cafés, to meet riff-raff! In fact, these places were much more the nurturing ground of a generation of skiffle, folk, jazz, blues and rock 'n' roll musicians and their fans, the very bedrock of the modern recorded music industry. Nowadays, with musicians perhaps more pub-and festival-based, Starbucks, Costa and Café Nero are as likely to be full of young mothers and babies.

But two historic London coffee houses also still influence our world.

By the late 17th century, the coffee houses of England had become vital sources of gossip and important information. The famous diarist, Samuel Pepys, went further than most in his reliance on coffee houses. Indeed, he declared that he received more valuable information there about shipping than he did in his role as Secretary to the Admiralty!

One of the most important of these gathering places was 'Jonathan's Coffee House', which Jonathan Miles had opened in 1680 in Change Alley in the City of London. By 1689, the Huguenot broker John Castaing was posting up prices of stocks and shares there as well as commodities. More dealers arrived, who had apparently been expelled from the Royal Exchange for their unruly behaviour! This coffee house was involved in one of the first share-dealing crises, the 1720 'South Sea Bubble', but grew larger in 1761 when 150 brokers and jobbers formally combined to trade stocks. 'Jonathan's Coffee House' moved to Sweeting's Alley in 1773 and was renamed 'The Stock Exchange', which it has remained ever since. The

London Stock Exchange is not the oldest in the world (it followed Amsterdam, Paris and Philadelphia) but it was the only one to start as a coffee house.

The most important was 'Lloyd's Coffee House', which became so crowded with traders and ship owners that Edward Lloyd had to move to Lombard Street in 1691. Five years later he began publishing Lloyd's List; full of worldwide shipping news. Insuring ships and their cargoes had always been vital and, in the coffee houses, brokers would visit 'risk takers', who would sign the deal by writing their names under the contract. Nowhere was more popular with these 'underwriters' than Lloyds. In 1771, 79 of them formed the Society of Lloyds, the first 'Names', as they are still called.

For three hundred years, Lloyd's, which started as a coffee house, has been the centre of world insurance.

Nowadays, most people drink what we call 'instant coffee'. The first popular brand arrived with American troops in the trenches of 1917. It was called 'George Washington' coffee, which curiously referred to the name of its maker – not of the first great President! Now a drink of real convenience and in huge demand, there are 50 countries producing coffee today with 150 million people involved. And all that may be at risk, with the usual suspect – climate change. Global warming is forcing coffee plant growing ever further up into the cooler hills and into ever smaller areas. Hopefully, resilient species and cultivars may come to the rescue, and probably long before any reversing of climate change can.

FIGS, EVER-USEFUL AND SACRED

Figs have frequently had a bad press. Too often they are seen as a funny fruit: with allusions to the laxative Syrup of Figs, or in the continental rude gesture, analogous to the Anglo-Saxon V-sign, of thumb poking out between first and second fingers, and in the related expression 'I don't give a fig' to emphasize something unimportant. All this is a mystery, because in reality, figs were once greatly esteemed items of enormous commercial and social value.

Part of a large family (Moraceae) of mostly tropical trees, **Common Fig** (*Ficus carica*) has served humankind for millennia. The fruits are a nourishing food, readily dried for storage, transport or trade, pleasantly sweet (in a world before plentiful sugar), certainly mildly laxative, and steeped in religious and sexual symbolism. Good to eat, they are rich in fibre, manganese

and potassium.

Now grown worldwide in warm and temperate and temperate regions, figs probably originated in Iran or nearby SW Asia, but spread east to China and west through the Mediterranean. One of the most ancient and important of all Mediterranean fruit crops, fresh and dried figs are still eaten and exported in large quantities. There are hundreds of cultivars varying in hardiness, size, shape and colour.

A small, much-branched deciduous tree around 2–7 metres tall or a sprawling shrub, with smooth grey bark, broad hand-like leaves and milky sap, it is both cultivated and a wild plant of cliffs, rocky ground and ruins, and along streams – tolerating heat and drought while the roots tap water from deep underground.

The fleshy apple- or pear-shaped fruit or *syconium* is a hollow envelope filled with swollen hairs and minute flowers, each of which forms a seed. Tiny fig wasps enter through the pore or 'eye' at the tip of the fig to pollinate the flowers, although most cultivated figs set seeds without pollination.

Figs have been cultivated since possibly 9,000 BC, and were probably one of the very first domesticated crops that allowed the evolution and development of civilizations. Today, several countries grow figs, but Turkey, long famous for its Smyrna figs, Egypt and Morocco account for more than half the world crop of 1.15 million tonnes. Spanish Franciscan friars brought figs to California in 1520, and Smyrna. Figs arrived there in the late 19th century. Today California and Texas now produce most of the US crop.

Native to East Africa and widely grown in Egypt and formerly Palestine, the larger **Sycamore Fig** (*Ficus sycamorus*), with usually evergreen unlobed leaves, produces smaller, less tasty figs on older branches. These figs have been found in the tombs of the ancient Egyptians, who made coffins from their soft light wood, and in Africa local people carve the wood into household utensils, drums and dugout canoes. The 'sycamore' of the Bible, this is the tree into which wealthy Jericho tax-collector Zacchaeus (Luke 19:4), 'little of stature', climbed for a better view of Jesus during his visit to Jericho. Zacchaeus ended up inviting Jesus to his home, confessed his bad behaviour, and then gave half his possessions to the poor and those he had defrauded!

The word sycophant derives from the ancient Greek sycophantis, 'revealer of figs', meaning slanderer or unjustified accuser, retaining this meaning in modern Greek and in French, though the English has shifted to mean 'insincere flatterer'. The original derivation may have referred to those who informed on anybody breaking over-strict ancient Athenian laws forbidding export of the best quality figs, or just stealing figs from a garden. Whatever, it reflects the cultural importance of figs to a society that lacked the array of fruits one sees in modern Greece.

The Romans too, regarded figs with almost mystical reverence and Romulus and Remus, the twin founders of Rome, were said to have been found under a fig tree by the she-wolf that raised them. A venerable specimen survived for centuries in the city's Forum.

The Bible mentions figs frequently: for example, Jesus cursing a barren fig-tree (Mark 11: 12–14).

Of the 750 species of fig trees, mostly tropical and found in South-east Asia, several have religious significance.

In Buddhism, they have a central role. The **Peepul Tree** (*Ficus religiosa*) (above) grows up to 30 metres tall, with many aerial prop roots, heart-shaped, long-tipped leaves and only small figs. Buddhists, Hindus and Jains regard it as sacred, but the most famous of all specimens is the actual **Bo Tree** or Bodhi Tree in Bodh Gaya, Bihar, eastern India, under which the Buddha is said to have gained enlightenment. Repeatedly destroyed by both insensitive rulers and the forces of nature, it was always replaced by cuttings from the original tree.

The famous Bodhi tree at Anuradhapur in Sri Lanka grew from a cutting brought by the daughter of Emperor Ashoka, the enlightened ruler of almost all India who did much to nurture and spread Buddhism – and who loved and planted trees. Planted in 249 BC, this is the oldest tree in the world of which we know the date of planting. The original tree has died but others grown from cuttings and planted elsewhere on the island survive as living clones of Ashoka's ancient gift.

These tropical fig species are 'strangler figs', whose seed germinates on the trunk or branch of another tree, or in rocks or old buildings like the temples of Angkor Wat in Cambodia, and puts down successive descending roots that gradually envelop the host tree. Further roots produced as the tree matures become the prop roots. One of the largest of such figs is the **Banyan Tree or Bengal Fig** (*Ficus benghalensis*), but 'banyan' has become a general name for all strangler figs, derived from the merchants (Gujarati, *banya*: merchant) who gathered in its shade to sell their goods. Sacred for Hindus, for whom it represents immortality, the Banyan is the national tree of India, providing welcome shade and a village meeting place; and it features on the national coat of arms of Indonesia – denoting the unity of that country of scattered islands.

The Great Banyan tree of the Acharya Jagadish Chandra Bose Indian Botanic Garden or Kolkata (Calcutta) Botanic Garden in Howrah, India, attracts more visitors than all the rest of the garden's 12,000 plants. It is only 25 metres tall but forms its own small wood of prop roots. Covering 1.89 hectares (4.67 acres), it has even outgrown a 330-metre long road built around it.

The Great Banyan is at least 250 years old, and has survived cyclones, and in 1925, the removal of its main trunk. And an older tree in Anantapur, Andhra Pradesh, also covers a similar area.

A hugely impressive sight!

CORK OAK AND ITS REMARKABLE BARK

We encounter cork pretty much every day in our kitchens and elsewhere. It looks and feels like soft wood but is actually specialized bark. One of the landscape features of the western Mediterranean region, especially Portugal and Spain, is open woods of evergreen oak trees, many with stripped, smooth, reddish to chocolate-brown trunks. Their outer bark has been neatly removed – harvested for the cork – of which seventy percent goes to make wine bottle stoppers.

The **Cork Oak** (*Quercus suber*) is a tree up to 20 m tall with a spreading crown, rugged but soft greyish bark, and rather small, oval to oblong leathery leaves that are dark green on the upper surface and greyish-hairy beneath. All woody plants produce at least some cork, impregnated with the water-resistant natural polymer suberin, but the Cork Oak has extra-thick bark to resist fire. The trees regrow after the forest fires, a natural factor in Mediterranean ecosystems, have swept through.

Cork is harvested in great longitudinal plates when the trunk diameter reaches 60–70 centimetres, after which it is removed every 9–12 years without damaging the tree, followed by regrowth. The cork industry we know today dates from the 17th century, when glass bottles became widespread for storing and selling wine. An enterprising Benedictine monk, Dom Pérignon, used cork's compressibility to stop his wine bottles exploding dangerously after a mysterious second fermentation, and thus created sparkling champagne almost by chance (page 227). Cork provided the perfect material for wine stoppers, being easily cut, elastic, light and impermeable to water. We still refer to them simply as 'corks'.

We associate Cork Oak mostly with Portugal and Spain – indeed half of the world crop of cork comes from Portugal – but it occurs from NW Africa to southern Italy and Sicily, always on lime-poor soils. It grows in native woodland, in much reduced stands, but is particularly characteristic of the more than 450,000 hectares of managed, savannah-like wood pastures known as *montados* in Portugal and *dehesas* in Spain. These semi-natural habitats of oaks, scrub, grassland and winter-wet hollows and pools are rich in plant and animal life, including the threatened Spanish Lynx and Imperial Eagle. The acorns, along with those of the

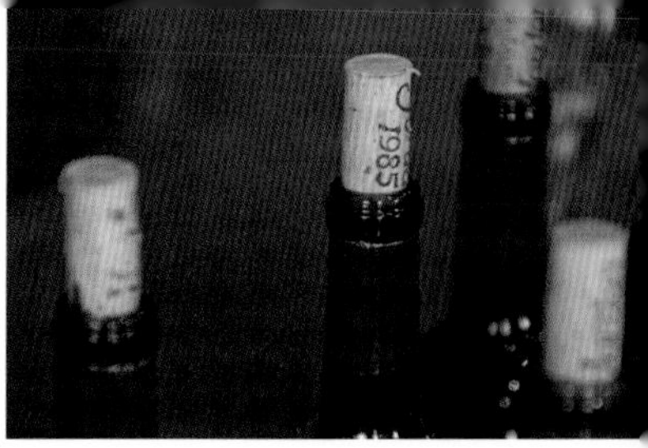

dark-leaved evergreen **Holm Oak** (*Quercus ilex*), provide forage for pigs, especially the free-range black Iberian pigs so greatly prized for their ham, the dry-cured jamón ibérico.

Impermeable and light enough to float in water, cork has a wide range of uses: as stoppers for bottles and jars, linoleum and floor or insulating tiles, table mats, bulletin boards, lifebuoys and fishing floats, the central core of balls for baseball and cricket, even rock outcrops for architects' models and model railway layouts! Cork has also long been used to make soles for shoes, especially in wedges and platforms for women, to the extent that in the early 1970s the craze for higher and higher platform shoes (for both women and men) caused a temporary world shortage.

Cork has an honourable place too in the story of botany and biology. Indeed, after microscopic examination of thin cork sections, the English scientist and polymath Robert Hooke (1635–1703) coined the term 'cell' for the basic structural and functional unit of life, which he illustrated in his *Micrographia* (1665).

But in recent decades and after three centuries of valuable service, cork fell under a cloud with many wine producers. Rising demand for wine and quality control for consistency caused suppliers, especially in the New World and Australia, to turn to plastic stoppers or screw tops as a substitute for cork. With so many modern 'corks' now made from plastic, farmers were unwilling to plant new trees and the long-term future of Europe's cork forests was uncertain.

Fortunately, cork is making a comeback and still accounts for more than 60% of wine stoppers. The growing environmental awareness certainly offers the Cork Oak and cork a bright commercial future, with numerous ecological benefits to the countryside of Portugal and Spain. It also offers a future to a skilled workforce and the rural economy of important Mediterranean woodlands and wood pastures. Cork is also sustainable and recyclable with the advantage of having just a fraction of the carbon footprint of plastic and metal – not to mention expanded polystyrene, which has replaced it in other spheres. And, as a biological material that can let in just enough air and has antioxidant properties, it will always hold its place at the high-quality end of the wine market.

Portugal's 'Whistler Tree'

Cork Oak is the national tree of Portugal. The largest specimen in the world, which was voted European Tree of the Year in 2018, grows at Águas de Moura in the country's Alentejo region. Planted in 1783, it is known as the Whistler Tree after the numerous songbirds that throng its branches. It is also the most productive Cork Oak tree in the world and has been harvested more than twenty times over its long life. It remains healthy and in 1991 yielded a record 1,200 kilograms of cork, enough to stopper well over 100,000 wine bottles!

CLOVER AND THE ENGLISH AGRICULTURAL REVOLUTION

From the mid-17th to the 19th century England went through not only an Industrial Revolution in the factories and in transport but also an Agricultural Revolution on the farms. Several factors came together; including technological innovation in machinery, improved livestock breeding, use of new crops (such as potatoes), and better crop rotation, along with the enclosure of fens, upland pastures and other marginal land to create more farmland.

One of the most important innovations was the widespread use of leguminous (i.e. pea and bean family, Fabaceae) fodder crops, which have bacteria in nodules on their roots that fix atmospheric nitrogen and make it available as nitrates. Of these legumes, perhaps the most significant was a native meadow wildflower, **Red Clover** (*Trifolium pratense*) (above), a leafy short-lived perennial with dense round red or pink flower-heads and 'clover' leaves; and **White Clover** or **Dutch Clover** (*Trifolium repens*), creeping to form leafy patches and with looser heads of white flowers.

Clover was to prove a simple but effective factor in improving farm yields. This was because from the 16th century farmers in Flanders had pioneered a four-field arable 'crop rotation' of wheat, turnips, barley and clover. The system was gradually adopted in England, and in the 18th century famous English landowners such as Thomas Coke of Norfolk, Charles 'Turnip' Townsend and Jethro Tull promoted this new agriculture. They are often credited for kick-starting the Agricultural Revolution, but they and others were more enthusiasts and self-publicists who talked and wrote about it – tapping into an English national love of nature, farming and the landscape.

The four course 'Norfolk' crop rotation restored and enhanced soil fertility, and records show its correlation between increased cereal yields and the more widespread sowing of clover. More livestock could be kept through the winter, which increased the availability of meat, milk products and manure. The better fodder provided by legumes and turnips supported the larger, fatter breeds of cattle and pigs that were being bred, and overall promoted a rise in food production to feed ever more people. In 1700 the population of England and Wales was no more than five and a half million. But at the end of the century it was up to nine million. Now with mechanisation and higher productivity, the number of farm labourers fell, enforced 'Enclosures' of common land took away their grazing, and they migrated to the towns to work in

the expanding manufacturing sector of the Industrial Revolution.

By the mid-18th century, while half the population still lived off the land – in 1850 it would be more like a fifth – and the whole tenor of farming was changing, from traditional subsistence husbandry to a more conventional economic model of profit or loss, with middle-men buying the harvest for the market, leading to the rise of capitalism in the countryside as well as the towns. Britain had made huge strides in agriculture in parallel with other scientific advances, and farming had moved into the modern age.

Over the next century many farmers continued to industrialize farming and make it more intensive. But by the 1880s, better transport links, refrigerator ships and the opening of the Suez Canal meant that British

farming was having to compete with cheap imports of meat and grain from the New World and Australia.

Today Red Clover is popular as an attractive plant of wild gardening and amenity 'wildflower meadows' and one that attracts bumble-bees. Farmers still sow it in leys or short-term grass swards, but Red Clover is no longer the major crop it was when it helped to power the Agricultural Revolution.

Red Clover flowers are pollinated by bumblebees, and those of White Clover by honeybees. In the 19th century Charles Darwin noted how cats protect these vital pollinators by hunting the mice that raid their nests. He observed how one or more cats on a small farm ensured a good crop of clover seed.

A century later, Irish humorous writer Flann O' Brien went even further: ladies in the country should be discouraged from marrying – as a single lady frequently had a cat to keep her company, which would help the clover!

Red Clover is the national flower of Denmark and the state flower of Vermont, USA.

THE 'DUST BOWL' AND THE SHORTGRASS PRAIRIE

The wide, almost treeless prairies of the Great Plains of the Midwestern United States and southern Canada are today North America's breadbasket. Only the memorable photographs and movies remind us that they were once the scene of one of nature's great ecological disasters.

With white settlers expanding ever westwards from the late 19th century, the Sioux and other Native American tribes of the plains were displaced and the buffalo on which they had always depended were driven almost to extinction. Most schoolchildren in America or elsewhere can probably only remember the drama of the Battle of the Little Bighorn and 'Custer's last stand', but not why they happened.

The ecologically rich habitat, once coloured by wildflowers and grazed by the buffalo, pronghorn antelope, deer and other animals has now all but disappeared, with most of the original tallgrass prairie converted to farmland.

The drier shortgrass prairie lies in the southern and western parts of the Great Plains. The grassland is dominated by **Blue Grama** (*Boteloua gracilis*) and **Buffalo Grass** (*Boteloua dactyloides*), which form a dense turf with extensive fine roots that bind the soil and retain its moisture on these open windy plains. This southern prairie region was opened up for wheat farming in the early 20th century as the US Government encouraged landless settlers to flock to the area, which was then enjoying a period of wetter weather. Cheap land, increased mechanisation and high wheat prices during and after World War I created an agricultural boom. During the 1920s came massive expansion of arable land by ploughing up the virgin soil of the shortgrass prairie. Soil was seen as an infinite resource and the grass as merely an impediment to

progress. Few realised the danger.

Then, a sharp fall in wheat prices from 1930 encouraged farmers to grow even more wheat to recoup their losses, and 1931 was a bumper harvest. This over-production coincided with the start of a decade of drought, and throughout the 1930s, the Depression Years, the prairie winds whipped up ever more frequent catastrophic dust storms. Now, the dry soil was no longer stabilized by native grasses, and 'black blizzards' of sand and finer particles ruined crops, vegetable gardens, livelihoods and health across the 'Dust Bowl' in Colorado, Kansas, Nebraska, Oklahoma and northern Texas. Nature itself seemed to gang up on the farmers. **Russian Thistle** (*Salsola tragus*), the tumbleweed of 'Western' films, which had arrived only in 1873 in South Dakota with imported flax seed, piled up into 'head-high impassible banks' that accumulated dunes of dust. Later, there arrived almost biblical plagues of jackrabbits and grasshoppers. Farmers were evicted when they could not pay their rent or mortgage payments. Tens of thousands of ruined farmers loaded their starving families on to half-wrecked cars and trucks and set off for the dream of better times in California and the West Coast. Two and a half million eventually left, and regardless of where they came from, Californians disparagingly called all their rather unwelcome guests 'Okies' – although Oklahoma had indeed suffered the worst, with 18% of its people abandoning their state to the driving dust.

From 1939, wetter weather conditions thankfully returned and the US Government, as part of President Franklin D. Roosevelt's 'New Deal' to alleviate the Great Depression, bought back land, planted trees for shelter, addressed the conservation of soil – including setting up the Soil Conservation Service – and restored and consolidated over 5 million acres of grassland, so much of which was almost beyond repair. Wheat cultivation resumed, irrigated in dry periods by water from an aquifer that had always lain beneath the plains. The grassland is mostly made over to livestock farming, although the high plains of Colorado retain substantial areas of the original shortgrass prairie habitats.

The loss of the grass and turf and the resulting devastating 'Dust Bowl' years, left a huge mark on North American history and a vivid cultural legacy. There are the haunting black and white photographs by Arthur Rothstein, Margaret Bourke-White and Dorothea Lange and an enraged John Steinbeck in 1939 wrote his novel *The Grapes of Wrath*, about displaced farm workers and their families going to California. The next year it was made into an award-winning John Ford film starring Henry Fonda, which some regard as the best film ever made in America. Many songs were recorded including the 'Dust Bowl Ballads' album (1940) by Woody Guthrie.

We can only hope that future ecological disasters will attract the same dramatic and artistic effort.

People might start paying more attention.

How many of us don't possess a few bamboo canes? Bamboo is familiar, but is one of those everyday woody plant materials that don't have an obvious origin. The familiar canes are simply the harvested robust stems of certain tropical grasses. People have long used them to stake or support their plants and may also grow some of the hardier bamboos for attractive evergreen features or leafy screens. But over much of South, South-east and East Asia and other regions, bamboos form a major part of the native vegetation and make an essential contribution to human society and its well-being. Ranging in size from short swards to plants the size of trees, the different types of bamboo are a major ecological and economic resource.

This group of more than 1,400 species of tropical and warm temperate regions belongs within its own sub-family, Bambusoideae, of the large grass family or Poaceae. Bamboos include both the largest of all the grasses and the fastest-growing, some able to increase their stem length by almost a metre in 24 hours! They have branched underground stems or rhizomes and can form extensive thickets of hollow woody stems, sometimes spiny, which are branched and leafy in the upper part.

The most familiar of them is **Common Bamboo** (*Bambusa vulgaris*), native to Indo-China and China's Yunnan province, but widely cultivated even outside the tropics, which provides the canes sold in great quantities at garden centres and super-markets. All across the Far East, the much larger **Giant Thorny Bamboo** (*Bambusa bambos*), with stems up to 30 m tall and 25 cm in diameter, is even more important than timber as a building material, regrowing readily and being strong, light, flexible and relatively resistant to earthquakes. It is widely employed in a range of structures and domestic items: scaffolding, walls, floors, fences, water pipes, gutters, furniture, buckets, bowls and mugs, and woven into baskets, cloth and paper. In addition, the thick, pointed young shoots of **Moso Bamboo** (*Phyllostachys pubescens*) and other species are harvested as popular foods

in China Korea, Japan and elsewhere, and eaten either fresh or canned.

Thus, bamboos have long proved themselves essential to people, and properly managed, offer a sustainable, fully renewable resource. Able to grow in degraded forest habitats, their rapid growth, huge productivity and potential to sequester more than twelve tonnes of carbon per hectare can also help to alleviate the CO_2 emissions that increase global warming. Nevertheless, bamboos are often invasive and should not be allowed to replace natural forests.

The native distribution of bamboos extends in an equatorial belt through Earth's tropical and sub-tropical regions, as far north as Sakhalin and as far south as northern Australia. They also occur in sub-Saharan Africa and through South and Central America, extending to the south-eastern USA, where **Giant Cane** (*Arundinaria gigantea*) and two other bamboo species are native. Cane thickets or 'canebrakes' were once common there in valleys and on floodplains but have, like the prairies, largely been destroyed and replaced by farmland. The canes themselves were put to many uses by the native Americans and were as important to them as they are to the people of Asia. Travellers, scientists and writers commented on the extent of the canebrakes, and legendary Tennessee frontiersman Davy Crocket was known not only as 'the King of the Wild Frontier' but also as 'the Canebrake Congressman'.

It's often forgotten that bamboos are a significant constituent of some rainforests in South America, and here too they were always important to native people. They are a feature of the Orinoco basin, in Venezuela and Colombia, where **Guadua** (*Guadua angustifolia*) is a traditional and contemporary construction material with potential as a plantation crop.

Brazil has the greatest diversity of bamboos in the Americas, with over 250 species, most of them endemic. The Atlantic rainforests along the country's east coastal region are a global centre of bamboo diversity, and more than 18 million hectares of south-western Amazonia is dominated by Guadua bamboo species. These semi-climbing plants form impenetrable thorny thickets, either in pure stands or intermixed with trees. One of them, *Guadua sarcocarpa*, has edible fleshy fruits.

Perhaps the strangest property of these extraordinarily useful plants is their mass synchronized flowering. Bamboos rarely flower, but when they do, it is at intervals from 20 to 80 or even up to 130 years. We have nice evidence for this from Chinese records going back more than a thousand years. The green flowers are pollinated by the wind rather than by insects. Then, all or almost all of the plants die, and a new generation arises from the enormous quantity of seed produced. Plants propagated from division or root cuttings still flower at the same time as the parent plants – wherever they may be grown in the world. This striking phenomenon remains unexplained, both the mechanism and the ecological significance, but may be a means to clear the habitat, the dead stems being susceptible to fire. There is also 'predator satiation', an idea put forward by the creative US evolutionary ecologist Daniel Janzen, whereby rodents and other predators cannot eat the huge excess of seeds and enough survive to produce the new generation of plants. The origin of mass flowering is lost in the mists of evolutionary history!

However, a bamboo flowering event can be traumatic for human populations who depend on the bamboo for building and other materials and are also victims of subsequent population explosions of rats and mice that eat their food stores and spread disease.

It is a problem too for animals that depend on bamboos, not least the iconic Giant Panda but also the Red Panda and the bamboo lemurs of Madagascar.

How many of us gardeners, propping up our plants with bamboo canes, ever stop and think about such bamboo dramas?

We doubt that many people do!

FLAX AND THE OLDEST OF FIBRES

We've looked at several places that can claim to be the 'world's centre' for a plant-based product – Liverpool for timber, Glasgow for tobacco, Bristol for sugar slavery, Manchester for cotton, even Alresford for watercress. For Flax and Linen, it would have to be Northern Ireland – only one, sadly, with continuing political consequences.

Not many crops are valued for yielding both fibre and oilseed. When the Neolithic farmers were domesticating wheat and other cereals in the 'Fertile Crescent' of the Middle East (page 173), they also cultivated Flax. From 5,000 BC, this versatile plant gave the inhabitants of ancient Mesopotamia and Egypt the fibre that made the linen clothes they wore – together with a healthy and nutritious edible oil.

Flax (*Linum usitatissimum*) is a slender annual up to a metre or more tall, with numerous small spear-shaped leaves and loose branches of attractive 5-petalled, sky blue flowers and small spherical seed-heads. The seeds, like tiny apple pips, give a yield of 40% linseed oil when crushed. The crop comes in two versions: taller, unbranched plants grown for the long, strong, flexible fibres in the stems (flax), and more branched plants with larger seeds (linseed or flaxseed).

Linen cloth has since Antiquity been held in high regard. In ancient Egypt it clothed the priests, nobility and officials, as well as wrapping and stuffing mummies, not least the embalmed body of Tutankhamun. The Biblical book of Genesis has Pharoah promoting Joseph, a Jewish immigrant to his country, to high office and dressing him in linen robes. Linen is mentioned over a hundred times in the Bible, usually as 'fine linen', and most notably as the cloth wrapped round the body of Jesus in the tomb following the Crucifixion (page 277). In the ancient world, as well as clothing, flax was made into ships' sails, ropes, fishing nets and wicks for lamps. The cultural legacy of flax extends far. The Bible's Book of Ezekiel talks of a man measuring distances '*with a line of flax in his hand, and a measuring reed*', hence we use words like linear and lineage.

Flax remains the world's most important natural fibre after cotton, jute and wool. Flax fibres are much stronger and straighter than cotton, making linen into a smoother, more lustrous, higher quality cloth, but they are difficult and more expensive to process after harvest. To separate the fibres from other stem tissues, the harvested plants need to be 'retted', literally rotted by micro-organisms – a smelly process – by being kept for a while in damp conditions or in water. Then they are rolled, combed and spun into yarn.

Having contributed greatly to the Neolithic Agricultural revolution, Flax spread into Europe by 4,000 BC and was then widely grown. In Ireland, a country frequently associated with Flax and linen, it had been present since at least the Iron Age and was well established by medieval times, but did not take off until the the 17th century. Then the English Parliament sought to prevent Irish wool competing with the higher-priced English wool. Finally, an Act of 1699 prohibited the export of Irish woollen goods to any country but England, as well as imposing high tariffs. So Ireland, particularly Northern Ireland, turned to growing flax and making linen, augmenting the flax supply by importing fibre and yarn.

Then after 1685, when Louis XIV revoked the Edict of Nantes that had granted religious tolerance to Protestants, many skilled Huguenot linen manufacturers fled to Ireland. One can imagine that nothing could be more powerful to preserve and strengthen the unfair Protestant political and economic dominance in Northern Ireland than to

introduce Protestants who had been *really* badly treated by Catholics back in France!

As many of the Huguenots, along with English Quakers, settled in and around

Belfast, the linen industry of the city and nearby Lisburn expanded to become the world's linen manufacturing centre, known in the 19th century as 'Linenopolis'. Flax was woven in former cotton mills and the industry grew and prospered for a century. But in the face of modern fabrics, in the 20th century the industry declined greatly, and Flax ceased to be grown in Ireland by the 1970s. Today the fibre and yarn for Irish linen is imported.

Fewer people buy or wear linen rather than cotton clothes today, but Irish linen and lace especially continue to be prestigious, high-quality fabrics for tablecloths, napkins and handkerchiefs, and there is always a demand for fashionable linen clothes like skirts, dresses, jackets and suits. Linen creases easily, but is cool, elegant and breathable in warm weather.

While Flax's linen is now less in demand, linseed oil, now mainly produced in China, is vital as food for livestock. But that other product of the Flax plant, linseed, has a huge variety of uses. One of its most famous was as a component of linoleum, being used again, due to reaction against vinyl and other non-natural products, while appearing to provide a more hygienic surface for hospital floors. Stretched linen canvas is employed by artists for oil painting and the oil paints themselves are often linseed-based. Linseed oil is used as a wood preservative and to make glazing putty, paints, varnish and printing inks. After milling, the crushed, protein-rich residue is fed to livestock. As a human food, linseed and linseed oil are rich in healthy omega-3 fatty acids and have anti-inflammatory properties, with evidence that they are good for cardio-vascular and general health.

Flax has indeed served people well, certainly for longer than most other crops – the seeds and oil undoubtedly assuring it a bright future. And few farmland vistas are so uplifting a sight on a summer morning as a field of Flax in full flower.

A glorious spectacle!

ENGLAND'S PASTURES AND HER WEALTH

England of course is famously green. So much so that its lush pastures inspired William Blake's poem 'Jerusalem', which has become an unofficial English national anthem:

'And did those feet in ancient time
Walk upon England's mountains green?
And was the holy Lamb of God
On England's pleasant pastures seen?'

Ireland too is green, so green that

it is known everywhere as 'The Emerald Isle'. Ireland and England have always had extensive pastures for cattle and other livestock, but in England's slightly drier climate the grass turned out to be ideal for raising large numbers of sheep, which yield both meat and wool. Most natural fibres come from plants, but wool too depends on plants – pasture grasses grazed by flocks of sheep.

For centuries wool generated much of the nation's wealth. From as early as the 10th century, the weavers of towns in Flanders like Bruges, Ghent and Ypres greatly prized the English wool, especially from the Pennines, the hills of the Welsh borders, the Cotswolds, the Downs of the south and the Wolds of the north. Wool for cloth was a major commodity and the mainstay of the economy of Medieval England from the 13th to the late 15th century, by which time English weavers were producing their own local quality product for home use or export. Some Flemish weavers had also moved to England, for example to Worstead in Norfolk, which gave its name to worsted cloth.

The country grew rich on the trade, as did the King, who levied a tax on each sack of wool exported to Flanders, France or northern Italy. The gentry and Church, especially the abbeys and monasteries, also became rich. King Edward I used the money to pay for his wars in Wales and Scotland. So did his grandson Edward III, who needed money for the first, successful phases of the Hundred Years War (1337–1453), one cause of which was English support for Flanders and its wool industry against the French. A reminder of this prosperity is the 'woolsack' on which the Lord Chancellor sits in the

House of Lords. Another is the great village 'wool' churches of the villages of Norfolk, Suffolk and the Cotswolds.

The rural depopulation that following the pandemic of bubonic plague or Black Death in 1349 also led to an expansion of sheep, and wool remained a dominant industry until Tudor times. By then the wool economy was in decline, and a 1571 law from Elizabeth I's reign decreed that Englishmen must wear a woollen cap to church in order to support wool production. A century later, another government law, the Burying in Woollen Acts of 1666, specified that witnesses to English burials should swear that the shroud around the corpse was

'*made of Sheeps Wooll onely* ...', a practice that continued for another century.

From the 16th century the wool trade declined, but sheep were now still needed for their meat to feed the growing towns. The poorer mountain pastures of highland Britain supported large numbers of sheep. In Scotland, this sadly led to the wholesale and notorious eviction of tenants by the landowners between 1750 and 1850 to make way for sheep, forcing many Highland Scots to emigrate to North America.

The Industrial Revolution saw an expansion of wool mills and weaving in the towns of the West Riding of Yorkshire and in the Scottish borders, but gradually local wool was replaced by imports from Australia, South Africa and temperate South America. However, British high-quality tweed, worsted cloth and knitwear continue to be esteemed in Europe and elsewhere.

The green pastures of the English hills, often called 'sheepwalks', are a reminder of when grass, pastures and grazing sheep drove the country's economy and, for the first time, helped to give a small island a big influence in Europe.

GRASS AND THE LAWNMOWER

If there's one plant we take for granted it is grass, so 'common or garden' that we don't even think about it. Or rather, think about *them*, for the grass family or Poaceae (also known as Gramineae) includes some 12,000 species, found worldwide in almost every type of habitat. All are pollinated by the wind, which means that their flowers as well as their leaves are green as they don't need to attract insects.

In fact, grass covers a quarter of the world's land surface and thrives on every continent except Antarctica. Indeed, it dominates vegetation wherever there is enough rainfall, but not enough to support trees, forests and jungles. Or these habitats have been destroyed or degraded by human activity. In America these extensive grasslands are called 'prairies'; in Asia they are 'steppes'; in South America 'pampas' and in southern Africa 'veldt'. They often intergrade with savannah, mixed vegetation of grass and widely spaced trees transitional between grassland and woodland, which covers large areas of Africa, South America, Central and SW Asia and arid parts of the South West

Mediterranean region.

The grasses expanded greatly some 5–8 million years ago, during a time of a cooler and drier climate towards the end of the Tertiary Period, giving rise to grasslands like those which we know today but which then supported huge and diverse herds of grazing mammals. The last relics of these great ecosystems still survive today in places such as the Serengeti. They remind us that grass evolved to be grazed shorter and that short grass would have enabled African villagers to see danger coming from predators or an attacking tribe.

We could not live without grasses, and some of the goods and services which they provide (quite apart from their considerable contribution to carbon fixation and oxygen release during photosynthesis), such as cereal crops, sugarcane, thatch and bamboo, are considered elsewhere in this book. Either as semi-natural vegetation or grown as a farm crop they provide grazing for livestock (pastures) or yield mown hay and silage (meadows).

But it could be argued that short grass and the ability to cut it even shorter has been one of their most pervading influences on human society, certainly in recent times. Grasses possess the huge advantage to us that, apart from during cold or dry seasons, they continue to grow after repeated cutting – or artificial grazing, which is what mowing represents – making up for the loss of potential flowers by producing more leaves.

Short grass began to be called *launde* in Middle English or in Old French *lande*, meaning heath or clearing. We now call such stretches of turf grass 'lawns'. As the wealthy classes of Europe moved away from fortified castles and into vast manor houses surrounded by mown lawns, they became a social status symbol. Such large areas of grass could only be kept neat and tidy by teams of men with scythes or herds of sheep and other livestock – only available, of course, to the rich.

Even though a skilled man with a sharp scythe can produce a short neat sward, it was obvious that scything was both time-consuming and expensive. Some new method of cutting the grass short would be needed if the emerging middle class could ever benefit.

An engineer from Stroud in England, with the appropriately botanical name of Edwin Budding, provided the answer. In 1830, copying a cloth mill's trimming machine, he created the first lawn mower, pushed across the grass by hand, with a roller and knives in a cutting cylinder that we would recognise today. In the next few years, bigger mowers could be pulled by horses and then by steam power. The motor mower would inevitably arrive.

The mower transformed two features of our lives – gardening and sport. From the 15th century, European houses were surrounded with ornamental lawns or even parkland as designed by 'Capability Brown' (page 286). For the less privileged, grassy municipal and public parks, created first in a response to Victorian overcrowding and poverty, could now become a vital feature of urban life – with 27,000 parks today in Britain alone.

European immigrants arrived in America bringing grass seeds. Soon houses there, large and small, would be graced with manicured greenery. Most such houses now had a mower. The lawn in front of a home remains a symbol of respectable American suburbia.

The second huge influence was on a vital part of human life – sport. Many sports were transformed or even, like cricket, effectively created by the short grass and the mower that maintained it.

Today, hardly any outdoor sport does not benefit from mown 'turf grass' – soccer, rugby, American football, field hockey, baseball, lacrosse, hurling, and, above all golf, with its fairways and its immaculate trimmed greens. Such marvels of grass are now maintained by fertilizers, weed control and pesticides, which unfortunately makes them poor in biodiversity relative to the natural grassland from which they developed. Old established golf courses, on the other hand, especially those laid out on sand-dunes like at St Andrews in Scotland, or Lahinch in Ireland, often retain patches of grassland within the 'rough' that are refuges for rare wildflowers.

For millions of years grass has been an ecological success story. Today, in human -influenced habitats it's ubiquitous, not least through the invention of the rotary mower, helped by fertilizers, weed control and fungicides. But what of the future of lawns? These marvels of grass almost certainly have only one threat, but it is a large one – climate change, with both increased temperatures and decreased water supplies. The green summer lawns of Los Angeles may become a memory as the underground aquifers under south-west America dry up, with the ground now actually sinking above some of them as the water disappears.

Somewhat disturbingly, from an environmental point of view, artificial grass lawns are becoming a common sight.

GATHERING FROM THE WILD

Foraging for wild plant foods of course goes back to the very dawn of the human race. Today 'hunter-gathering' still survives in many societies, especially among indigenous peoples and in tropical regions, but the gathering of wild plants has also undergone a revival in Europe and North America. Often mocked as a mere fashionable pastime, foraging has recently made a substantial impact on Western cuisine and introduced many of us to new food flavours and eating experiences. These foods are also very healthy.

People forage without thinking – for mushrooms or **Blackberries** (page 232) and other hedgerow fruits, even for young **Nettles** (page 56) to make soup. Most of us foragers merely dabble, but in late winter and spring – traditionally a time of food shortages – in Greece and other parts of the Mediterranean region plenty of folk can be seen out in the countryside busily collecting basketfuls of edible wild herbs and greens. These include wild **Cabbages, Cresses**, **Mustards and Rockets** (*Brassica*), assorted **chicories** (*Cichorium*), **Dandelions** (*Taraxacum*) and **Sow-Thistles** (*Sonchus*), shoots of **Spiny Asparagus** (*Asparagus acutifolius*) bulbs of **Tassel-hyacinth** (*Muscari comosa*), **Fennel** (*Foeniculum vulgare*) and **Wild Leeks** (*Allium*). You still come across Greeks up in the scrub and rocky hills doing the same in order to earn a hard living selling wild foods and medicinal plants to local markets. The forebears of these tough mountain men were the *botaniki* or 'herb gatherers' of ancient Greece, from whom, perhaps surprisingly, we derive the word 'botanist' for somebody who studies plants – and the science of botany itself.

Foraging as we know it today emerged from the hippie era of the 1960s and early 70s. The first modern foraging field guide, Richard Mabey's *Food for Free*, caused quite a stir when it was published in 1973. In the Introduction he wrote of his sadness '*that this enormous storehouse of free, wild food is now all but ignored, and that the ability to capitalise on it is in*

danger of vanishing from popular knowledge.' Mabey began his own foraging with **Glasswort or Marsh Samphire** (*Salicornia europaea*), a fleshy annual plant of muddy salt marshes long collected by local people. This and other flavoursome wild-collected 'sea greens' such as **Sea Beet** (*Beta vulgaris*) are now almost mainstream. For in the decades since *Food for Free*, the ecological, self-sufficiency and foraging communities have grown, along with associated books, magazine articles and TV shows, and the fame and creativity of chefs, hoteliers and specialist suppliers.

Thirty odd years after Mabey's book, Miles Irvine expanded wild cuisine in *The Forager Handbook* (2009), noting how gathering, cooking and eating a wide range of wild foods not only yields a variety of flavours but also provides health, well-being and sheer pleasure. Wild foods – often bitter to those unfamiliar with them – are packed with the vitamins, roughage and the complex chemicals that have been partly bred out of supermarket fruits and vegetables in exchange for longer shelf life, blander taste and visual appeal. It is mostly a local and non-intensive harvest, analogous to predation by wild animals rather than wholesale pillage, and they are for the most part widespread weeds. With agronomists and conservationists warning of the limited number of commercial crops, many of them threatened by global warming or by pests that thrive on monocultures, while dieticians are encouraging a greater variety of plant foods, an expanding range of edible plants takes on a new significance – while supporting ancient links between people and places.

Also, some plants are just too difficult or impossible to cultivate. A good example is **Bilberries or Whortleberries** (*Vaccinium myrtilis*), the blackish-purple fruits of a dwarf shrub related to the heathers, which once provided a bountiful wild harvest. Known in Ireland as *fraochán*, this plant was important enough to lend its name to the last Sunday in July, Frochan Sunday, associated with the old Celtic festival of Lughnasa (Lammas in England), when country people traditionally gathered them. In the hills of Shropshire too, on the Anglo-Welsh border, they remained a significant wild crop until the Second World War. In her novel *The Golden Arrow* (1916), English writer Mary Webb described the communal picking of '*the small purple fruit*', and how at Shrewsbury market, '*the berries were brought in hampers that needed two men to lift them and the purple juice dripped from them as from a wine-vat.*'

Bilberries (as opposed to readily available commercial American blueberries) rarely feature today on British menus, although *tarte aux myrtilles* remains popular in France, particularly in the Vosges Mountains and Haute Savoie. In North America, several blueberry species were gathered from the wild for millennia by the First Nations peoples, and Canada still has a large wild harvest. The USA grows the larger cultivated crop, which is dominated by the **Northern Highbush Blueberry** (*Vaccinium corymbosum*), but the harvesting of wild plants continues – indeed wild blueberry pie has been deemed *the* state dessert of Maine, the largest US blueberry producer.

People who wonder why ancient battles only lasted a day may not realise the vital role of military foraging to supplying armies. In Napoleon's ill-fated invasion into Russia in 1812, his massive baggage train of 30,000 wagons was delayed by the primitive conditions. Normally, he would have relied on his well-organised foraging parties, but they encountered a 'scorched earth', made worse by an unexpected drought and a failed harvest. His men and horses actually began to starve.

How Napoleon would have appreciated the supply capabilities of the new railways, which in just a few years were to change warfare for ever, with battles that could, sadly, last for bloody months.

PLANTS IN WORDS

As you might imagine, our everyday language is peppered (there we go again!) with plant references. It is not surprising. It took only a decade or two after the steam engine was invented to fill our vocabulary with steam or railway phrases. Plants have been around for millennia. No wonder we refer to them all the time. So important are plants in our lives that they do, of course, provide us with many everyday favourable, practical and useful terms, as well as thoroughly insulting ones. Our faults and foibles, our many weaknesses;plants play an extraordinary part.

'Go a whole day without mentioning plants?
That's quite hard to do; not much of a chance.
In fact, it's quite hard to get through three hours
without some allusion to plants and to flowers.
Compliments, insults or just jolly chat,
plants will be mentioned, no doubt about that!'

'She's an absolute peach.'
'Everything's coming up roses.'
'It's lucky you're so rooted'.
'We've reformed it, root and branch.'
'He's the apple of her eye.'
'I'll use a carrot and a stick.'
'You're a budding genius!'
'Go out on a limb.'
'An apple a day keeps the doctor away.'
'That must be fruitful.'
'We got to the root of it.'
'You're wonderfully down to earth.'
'You'll get to the top of the tree.'
'It's lucky you turned over a new leaf.'

Plants & Us

'We'll walk the primrose path.'
'He's extended an olive branch.'
'That's a plum of a job.'
'He's the best of the crop.'
'She's really blossoming.'
'His plan bore fruit.'
'That's called Flower Power.'
'We're nearly out of the woods,'
'He's learned to branch out.'
'He's barking up the wrong tree.'
'That's a well-grounded decision.
'It's certainly taken root.'
'That's blooming marvellous!.'
'This is a quiet leafy suburb.'
'Thanks a bunch.'
'She's got a lovely, willowy figure.'
'Your plan is really flowering'.
'Life isn't all a bed of roses.'
'We're in the clover.'
'He's a tough nut to crack.'
'That's the root of all evil'.
'You shouldn't have grassed'.
'He's gone bananas.'
Out of mighty oaks do little acorns grow'.
He's slipped on a banana skin'.
You're such a stick in the mud'.
'He always gets the wrong end of the stick.'
'I blew a raspberry.'
'You upset the applecart.'
'You're always hedging your bets.'
'Don't beat about the bush.'
'He's been gilding the lily.'
'A rolling stone gathers no moss.'
'A rose by any other name would smell as sweet.'
'You should grasp the nettle.'
'Great oaks from little acorns grow.'
'I heard it through the grapevine.'
'I'm going to hit the hay.'
'You must know your onions.'
'Make hay while the sun shines.'

'Nip that one in the bud.'
'Oops-a daisy!'
'He led her up the primrose path.'
'Ring a ring o' roses, a pocketful of posies.'
'The menu's surf and turf.'
'The grass is always greener on the other side of the fence.'
'Touch wood!'
'He used a sledgehammer to crack that nut.'
'She's up a gum tree.'
'She's fresh as a daisy.'
'Hearts of oak.'
'Every rose has its thorns.'
'Don't let the grass grow under your feet.'
'She's got green fingers.'
'He was shaking like a leaf.'

'You should sow your wild oats.'
'It all goes back to the grass roots.'
'You're talking rhubarb'.
'Try to turn over a new leaf.'
'He sowed a seed of suspicion.'
'Wait a cotton-picking moment!'
'He's just a man of straw.'
'They're withering on the vine.'
'What a thorny problem!'
'Why can't you cotton on?'
'It's time we put him out to grass.'
'That's a fruitless suggestion.'
'They're having a roll in the hay.'
'Don't be a wet lettuce.'
'You're so lily-livered.'
'She's gone to seed.'
'She's pea-brained.'
'He's full of beans.'
'You must be guilty - your face has gone beetroot!'.
'You're such a weed'
'A total wet lemon'

PLANTS AND GIRLS' NAMES

Are you a female reader? Then there's a strong chance that your name may be inspired by a flower or plant, an extraordinary influence on what we call our children – but only if they're girls!

Acacia Alison Alyssa Amaryllis Angelica Anise Aster Aubretia Azalea Bay Begonia Belladonna Betony Blossom Bluebell Bryony Buttercup Calla Carnation Cassia Celandine Cherry Cicely Clematis Clementine Clove Clover Daffodil Dahlia Daisy Daphne Erica Felicia Fern Fleur Flora Forsythia Fuchsia Gardenia Genista Gentian Geranium Hazel Heather Hebe Hermione Holly Honesty Honeysuckle Hyacinth Iris Ivy Jasmine Heather Hebe Hermione Holly Honesty Honeysuckle Hyacinth Iris Ivy Jasmine Jenny Jessamine Jonquil Jordan June Juniper Kale Lantana Laurel Lavender Lilac Lily Linden Linnaea Lotus Lucerne Magnolia Maple Marguerite Marigold May Mina Minty Myrtle Nerine Nigella Olive Olivia Orchid Pansy Peony Peaches Periwinkle Petunia Petal Poppy Posy Primrose Primula Prunella Rosa Rosamunda Rose Rosie Rosemary Rowan Rue Saffron Sage Scilla Sequoia Se… …kimia Sorrel Tamarind Tansy Thyme Tiger Lily Twiggy Valerie Venus Vera Verbena Veronica Violet Virginia Willow Zinnia

But if you're male, the chances of being named after a flower or plant in the English language is virtually nil – unless you're Basil or Ivo! Trees for boys' names might have provided some inspiration. Curiously, it seems not.

Plants & Us

PLANTS AND BOYS' NAMES

We've seen that the English seem to be very keen on plant names when naming baby girls, but curiously reluctant when boys are involved, probably because plant names are seen as feminine. The parents in other countries show no such reticence, although girls named after flowers and plants still outnumber the boys by far.

In Holland, we have **Phlox**, **Aster**, **Senna** and **Lotus** for boys (both of these last ones can be used for girls), **Jared** and **Camiel**. In Spain, we have **Jacinto**, named after the **Hyacinth**, and **Narciso**, a male name that occurs in several languages, probably more related to the young man in Greek mythology who falls in love with his own image in the water when the Gods change him into a flower, the **Daffodil** (*Narcissus*).
In Sweden, we only have **Vide**, named after the **Willow** tree. The Germans have no trouble naming boys after plants. Among many, there are **Alon** and **Daron** which are both named after the **Oak**, **Oren**, the **Pine**, **Keiffer**, the **Fir**, **Ivo**, the **Yew**, **Kai**, the **Willow**, **Cedar**, **the Cedar tree and Oliver**, which refers not to the Olive or its tree, but its grower.

Portugal and Brazil, too, have lots of such plant-related boys' names. **Alisson** is named after the **Alyssum** flower and **Delfino** is named after the **Delphinium**, **Eriko** after the Brazilian heather **Erika**. The word 'flower' in Portuguese gives us several names: **Florian**, **Floriano**, **Florim and Florêncio**, and once again, **Narciso**, **Oliver**, in Portuguese, relates to the Olive tree and **Tales** comes from the Greek meaning to flower or flourish. With Cicero, Latin admirers of that great scholar and orator may be surprised and saddened that this revered name comes from someone who merely grows **Chickpeas**!

50+ COOL FLOWER NAMES FOR BOYS!

THE MOM FRIEND

In Israel, **Narcissus** crops up again in Hebrew, with the boy's name **Narkis**. Then there is **Tidhas**, named after the **Ash** tree and **Arava**, **the Weeping Willow**, **Savyon**, a type of **Daisy** and **Nitzan** meaning a bud.
In Poland, there are plenty of girls' names from plants, like **Dalia**, **Roza**, **Wioleta**, **Hortensia**, **Jasmina** and a fair share of ones for boys, like **Bazyli (Basil)**, **Olivier (Olive)**, **Florian** (flower), **Jaceth (Hyacinth)** and **Narcyz**, our old friend **Narcissus**.

In India, girls' names as usual outnumber the ones for boys, but **Kamal** (Lotus), **Kairav** (White Lotus) and **Kesar** (Saffron) are all popular boys' names.

There seems, in general, to be a natural reticence about naming boys after plants, though the English seem more reticent than most – perhaps as plants are seen as pretty rather than handsome. Cool flower names for boys? It's unlikely they'll ever catch on!

PLANTS AS INSULTS

For some reason, plants seem to be a rich source of words that are insulting or less than complimentary – at least in English. Here, in red, are several examples of that – when someone's getting fired from his job.

'Basil, I'm not going to beat about the bush. Frankly, you've been a blooming disaster here, a real thorn in our side. You need to move on to new pastures and turn over a new leaf. Working with you hasn't exactly been a bed of roses from the start, and you're daffy if you think you can stay here after that wooden presentation last week – completely nuts. I can see the seeds of disaster if you stay here. None of your projects have ever borne fruit, and none of your plans have blossomed successfully. All of them have gone pear-shaped, and cost a bomb. Money doesn't grow on trees, you know.

The fact is you're too rooted in the past and plum rotten at presentations. You're off your tree if you think you can stay here.

What's more you drive the rest of us bananas, especially the girls. They say you're so seedy and that really nettles them. And you seem to see everything through rose-tinted glasses. What's more, you get prickly if anyone disagrees with you. We all reap what we sow. And please don't tell me that all this is just sour grapes. That's poppy-cock and anyway that excuse won't butter any parsnips. I don't give a fig what you think. Frankly, you're deadwood and we need to prune our staff.

Everyone thinks you're a bad apple. And thanks a bunch for losing us our biggest account because of that corny presentation, peppered with irrelevant stories and in that plummy voice of yours. And you thought you were a real hot potato! Well, you're totally bananas.

You've never really got dug into the job and what it takes. You're a disaster in this field and you just can't see the wood for the trees. I can't wait around for you to spruce up. I'd be pushing up the daisies by then!

So it's time we put you out to grass, and turf you out of here.

And don't expect a flowery reference, old fruit, not after nearly bringing this branch to its knees. Quite frankly, I rue the day I hired you.

Good luck, buddy!'

PLANTS AND LOOKING GOOD

'HERE'S LOOKING AT YOU!'

'Cure yourself of the condition of bothering about how you look to other people. Be concerned only with the idea God has of you.' That piece of advice from the brilliant and insightful playwright, novelist and poet Miguel de Unemono (1854–1931) has certainly fallen on deaf ears!

Understandably, for most of history – and particularly since the arrival of the first mirrors around 6,000 years ago – people have wanted to look as good as possible; not least to attract partners. How incredibly frustrating it must have been to have to rely on ponds, streams and rivers to have any idea of one's appearance – that's if there were any sources of clear or clean water nearby!. Incredibly, Queen Elizabeth I was the first English Queen to see herself in a clear glass mirror in the late 16th century, though such mirrors were subsequently banned at Court. (See panel).

But the use of cosmetics goes back much further than the arrival of mirrors. It probably dates back 8,000 years, when the beneficial properties of plant essential oils were discovered in Egypt. Used by men as well as women, they became an important part of religious rituals, reserved for the upper classes, and were associated with welfare and health – even though we now know some of the ingredients to be toxic. As early as 7,500 BC, the concept of protecting the skin had arrived, with Egyptian shepherds and hunters in the Nile Valley using oil crushed from the bean-like seeds of **Castor-oil Plant** (*Ricinus communis*) (page 31) to protect their faces from the strong sun. Wrinkles were treated with gum of **Frankincense** (page 131) and fresh **Moringa** or **Drumstick Tree** (*Moringa oleifera*) from India. Women in Egypt used dyes made from the shrub **Henna** (*Lawsonia inermis*) to colour their feet and hands. In China, legend has it that Princess Shou yang, the daughter of Emperor Wu, felt a blossom of the **Japanese Plum Tree** (*Prunus mume*) fall on her face. The flower-like imprint led to the floral fashion of Meihua zhuan or 'Plum Blossom makeup', popular in the Tang and Song dynasties.

Soon plants began to be used in other parts of the world for cosmetic purposes, including Rome and Greece, but now more for their role in sexual attraction.

In ancient Rome, incredibly, women were not considered beautiful if they *weren't* using cosmetics, which led to a boom in the sales of beauty products – and a sharp increase in prices. Roman women used

Saffron (*Crocus sativus*) dye to create a golden effect around their eyes and then wood ash

to blacken their eyelids.

The Roman poet Ovid wrote a book on cosmetics and also promoted smooth skin by concocting a recipe of **Barley** bean flour, egg and mashed **Narcissus** (another poison!). Italy would not be the only country where make-up tended only to be worn by upper-class women or prostitutes!

Later, the Greek physician Galen of Pergamon created a cream of water, beeswax and olive oil, almost identical to the 'cold cream' of today, and with the same cooling effect.

In Japan, noble women were even prevented from leaving their homes if they *weren't* using cosmetics, while the poor were not allowed to wear them at all – though the prices would have been prohibitive anyway.

Later, in the European early Middle Ages, except to hide the ravages of disease, cosmetics all but disappeared – becoming associated with questionable morals and the concept of accepting the face you were born with. However, in many countries, pale skin for both women and men, became the mark of wealth, indicating you did not have to go out and work in the sun. The remedies could be dangerous, including the application of white lead, containing both lead and arsenic, or even women bleeding themselves in an effort to stay pale (See Panel).

In England, the use of cosmetics was rather frowned upon right up to the Victorian era. But in the 19th century, cosmetics became gradually more popular. Skin care was aided by moisturizers containing **Rosewater**, **Cucumbers** and **Strawberries**. The desire to look pale (and rich) continued, but now with safe powder made of rice flour. Rouge could be made from various flowers, while **Geranium** and **Poppy** petals stained the lips. However, cosmetics were still associated with 'ladies of the night', and products could not be bought in normal stores, but only in theatrical costume outlets.

In fact, it was indeed the theatre that began to change attitudes. The Russian Ballet arrived in New York in 1910 and women began copying the look of dancers and also actresses like Sarah Bernhardt. However, a Kansas court in 1915 seriously debated making it a misdemeanour for women under 45 to wear cosmetics 'for the purpose of creating a false impression'! Now the film industry changed

everything. Max Factor opened in 1909 his Los Angeles store for actresses, but other women started turning up. In Hollywood, Helena Rubinstein, used kohl to create the eye make-up for star Theda Bara. The 'Flapper' era saw the suntan look pioneered by Coco Chanel. Now, in contrast to previous eras, in Paris or in Britain having a tan meant you were rich enough to afford to travel on a train to the Riviera and later to fly. The eyebrow pencil was then invented using **Cottonseed** oil.

Today, of course, beauty is a booming industry, with increasing demand for products made with natural plant-based ingredients.

The white-faced Queen

On 10th October 1562, the royal halls of Hampton Court Palace echoed to cries of anxiety and fear. The young and beautiful Queen Elizabeth, who had been on the throne for a mere four years and was only 29 years old, had fallen ill.

She nearly died, but after a week recovered slightly. Her physician, when asked, hesitantly told her she 'had the pox'. He was curtly dismissed from her furious presence. But after a week, he was re-admitted and the young Queen reluctantly began to face up to the truth. She was indeed a victim of smallpox, a disease that had infected millions in Europe, killing tens of thousands and leaving the survivors with scars disfiguring their faces.

Cosmetics came to the rescue in the form of a rather strange white application called 'Venetian Ceruse', which some equated with a clown's make-up – and so she banned mirrors from court!

This mixture consisted of vinegar and white lead. The vinegar, plant-based, literally *vin aigre* or 'sour wine', produced by a bacterial fermentation that converts cider, wine, beer or grain alcohol to acetic acid, would have done her no harm. But the white lead, containing arsenic along with the mercury in her lipstick, almost certainly did. Her reported loss of both hair and memory, and her fatigue and digestive ailments rather suggest lead poisoning.

When we think of protest movements, especially those against the Vietnam War, we probably picture 1968 and London's violent Grosvenor Square riots or Mayor Daley's brutal police at the Democratic Convention in Chicago. Probably the last thing many would think of is flowers, or flowery patterned clothes, with both sexes wearing blooms in their hair and even presenting them to the forces of law and order. Yet this was precisely what made the American Beat poet Allen Ginsberg's 'Flower Power' protest rallies so memorable in the late 1960s. It was also a cultural turning point, as if the modern world we know had cut loose.

It was Ginsberg's dream to change angry and aggressive anti-war protests into orderly and positive ones with 'Hippie' marchers handing out flowers to the crowds lining the streets – along with anti-war literature. And not just to the crowds, but to the police, the media and politicians if possible. There was even the remarkable sight of carnations being inserted down the gun barrels of the National Guard.

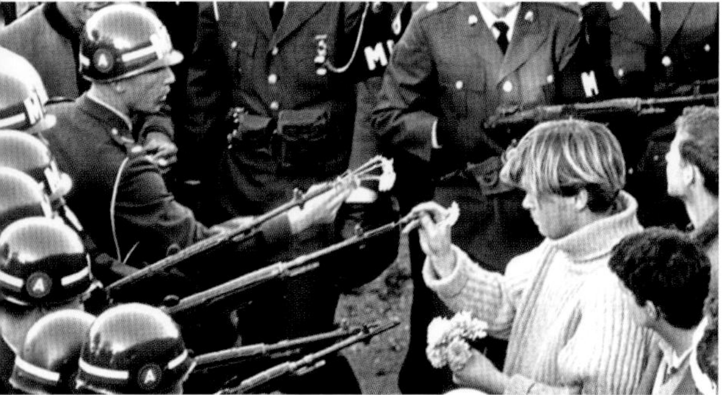

The 'Flower Power' movement started in California, in Berkeley and in San Francisco, especially at the Haight/Ashbury street intersection, where Bay Area music legends such as Janis Joplin, Quicksilver Messenger Service, Jefferson Airplane and The Grateful Dead lived and performed. Soon hundreds of thousands of young people arrived, swarming into the area for the 1967 'Summer of Love', with free food, free drugs and free love as much of an attraction as the protests.

Music was a huge catalyst and soon went mainstream. Scott MacKenzie's 'San Francisco (Be sure to wear some flowers in your hair)' took the message all over the world. John Lennon was, and remained an active supporter, and a debut performance of the Beatles' hit 'All you need is love' was beamed to over 400 million as part of a special 'One World' BBC broadcast.

But what also went all over the world, and lasted much longer, was the fashion that Flower Power generated. It not only applied to clothes, but to many other forms of design, especially rock album covers, rock and protest posters, psychedelic art and even advertising campaigns.

Fashion leaders who took up Flower Power designs and ideas, included Biba, Pucci, Laura Ashley, Mary Quant and Zandra Rhodes who featured it at the Fashion and Textile Museum in London.

These days there's nothing strange about seeing men in floral shirts or sporting flower design ties, although it's probably true that most still prefer plain ones. But floral attire for males was pretty well unheard of before 'Flower Power', when it was seen as 'pansy', curiously another floral word. All that started to change with Flower Power.

Plants & Us

NICE TO KNOW

Of all the struggles and challenges that we human beings have endured, that of simply remaining clean and odour-free and pleasant to know has been one of the greatest in history, yet the least thought about today. Indeed, there was a long period when 'The Dark Ages' could well have been called 'The Smelly Ages'.

Small wonder that people turned to aromatic plants for the answer, to scatter in their homes and churches, so when trodden they would release a pleasant fragrance; to arrange in containers; and to mix into potions to rub on to their skin.

The ancient Egyptians took a strong lead in using plants and flowers to aid their hygiene, using natural plant oils to wash with as far back as 3,000 BC. The Romans went further. All over their Empire, they constructed and then luxuriated in heated bath houses – not least in the West of England in the aptly named city of Bath – and using a number of plants to aid the cleansing process.

One of them, **Lavender** (*Lavandula*) was thrown into the baths, and not only to scent the water but to use as a disinfectant. Indeed, the scientific name for the plant comes from the Latin *lavare* – to wash. The soaps of the Romans included a mixture of goat tallow and **beech** ash.

Unfortunately, the Romans' admirable and social habit of bathing disappeared with their Empire, after which a period of several hundred years of European uncleanliness followed. By contrast, from the 7th century, the Islamic world held bathing in the highest regard, with the '*hamam*' or public bathhouse becoming a central feature of towns, especially in Turkey under the Ottoman sultans. Even in the West we still have 'Turkish Baths'. Bathing was one of

the innovations the Crusaders brought back from their wars in the Middle East, but several centuries would pass before it was a widespread habit in Europe. They also introduced the know-how for making soap.

Some soap-making started in Bristol in the 12th century, but it was Spain, much influenced by its Islamic conquerors, that took the lead two hundred years later with its 'Castile' soap – giving the name to a famous British soap, Knight's Castile.

Marseilles and Venice also became known for their soaps, and Savona in Italy was

to give us the word for soap in French – savon. Initially, burning seashore plants such as **Saltwort** (*Salsola kali*) provided the alkali to mix with animal fat for soap production, but today African **Palm oil** and **Coconut Palm** oil are the key ingredients, along with **Soya** and **Groundnut** oils.

One plant that was used in Europe to produce soapy and frothy conditions was the aptly named **Soapwort** (*Saponaria officinalis*), also called Latherwort, Crow's soap and Soaproot. (page 8). Now superceded by plant oils and animal fats, Soapwort is still used to clean delicate fabrics such as tapestries.

Crowning Glory

Huge effort and a great deal of money has always been spent on human hair, and plants are both used and their use promoted vigorously today.

Jojoba (*Simmondsia chinensis*), a plant from Mexico, is now an essential element, combined with Coconut and Palm Oils. Thickeners are usually provided by plant cellulose, which can come from cotton and also wood pulp from South African, mostly Eucalyptus and Wattle, and from North America, mostly Oak and Western Hemlock. Having cleaned their hair, many would like to alter its colour. The most famous hair dye comes from **Henna** (*Lawsonia inermis*), which also has great religious and mystical

significance in the Middle East, and especially among the Berbers. Indeed, the prophet Mohammed is said to have reddened his beard with this plant. To blacken hair, two plants were used; **Black Walnut** (*Juglana negra*) and **Oak Galls**, with botanic acid created by wasps. If you'd prefer to be blonde, you might be surprised that the roots of **Rhubarb** (*Rheum hybridum*) are still used to

lighten hair, along with two daisy-like plants, **Chamomile** (*Chamaemelum nobile*) and **Scented Mayweed** (*Matricaria recutita*).

FLOWERS AND JEWELLERY

Ever since people started finding gold and precious stones, they have made them into ornaments or jewellery to adorn the body.

But it is a curious fact that for most of time, nearly five thousand recorded years, images of plants and flowers were only used rarely as an inspiration for jewellery.

This is, after all, in contrast to what we see in language, poetry, paintings, architecture, music and clothing, where flowers, trees and plants appear all the time. The Egyptians, in their jewellery, preferred serpents, vultures, falcons, lions, sphinxes and even scarabs (dung beetles), Minoans liked their bulls. Etruscans favoured sphinxes, lions, chimera and giraffes. The Greeks and Romans portrayed human figures, both men and women and also horses.

Perhaps plants and flowers for people in hot climates have been less familiar and symbolically important. But certainly it was in Europe in the 17th century, that flowers suddenly began to feature in jewellery. This coincided with a great vogue for the collection and cultivation of new flowers, and, in the case of Tulipomania in Holland, crazy over-enthusiasm (page 128).

In modern Britain, flowers again are providing inspiration to designers. This may be because Britain has one of the richest variety of plants and flowers. The English country garden with all its myriad shapes and colours has always been an inspiration for jewellers.

Flowers of all shapes and sizes have long been a huge inspiration for jewellers almost certainly because their shapes are feminine and there are such a variety of colours. They are easily made into earrings, necklaces and brooches but less so rings. Little flowerheads are often used for decoration in grander designs to add a lightness of touch. **Sunflowers**, **Daisies** and **Forget-me-nots** are probably the most popular.

Britain's Royal Family have always worn fabulous jewels, notably Queen Mary. The Princess of Wales particularly favoured jewels with a floral theme as does the Duchess of Cambridge (below).

COTTON AND DENIM

One of the most important uses of cotton emerged from a town in in France. Nîmes, the capital of the Gard region, was already a major town even before Christ was born. As Nemausus, it was one of the finest cities in Roman Gaul, and its magnificent arena, seating 24,000, is still in use today, while its Maison Carrée is regarded as one of the most beautiful of surviving Roman temples.

But it could be argued that it is yet more famous for a cotton product that is now worn all over the world. 'Serge de Nîmes' was a fabric woven in the town and exported in the 17th century to England, where it was called 'Serge de Nim', soon shortened to denim. The blue colour came from a dye extracted from **Woad** (*Isatis tinctoria*), a member of the cabbage family or Brassicaceae, with yellow flowers and distinctive hanging seed-pods. Perhaps best known as the blue face paint of Boudicca and her Iceni warriors, Woad is native to dry, open or grassy places from southern Europe to Siberia, and was long cultivated as a dye plant in Germany, England and especially southern France. Following the 16th century Portuguese voyages to India, a similar dye from **Indigo** (*Indigophora tictoria*) largely displaced woad. The blue colour gave us another name from another city – 'blue de Gênes' – reflecting the fact that Genoa was also exporting blue denim. From that we get the word 'jeans'.

In 1853 a young German immigrant, Levi Strauss, (above) moved to San Francisco to open a dry goods store which sold clothes, especially strong denim, to the miners during the Gold Rush. In 1872 Jacob Davis, a tailor in Nevada, wrote to Strauss suggesting that they patent his idea for metal rivets. Levi Strauss brought him to San Francisco to make their copper-riveted denim 'waist overalls' together. Jeans would become a hit.

By the 1920s, Levi's 'denims' were America's leading work trousers, and soon Hollywood saw to it that denim 'jeans' became associated with the individualism of the cowboy. By the 1960s, *American Fabrics* magazine was to write '*What was once a fabric only for work clothes has now become an important fabric for play clothes.*' Denim had, in short, become a fashion item for both men and women, as well as a symbol of various youth subcultures and the subject of pop songs like 'Venus in Blue Jeans', and 'Blue Jean Baby'. Styles vary, but Levi's classic '501' remains their best-selling line.

The worldwide denim market is now worth a colossal $110 billion.

Plants & Us

THE BEAUTY OF MARULA

Did you wash your hair today? Or use a moisturizer? Or apply cosmetics? There's a good chance you may have a tree called Marula partly to thank. Its oil is one of the new and important ingredients in today's skin and haircare industry. Its pale yellow oil has antioxidant as well as anti-inflammatory and also anti-microbial properties, providing hydrates and goodmoisturizers for skin, hair and nails, and is increasingly added to soaps, shampoos, hair tonics, body lotions and other beauty products. While most hairdressers should know about it, most people don't, or may only associate it with an increasingly famous drink.

Yet for those who live in southern Africa, the **Marula Tree** (*Sclerocarya birrea*) has a much greater significance. For thousands of years it has been a food, medicine and part of sacred ritual. A member of the cashew and pistachio nut family or Anacardiaceae, Marula is a hardy, deciduous, savannah tree up to 18 metres tall, with a spreading crown, red or purplish-white flowers and compound leaves that are shed during the dry season. It is not restricted to southern Africa, but occurs through sub-Saharan Africa from Kwazulu-Natal and Namibia north to Ethiopia. There is evidence that it has been spread and domesticated by migrating peoples.

Many large mammals, including antelopes, baboons, elephants, giraffes and warthogs feed on the leaves and, especially, the fleshy, plum-like fruits, which turn yellow after they have fallen to the ground where they ripen. They are even richer in vitamin C than oranges.

The fruits are a major human food resource in Africa, especially in the southern part of the continent, where they are collected from the wild and eaten raw or in jam, or fermented to make marula beer or wine.

The inner hard-skinned kernels containing the seeds are crushed to extract the oil, which is also eaten and is an important part of the diet of San people or Bushmen and other hunter-gatherers.

It is for a successful drink that the Marula tree has become best-known. The fruit pulp is processed on a commercial scale into juice creating a cream liqueur, Amarula, which has achieved international success. Because elephants particularly enjoy eating the fruits, it is sometimes called the 'Elephant Tree' and the drink is marketed using an elephant symbol, with the manufacturer generously lending support to elephant conservation. The collection of the Marula fruits has become a significant

source of income for rural communities, especially for women, across large areas of Africa.

Marula is important as well in traditional ritual, its abundant fruit production being regarded as a symbol of fertility and a good omen for a marriage, so it is often called the 'Marriage Tree'. The trees, being either male or female, have led to a belief in southern Africa that they can influence whether an unborn child will be a boy or a girl through the mother drinking an infusion of the bark of either a male or a female tree.

Here is one of those remarkable trees that possess an infinite range of useful attributes and is fortunately valued and protected by local people. The whole plant is of cultural, social and economic importance. The bark yields fibre and dye and the bark and leaves have several traditional medicinal uses. In Africa, the oil is applied to the skin for moisturising and cleansing – just as we do now in our own societies.

Marula is already legally protected in South Africa, and provided that the harvesting of its fruits is managed sustainably there and elsewhere, it is indeed a tree with a bright future.

RELIGIONS AND RITUALS

With plants, trees and flowers playing such a huge role in human history, it would be very surprising if they didn't have a similar prominent place in our religious beliefs and rituals.

In ancient times, the relationship between nature and people was much closer and more intense than today. After all, our ancestors' very existence depended on plants – for food, buildings, protection, weapons, fire, medicines and even hallucinatory drugs.

All ancient religions had myths about trees and plants that were strongly believed. The Egyptians believed that the Goddess Nut shed the water of immortality from the Sycamore Fig tree on to the dead; Scandinavians thought that the universe was linked to an immense Ash; the Greeks were convinced that the golden Apples of the Hesperides (perhaps in fact Pomegranates) conferred immortality; the Olive was sacred to the Goddess Athena as were the Laurel and the Cypress to the God Apollo.

In Norse mythology, the **Lily-of-the-Valley** was associated with Ostaria, the Goddess of springtime. The **Acacia**, with its hard and resistant wood, was linked to knowledge by both the Chinese and Egyptians. The **Spruce** was a symbol of fertility for Celts and of hope for Greeks, and later of course for Christian families,

in the form of the Christmas tree. **Aloe** was a symbol of eternal life for many cultures. **Cedars** represented strength and knowledge, **Figs** meant abundance and prosperity, **Lilies** virginity, **Almonds** rebirth and fertility. The blooms of **Passion Flower** each have five symbolic structures recalling the death or passion of Christ (see panel), and the branches of the **Olive Tree** were, and still are, seen as symbols of peace.

With plants, flowers and trees regarded as holy and sacred, such symbolism appears in many of the world's religious ceremonies. In the Christian faith, Holy Communion, stemming from the Last Supper, is celebrated with bread (Wheat), and wine (Grapes), representing the body and blood of Christ, in what Catholics call 'transubstantiation'. Churches set great store by their displays of varied and seasonal flowers on the altar, and on the last Sunday before Easter the tradition is to include Palm fronds, or at least small crosses made of palm, to recall Jesus's entry into Jerusalem before the Crucifixion.

Wedding ceremonies are, of course, full of flowers of all kinds, redolent of romantic love, not least with the bouquet carried by the bride. In the Middle Ages, bouquets were made up of **Dill** – representing lust! Brides were considered lucky, so the guests tried to grab at things – flowers, their dresses or even their hair, so a bride would throw the bouquet into the crowd to escape such attention. (Not, as is the belief today, to see who is to be the next girl to attract a husband).

Queen Victoria as a bride started a trend in carefully planned bouquets. She carried **Snowdrops** (*Galanthus*, Prince Albert's favourite flower), **Orange Blossom** and **Myrtle**, the last of which has become a royal wedding tradition, most recently in 2011 for the wedding of Princess Catherine. In fact, the Victorians went on to create a very complicated 'language of flowers', of which some seem a little strange: such as **Burgundy Rose**, lust; **Pink Carnation**, boldness; **Lilac**, love's first emotion; **Yellow Tulips**, hopeless love!

Most other religions have flowers as a central part of their beliefs. For Hindus, the **Tulsi** plant (known as **Basil**), symbol of the Goddess Laxmi, is so sacred that there is a Tulsi plant in every Hindu house that is worshipped daily.

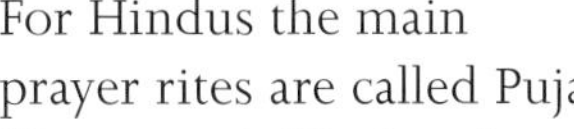

For Hindus the main prayer rites are called Puja, meaning the 'flower act'. Hindus also revere the **Lotus waterlily**, the **Banyan** tree, the **Mango**, **Coconut** and the **Pipal** tree.

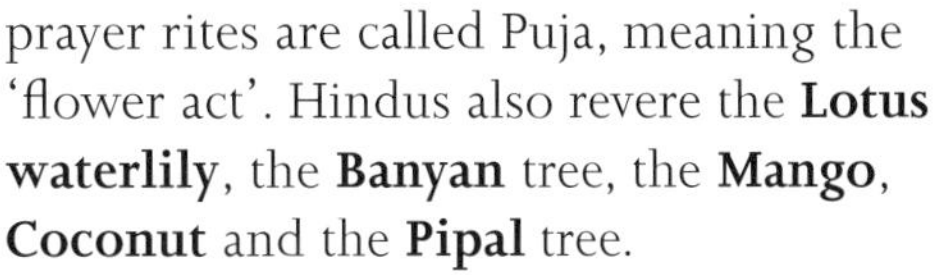

The Pipal is important for Buddhists too, also known as the **Sacred Fig** or **Bodh Tree**, and it is thought that the Buddha attained enlightenment under its shade. The Lotus is revered by Buddhists as a symbol of the highest spiritual elevation and knowledge.

The Prophet Muhammed several times stressed the value and importance of trees

and plants, notably the **Date Palm**. Islamic ceremonies like funerals and marriages feature **Roses** and **Jasmine**, with floral patterns drawn with Henna on the hands and feet of brides. **Myrtle** branches are laid on graves in Moslem cemeteries. The Holy Qur'an referred often to gardens – which were seen to symbolise Paradise – and the Persians, especially, created many Islamic gardens for coolness, rest, reflection and contemplation, often with water features.

Among the many plants, trees and flowers that the Jewish religion features, there are those called the Seven Species listed in the Bible, Deuteronomy 8:8. Only the first fruits of them could be brought to the Temple in Jerusalem as offerings.

Wheat and **Barley** were the two vital cereals mentioned in the Seven Species, and both were celebrated in festivals. **Grapes** were eaten fresh or dried, and used to make wine. **Figs** were cultivated throughout Israel and were eaten fresh or dried. **Pomegranates** were used to make wine or juice, and eaten fresh. They were also religiously symbolic, adorning the hem of the High Priest's robe, the Temple pillars and appearing on coins. **Olives** in ancient times were even more important than they are now, used for food and cooking but also in lighting, sacrificial offerings and ointments. **Dates** were eaten, but they had a more important role, being boiled into a thick and long-lasting syrup, called 'date honey'. This was needed as a sweetener. Sugar had not yet become available and honey had disappeared because bees had died out in Israel. Thus, the 'land flowing with milk and honey' may have been referring to date honey.

White Flag Iris (*Iris albicans*), with spear-shaped leaves and fragrant flowers, is frequently planted in Moslem cemeteries. Unable to set seed but spread by dividing the rootstock, this most ancient of cultivated Iris is depicted in a wall painting of c. 1420 BC in the Temple of Amun at Karnak in Egypt.

Passion Flower (*Passiflora*), is a tropical climbing vine with large edible berries, the passion fruits of desserts and drinks. Catholic missionaries in South America found the intricate and beautiful flower to be a useful aid to teach the Easter story of the Crucifiction or 'Passion' of Jesus Christ. The ten 'petals' (five sepals, five petals) denote the Apostles, the circle of filaments is the crown of thorns, the five male stamens are the wounds to hands, feet and side, and the central three female stigmas are the nails holding Christ to the cross. The lobed leaves and tendrils represent the hands and whips which did the scourging before the Crucifixion.

JESUS CHRIST AND THE WOODEN CROSS

As we see in this book, so many plants have influenced our world. But perhaps the greatest influence was not the yew in bows, the oak in ships, the fir in railway sleepers, the charcoal in gunpowder or even the cotton we wear. The single greatest influence was the piece of wood used for the cross on which Jesus was crucified.

Crucifixion was a standard punishment in the Roman Empire, designed to humiliate, to act as an example and to cause an agonising, slow, literally 'excruciating' death. The victim would be stripped naked, flogged and then forced to drag the crossbeam to the place of execution. He or she would be tied or nailed to the cross, now assembled with its crossbeam, and left to die. This cruel end was normally reserved for slaves, criminals of the worst sort or perceived traitors like the gladiator followers of Spartacus, 6,000 of whom were crucified, their crosses lining the Appian Way into Rome. Roman citizens were not allowed to be crucified. All the many pictures of Christ dragging the whole cross through Jerusalem are artistic licence. The weight would have been impossible, which is why it was not part of the Roman ritual before crucifixion.

It has often been suggested that the wood of the cross came from **Wild Cypress** (*Cupressus sempervirens*), a cedar-like coniferous tree of the eastern Mediterranean that still grows in a few woods on the mountains of Jordan and elsewhere. **Aleppo Pine** (*Pinus halepensis*), more widespread in the region and with a long straight trunk and less valuable wood, is an even stronger candidate.

Whatever the political motives of the Romans were to crucify Jesus, they failed. Because at a stroke it gave his followers the most powerful and simple symbol – the cross. It subsequently appeared in all churches, on gravestones and vestments, necklaces and ornaments, even the white and red livery of medieval 'crusaders'. It helped Christianity to become the world's largest religion, now with over two billion followers. In *Sylva* (1664), the passionate tree lover and devout Christian John Evelyn wrote: '*In a word, and to speak a bold and noble truth, trees and woods have twice saved the whole world; first by the ark, then by the cross.*'

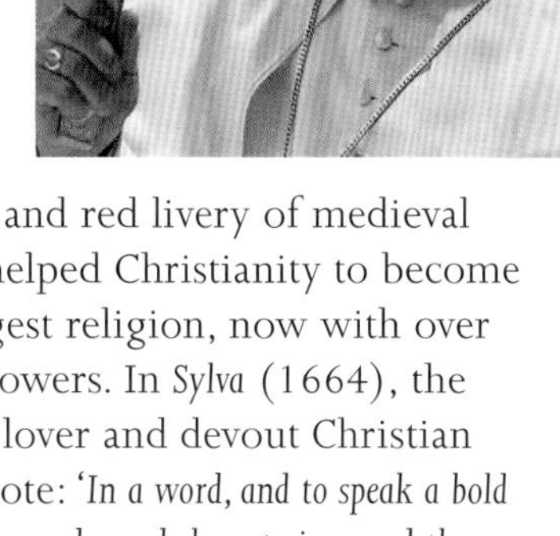

No other religion has such a simple and potent symbol and no other piece of wood, or any plant, has had such a lasting effect.

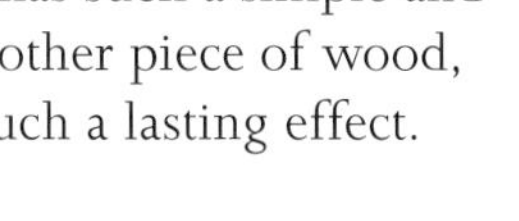

SALVATION FROM THE AIR

John Akeroyd vividly remembers years ago hearing the late Professor Aubrey Manning of Edinburgh University say in a lecture that 'Only technology can solve conservation's problems'. Most of us today are aware of how so much of the natural world is under threat. Indeed, the race is on to restore 2 billion hectares of damaged land globally, including the alarming 24 billion tons of fertile soil being lost each year. But two pieces of technology that are already transforming many other aspects of our lives are now coming to the rescue of habitats – the aerial drone and AI.

An Oxford company, Dendra Systems, uses such new generation drones first to map and analyze from the air the land that needs to be rehabilitated, AI and data science making the process thousands of times more accurate than satellite imagery. Founder Susan Graham says, 'High resolution imagery means we see every blade of grass, every leaf on a tree, every piece of dirt moved by ants, every animal, however small, and we analyse every bit of it. One team can map 300 hectares, the equivalent of 400 football pitches a day and can identify 120 different species from the sky.' Land damaged by the search for and use of natural resources or by increasingly frequent and devastating wildfires can be analyzed and, when a full picture is achieved, Dendra then uses bespoke drones capable of carrying enhanced payloads to carry out aerial seeding. A swarm of ten drones can methodically spread 800 million seeds a day, 11 times faster than any traditional manual or mechanical method.

On Lord Howe Island off New South Wales, Australia, Dendra's drones have helped to identify and limit the spread of invasive, non-native species – plants like **Cherry Guava**, **Sweet Pittosporum**, **Ochna**, **Ground Asparagus** and **Bitou Bush**.

Dendra is involved in over 44 restoration projects in 11 countries, and there is no doubt that drone technology is a key new element in the battle to save plants, animals and their habitats. Hopefully not too late.

THE STRANGE PLANTS OF CHRISTMAS

All Christians know the story of the birth of the baby Jesus in Bethlehem and of the three Wise Men or 'Kings' bringing the presents of Gold and very expensive Myrrh and Frankincense (page 131).

But then there is the seemingly disconnected story of snow, Father Christmas and Christmas trees, with Holly, Ivy and Mistletoe thrown in. Much of this appears to have come from ancient pagan religions, that have been adopted in Christian ritual – mostly now

for commercial purposes!

As for snow, global warming means that many are much less likely to experience again the magic of a White Christmas, midwinter snow having long been infrequent in regions such as much of the British Isles, so imitation snow rather than the real thing sits alongside the traditional sprigs of evergreen foliage that help to create the festive atmosphere of Christmas. These plants brought indoors are an essential element of seasonal celebration, family and fireside fellowship, and the turning of the year.

Outdoors, the evergreen woody plants **Holly** (*Ilex aquifolium*), **Ivy** (*Hedera helix*), and sometimes **Mistletoe** (*Viscum album*), colour otherwise leafless gardens, hedges and woods, and all bear ripe fruits at Christmas. Safe and warm indoors, we surround ourselves with these and other symbols, recreating a winter scene of log fires and the snowbound forests of **Norway Spruce** or **Christmas Tree** (*Picea abies*) from Germany to Scandinavia and Siberia.

Presiding over the tableau of greenery, reindeer, sleighs and lights is 'Father Christmas', dressed as a Boreal shaman in the ritualistic red and white colours of the hallucinogenic fungus **Fly Agaric** (*Amanita muscaria*). Father Christmas is a long way from the original St Nicholas, a kindly, gift-bearing 4th-century bishop of Myra in SW Turkey; then, strangely, he travelled via Dutch tradition over to the USA, where from the 1920s he was adopted by Coca Cola's advertising to become today's friendly winter face.

Holly and Ivy, celebrated in the familiar carol, are an ancient part of Christmas:

'The holly and the ivy,
When they are both full-grown
Of all the trees that are in the wood,
The holly bears the crown…'

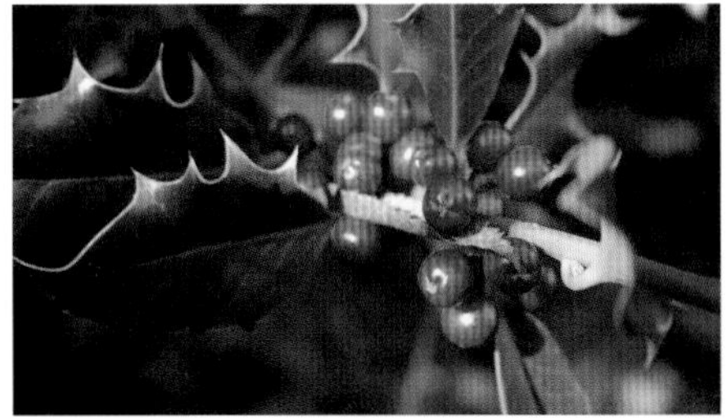

The Holly and the Ivy says little of Ivy other than in the chorus, perhaps because the Church once associated it with wine and drunkenness. Followers of the wine God Dionysius or Bacchus carried Ivy-entwined wands, and Ivy was formerly often depicted on inn signs!

Christmas carols rarely mention Mistletoe, a deeply pagan plant. Associated with oak trees, although mostly growing on apple and other tree species, including conifers, it was venerated by Druids, witches and other pagans because the winter green shoots appear to spring miraculously from the branch on which it is rooted. You rarely see Mistletoe in churches, since devout Christians frequently distrust it, and it has been retained more as a fertility symbol under which to kiss than integral to other leafy Christmas decorations.

Holly, on the other hand, is steeped in both pagan and Christian myth, its bold red berries evoking all manner of images. In northern Europe, Holly must always have been a token of hope in winter. After Christianity had largely absorbed pagan worship, the berries and dark, shiny, prickly leaves were seen to point beyond Christmas to Easter and the Crucifixion – the wounds, the crown of thorns and the bitter wormwood in the rough wine given to Jesus on the cross by a Roman soldier. As the carol says:

'The holly bears a berry, as red as any blood...
The holly bears a prickle, as sharp as any thorn...
The holly bears a bark, as bitter as any gall...'

Back in the modern world, Holly has long had to compete at Christmas in many US and UK homes with another green and red plant, **Poinsettia** (*Poinsettia pulcherrima*), (above)hailing originally from Mexico, its whorls of bright red, leaf-like bracts surrounding inconspicuous yellowish flowers. Yet, however handsome, it is neither evergreen nor has any associated folklore or real Christmas magic. That said, it sells in millions each year – a perfect last-minute gift.

ASTHMA AND 'PLANT POLLUTION'

Health problems caused by airborne pollution are now headline news. Cities that are banning vehicles from their centres include Paris, Madrid, Oslo, Brussels, Copenhagen, Rome, Athens, Berlin, Frankfurt, London and New York's Central Park. And in Britain burning plant material in the form of unseasoned, 'wet' or 'green' wood, recently identified as a major polluter, has joined the list of practices being proscribed by law.

But if you are an asthma sufferer, like 360 million people worldwide (6 million in Britain and 50 million Americans) you will know that some plants have always been your 'enemies'. You will, no doubt, have learned to dread the plant pollen seasons and also which plants to keep out of your garden or home, particularly those with visible pollen like **lilies, daisies**, **chrysanthemums** and **sunflowers**. In addition, you are rightly wary of certain trees and shrubs that are known to produce a lot of pollen, including many wind-pollinated, spring-flowering temperate

Plants & Us

forest trees, including **Ash**, **Elm** and **Oak**, also conifers such as **Pines** and (in autumn) **Cedar.** And wind-pollinated herbaceous plants such as numerous **Docks** (*Rumex*) and, in America but increasingly introduced into Europe, **Ragweeds** (*Artemisia*).

Plants can have both positive and negative effects. They do help to purify the air around them, absorbing pollutants, moulds and bacteria, but many also produce the clouds of pollen grains that are so bad for bringing on asthma and chronic obstructive pulmonary disease (COPD). Clearly this is a serious problem, with three people a day in Britain dying from asthma attacks, tragically many of them children.

At the same time, asthma varies strongly from person to person, and living with it can be a constant learning curve – although the internet can be a help with its lists of asthma-friendly plant species. For instance, your friends may include: **Azalia**, **Begonia**, **Box**, **Cactus**, **Cherry tree**, **Clematis**, **Columbine**, **Crocus**, **Daffodil**, **Dahlia**, **Geranium**, **Hibiscusv Hydrangea**, **Impatiens**, **Iris**, **Orchids**, **Pansy** and **Periwinkle**.

Your villains, your worst enemies, are probably, along with the grasses: **Ash**, **Elm**, **Cedar**, **Cypress**, **Birch and Juniper**, **Forsythia**, **Maples**, **Mulberries**, **Oaks**, **Pines**, **Russian thistle**, **Sagebrush** and **Walnut trees**. And, in the countryside each spring, asthma sufferers dread the blooming of the massed yellow flowers of modern farming's vast fields of **Oil Seed Rape** (*Brassica napus*).

Fortunately, there are some useful plant remedies for asthma. **Euphorbia** is even called the 'asthma plant' and **Chenille** in the same family is widely used in India to treat respiratory complaints. **Ephedra** in the form of Ephedrine, is used to give temporary relief for asthma attacks and shortness of breath. Anti-cough herbs such as **Elecampane** or **Marshmallow** may also give some relief. Homeopathic remedies that are used, depending on the symptoms, include: **Monkshood**, **Indian Tobacco**, regarded as a 'lung strengthener', and **Pasque-flower,** a strong childhood asthma remedy, all of which are toxic but only administered in infinitesimal doses. Other plant homeopathic remedies include **Sundew**, also a remedy for whooping cough, and **Elder,** which has many herbal uses. Most of us don't think of plants as 'enemies' or threats to our health. Sadly, asthma sufferers often do.

PUMPKINS AND HALLOWEEN

Each autumn in the UK, large numbers of pumpkins appear in supermarket vegetable aisles, greengrocers and corner shops. They sell well enough but few, if any, are actually eaten – they are bought to hollow out and carve into Jack-o'-lanterns for decorating and illuminating the festivities of Halloween. By contrast, in America pumpkin pie is an ever-popular autumn dessert and an essential part of Thanksgiving as well as Halloween.

Hallowe'en or All Hallows Eve on the 31st October

remains a pagan occasion. It began as the Celtic fire festival of Samhain, marking the end of harvest, the return of the cattle from summer pastures and the start of winter. It was also said that the boundaries between the living and the dead were blurred and ghosts and otherworldly spirits walked abroad at that time. Hence the spooky faces that are cut into the pumpkins, along with all the other imagery and costumes of devils, spiders and witches. Autumn produce, too, is part of these traditional rituals. Apple bobbing involves catching **Apples** (*Malus domesticus*), associated with immortality, in a bowl of water using only the teeth. **Hazel Nuts** (*Corylus avellana*), associated with divine wisdom and fortune telling, used be roasted on the fire, but today they are replaced by **Chestnuts** (*Castanea sativa*).

Rather than these other symbolic plants, **Pumpkin** or **Pie Pumpkin** (*Cucurbita pepo*) has come to epitomise or even dominate the Halloween festivities. This annual plant with trailing leafy stems and a huge orange fruit – in fact a hard-walled berry, which botanists call a 'pepo' – was first domesticated in Mexico some 9,000 years ago. The smaller pumpkins belong to this species, as do the courgettes, marrows and summer squashes, whereas the larger and the giant competition 'show' pumpkins and butternut and other winter squashes, belong to the related *Cucurbita maxima*, thought to have originated in Peru. Pumpkins are a part of the effective 'three sisters' corn-beans-squash cultivation system that sustained the Native Americans. In the 1840s, Irish and Highland Scottish and immigrants to North America encountered pumpkins and adapted their existing Jack-o'-lantern tradition of hollowed-out roots of **Swede** or **Rutabaga** (*Brassica napus*) and **Fodder Beet** or **Mangelwurze**l (*Beta vulgaris*). Another Halloween tradition was born and became commercialized. From the 1980s, celebration of American-style Halloween has been widely adopted in Britain, including 'Trick or Treat', and pumpkins are now grown as a field crop, if still little eaten! One Lincolnshire grower harvests 2 million pumpkins each year in time for Halloween.

However, the fashionable trend towards more plant-based foods has increased the popularity of Pumpkin, especially in soups or as a roast vegetable – a good source of fibre, potassium and beta-carotene (as in carrots), which the body converts into vitamin E. The seeds, rich in protein and healthy fatty acids, are also becoming more widespread in recipes and as a snack.

Despite America's love of pumpkin pie, these great orange berries will continue, in the UK at least, to be regarded as symbols of Autumn festive fun rather than food.

However, that may well change if we're encouraged to eat them!

PLANTS ON PARADE

VERSAILLES AND ITS TWO LASTING INFLUENCES

Imagine deciding to create a garden outside your house, while being rich enough to estimate that it needed 235 acres of pleasure spaces, 4,200 acres of ornamental park, and moreover, 15,000 more acres for hunting, all surrounded by a wall 26 miles long!

Such a house was the magnificent Château of Versailles, whose owner was the 'Sun King' Louis XIV of France, then the richest and most powerful country in the world. The gardens of Versailles would have two huge influences. The first was as the ultimate example of the strictly formal European style of gardens, much imitated but from which the English broke away under William Kent and 'Capability' Brown (page 286).

Its second and greatest influence was political. The gardens were statements of power and absolutism, celebrating the glory of Louis, who regarded himself as Apollo, 'the source of all light'. As he boldly reminded everyone, '*L'état c'est moi*'.

Versailles had started life in the 11th century as a tiny village of 50 houses, but by 1661 the forceful King Louis had acquired enough land to make the huge statement that he had planned. He appointed three master architects, Charles le Brun, Louis le Vau and, for the gardens, André le Nôtre. After their three years work, the King was able to enjoy the first of his Grandes Fêtes, an event lasting three days and nights designed to dazzle his guests.

The scale of everything is almost impossible to imagine. In 1687, the King's annual shopping list of garden plants included a hugely long and varied selection including **Antirrhinums**, **Campanulas**, **Candytuft**, **Cornflowers**, **Jasmines**, **Pasque-flowers**, **Pinks**, **Marguerites**, **Primulas and Violets.** Even more staggering were the 55,000 **Alder** seedlings, 3,700 **Ash** seedlings and bulbs of 2,700 **Hyacynths**, 7,000 **Irises,** 12,000 **Tulips**, 13,000 **Crocuses** and 20,000 **Narcissi**. There was also a 22-acre Potager, or vegetable and fruit garden, that was both ornamental and productive, and included heated glasshouses which enabled the King to enjoy **Figs,** his favourite fruit, for much of the year. The Orangerie contained no less than 1,000 **Orange** trees, brought outside in great tubs in summer, as well as many others. The mile-long Grand Canal was full of ornamental ships, with a shipyard to construct even more.

The massive Château itself housed the Royal Court and the Government of France and had no less than two thousand permanent residents, including many of the nobles of France, whom Louis liked to keep close to him.

In the gardens, Le Nôtre created vast

symmetrical layouts of avenues, water features with statues and fountains, formally planted trees, trimmed hedges, elaborate parterres and grand vistas. Plants and Nature herself were subjugated to the service of the Sun King. Water was always a problem and a huge and complex system was built to bring it three miles from nearby rivers. Even then, the hundreds of spectacular fountains had to be turned on as the King and his guests approached and then quickly turned off as they moved on. The lack of drinking water or even clean water and basic sanitation inside the Chateau itself was legendary!

The extravagant Château and its gardens managed to survive the French Revolution and the following century of social and political upheavals in France. While not quite as dramatic as in the days of the 'Sun King', Versailles remains one of the key destinations of any modern visitor to France.

Yet its greatest influence was not much to do with plants. Enacted there in 1919 was the 'Treaty of Versailles', the most important of the treaties that ended the First World War. This imposed harsh terms on the defeated Germans, and many argue that it sadly set the scene for the rise of Hitler and the terrible effects of the even more devastating Second World War, some of which we still feel today. It may also have had another influence, for it was said of Versailles that '*Louis XIV built it, Louis XV enjoyed it and Louis XVI paid for it*', literally with his head in the French Revolution.

28 JUNE 1919

PEACE CONGRESS

VERSAILLES 1919

SESSION OF 28 JUNE 1919

AGENDA

SIGNATURE OF THE TREATY OF PEACE BETWEEN THE ALLIED AND ASSOCIATED POWERS AND GERMANY

But for anybody who loves looking at plants and enjoys gardening, Versailles is quite simply the supreme, ultimate manifestation of an extravagant Baroque house and garden combined 'in the French style'.

Take a train from Paris and give yourself a visual treat! *Merveilleux!*

LANCELOT BROWN AND HIS 'CAPABILITY'

Most people hearing the name 'Capability' Brown would probably and quickly assume that he earned that nickname by his immense gifts as a landscape architect. In fact, the name arose because of his constant habit of politely telling his clients that their land '*had the capability of improvement*'.

However, Lancelot Brown (1715–83) was undeniably capable as a true visionary, foreseeing a whole new style of 'natural' English landscape gardens in marked contrast to the formal style in the rest of Europe, perhaps best typified by André le Nôtre's rigid patterns at Versailles.

His first commission was designing a new lake in the park at Kiddington Hall in Oxfordshire. Two years later he became an under-gardener at Lord Cobham's immense house of Stowe in Buckinghamshire, then one of the most important buildings in Britain, frequently visited by international royalty and also a political centre that would launch the careers of no less than four Prime Ministers. There, he worked under William Kent, a visionary founder of a whole new style of garden design, whose fame he would soon overshadow. When he became Stowe's Head Gardener, he created a landscape of lakes, grassy vistas and temples among the trees, beautiful to this day. He even moved the whole of Stowe village except the church, where he was married, which, to avoid spoiling the vista of the South Front, he hid with trees, including what has grown into an immense specimen of **Cedar of Lebanon** (page 161), his signature tree.

So impressed were Lord Cobham's wealthy friends that Brown was asked to 'take their gardens into the future', and soon he was working all over the country, becoming rich and earning in the 1760s today's equivalent of nearly a million pounds

a year! An excellent rider, he had the further advantage of galloping across the countryside to survey his clients' land far faster than on foot. His perceptive eye took in the natural landscapes he imitated and he not only replaced the conventional garden features of the time such as formal paths and fountains, but also hid the flowers, vegetables and fruits behind walls. He planted trees in belts and clumps, mostly natives such as **Beech** (*Fagus sylvatica*) and **English Oak** (*Quercus robor*) but also, as well as the **Cedars**, the garden hybrid **Lime,** the Mediterranean evergreen **Holm Oak** (*Quercus ilex*) and on water-sides, originally from China**,** **Weeping Willow** (*Salix babylonica*).

His growing fame led him to the very top when in 1764 he was appointed Master Gardener at Hampton Court Palace by King George III, a supreme honour.

How many gardens did he design? Around 170, including many famous ones like the Duke of Marlborough's at Blenheim Palace (bottom), Althorp, the seat of the Spencer family, where Princess Diana grew

up, Chatsworth, Highclere (above), where the mythical 'Downton Abbey' was filmed), Longleat, Petworth, Syon House and Woburn Abbey. They all possess his distinctive 'natural' style and many of them are open to the public today. Brown's style was also widely copied.

His most important legacy? Creating for grand houses the quintessentially English garden, using simple ideas to tremendous visual effect – with smooth swathes of grass leading up to the grand houses, strategically placed clumps of trees and often sinuous lakes created by damming rivers. If you look at them today, you might assume that such landscapes had looked like that for ever, rather than being the work of literally thousands of labourers working under 'Capability' Brown.

Orderly formality was not his style. Harmony, calmness and simplicity *were*.

EDWYN LUTYENS AND GERTRUDE JEKYLL

How extremely fortunate it was that one of the early twentieth century's greatest garden designers and writers, Gertrude Jekyll, was to meet in 1889 an equally talented and innovative young architect, Edwyn Lutyens. Over the next forty years they would create one of the most influential partnerships of the Arts and Crafts movement.

Edwyn Lutyens (1869–1944), later Sir Edwyn, was to become one of Britain's greatest architects, now perhaps best known for his war memorials like the Cenotaph in Whitehall, the Irish National War Memorial Gardens in Dublin or the moving monument to the 75,000 'Missing of the Somme' at Thiepval, in France.

The buildings and gardens they worked on together were not the grand structures of the aristocracy like Blenheim Palace and Stowe (page 286), but more approachable country and manor houses, yet still with enough outside space to display Miss Jekyll's considerable planting talents – particularly when it came to colour. In that field she was a radical pioneer, creating original and dazzling displays – especially in her flower borders. She also incorporated local stone, brick and timber and re-invented the rose garden, with an emphasis on pergolas and rambling roses (top).

Gertrude Jekyll (1843–1932) had trained as an artist, but it is said that deteriorating eyesight would later make her follow the looser, radiant colour styles of Turner and the Impressionists. Influenced by the plants she had seen on visits to the Mediterranean, the 'Lutyens-Jekyll' gardens (over the page, top left) had shrubberies and herbaceous borders filled with **Lilies**, **Lupins**, **Delphiniums** and **Lavender**. Together they created a new 'natural' style, rather as 'Capability' Brown had achieved for the vast estates of the nobility (page 286). Miss Jekyll was influenced both by her friendship with Irish garden designer William Robinson, author of the *The Wild Garden* (1870), and by the informal cottage gardens of the villages around her Surrey home, Munstead Wood(over page, top right). She had a keen eye for plants in the wild and in cottage gardens, and among those she selected and bred were garden

classics like a compact fragrant **Lavender,** (*Lavandula angustifolia* 'Munstead'), and a **Pansy,** *Viola hispida* 'Jackanapes', with reddish-purple and yellow flowers.

Amazingly, she never visited any of the 400 gardens that she designed in Britain, Europe and America. Rather, she made her clients send her detailed plans of the existing layout, together with soil samples.

Luckily, although she never saw the gardens, she did see the need to pass on her ideas to others, writing numerous articles and no less than fourteen books, including *Home and Garden, Gardens for small country houses, Colour in the Flower Garden* and *The beauties of a cottage garden* – all of them, remarkably, still in print today. Spreading the influence of the Lutyens-Jekyll partnership, the new magazine *Country Life* regularly featured the gardens they created.

As she herself observed, '*to have a good border of summer flowers, even for three months, is one of the most difficult horticultural feats*', but she certainly lived up to such a challenge. Her legacy lives on in countless country and suburban gardens.

She was unflinchingly critical of the potential waste of a poorly designed garden. '*Given the same space of ground and the same plant materials, they may either be fashioned into a thing of beauty, a place of perfect rest and refreshment of mind and body, a series of soul-satisfying pictures, a treasure of well-set jewels – or they may be so misused that everything is jarring and displeasing.*

To learn how to perceive the difference and do right is to apprehend gardening as a fine art.'

The marriage of skills between Jekyll and Lutyens gave us some of the greatest gardens of the 20th century, still a massive influence today. She was not to know that a more baleful legacy was her enthusiasm for **Giant Hogweed** (alas, a plant villain, page 68) – as a 'proud and sumptuous' plant for bog gardens!

KEW AND ITS BOTANICAL TREASURES

'Come down to Kew in lilac-time, in lilac-time,
in lilac time;
Come down to Kew in lilac-time
(it isn't far from London!)' - Alfred Noyes (1913)

The Royal Botanic Gardens, Kew, is both a much-appreciated green space for Londoners and an international byword for botanical study and expertise. It has not always been a Botanic Garden, but has always been Royal. For George II and his Queen Caroline it was, as usual, infuriating that their son Frederick (widely known as 'Poor Fred') should do something like set himself up on the Kew Estate next door to their Richmond Estate by the River Thames. '*My dear first-born is the greatest ass, and the greatest liar, and the greatest canaille, and the greatest beast in the whole world, and I most heartily wish he was out of it*', was Caroline's motherly opinion!

Frederick needed to settle down. One of his many mistresses was Madame d'Elitz,

who incredibly had been the paramour of both his father and grandfather. '*There's nothing new under the sun*'. George Selwyn, the noted wit, retorted, '*or under the grandson!*'

The Prince of Wales eventually settled on Augusta of Saxe-Gotha, and it was she who started the first 9-acre garden at Kew, with the support of Lord Bute and the architect Sir William Chambers, whose Orangery, Ruined Arch and Pagoda still stand – where the temporary gardener was a young William Cobbett, later famous as a radical politician, the founder of *Hansard* and author of *Rural Rides*, as well as two books on horticulture, *The American Gardener* (1821) and *Cottage Economy* (1822).

However charming Kew was as a Royal Garden under Frederick's son George III and Queen Caroline, it was to Sir Joseph Banks (pictured) that the credit must be given for its international fame. Banks, who had been with Captain James Cook on the voyage of the *Endeavour*, was the botanist who gave the name to Botany Bay in Australia and brought back numerous Australian trees and shrubs such as **Acacia**, **Eucalyptus** and named in his honour, **Banksia**. He had,with Royal approval, started the policy of sending collectors all over the world to bring plants back to Kew – where temporarily the King was confined, as we saw in the film 'The Madness of King George'. Known not unkindly, as 'Farmer George', the King himself had a keen interest in agriculture, not least the improvement of **Clover**, **Lucerne (Alfalfa)**, **Sainfoin** and other forage crops.

Kew's policy of collecting plants and either bringing them to Kew or sending them to other parts of the British Empire was to lead to Cook's tragic death in Hawaii in 1779 and, equally dramatically, the 1789 mutiny on HMS *Bounty*, when Cook's former sailing Master, Captain William Bligh, was transporting **Breadfruit** trees(*Artocarpus altilis*) from Tahiti to the West Indies as a food for the slaves of the sugar plantations. The little boat in which Bligh and 18 men were cast adrift travelled 4,000 miles, and his 'strongest helper' was the Kew botanist David Nelson.

After some years of decline, the Government took over Kew and, first under William Hooker and then his son Joseph, a friend and supporter of Charles Darwin, Kew continued to expand with its magnificent Palm House and Temperate House; a policy existing to this day of investing in state-of-the-art glasshouses and other facilities, and continuing to collect, curate, exchange and distribute its worldwide collection of plants, both living and preserved.

Many of these plants would change the world. It was a Kew gardener, Robert Cross, who joined the expedition to Ecuador to bring the **Chinchona** plant (*Cinchona*) to Kew, thence to Ceylon and India to create quinine in order to combat malaria which was killing a million people a year. Rubber, too, owes its success to Kew. Seeds of the **Rubber Tree** (*Hevea brasiliensis*) were brought to Kew from its native Brazil and sent to the Far East to create one of the world's greatest industries.

With its herbarium, laboratories, library, horticultural and educational resources, and influence in naming, studying and utilizing plants throughout the world, The Royal Botanic Gardens, Kew, has long been eminent among the world's botanical institutes, and in 2003 became a UNESCO World Heritage Site.

To most of us it is just 'Kew', a much-loved national institution that combines scholarship for staff and recreation and delight for visitors.

THE APOTHECARIES AND THEIR PHYSIC GARDEN

Hidden behind a wall in London's Chelsea is a place which has had a huge influence on the world's understanding and use of plants. The Chelsea Physic Garden is one of the most charming small open spaces in London, an oasis of peace just off the Chelsea Embankment of the River Thames. Many of those who enjoy visiting for the flowers and trees, the outdoor café, or perhaps an exhibition of paintings, are undoubtedly aware that here is an important historic garden. But one easily overlooks just how significant this miniature botanic garden has been in botanical and wider British history.

The Physic Garden was founded in 1673 by the Worshipful Society of Apothecaries. The Society had been established in 1617 as an offshoot of the Grocer's Company, a City of London livery company. Apothecaries provided healthcare as pharmacists and general practitioners for the sick and 'worried well', especially those unable to afford qualified doctors. Their vital skill was a knowledge of medicinal plants, from which they made up their own remedies for all sorts of ailments. The Society ensured medicine quality

control, trained apprentices and set and raised professional standards. Later the Apothecaries' Hall, London's oldest surviving livery hall, created laboratories to process medical plants grown at the Chelsea Physic Garden. These medicines stocked the medicine chests used by the Army, Navy and colonies, notably those taken on voyages of discovery such as those of Captain Cook – which themselves yielded new medicinal plants.

Apothecaries' Hall

Apothecaries actively sought not just medicines but any new and interesting plants – indeed, they were the first modern botanists. An early Society Fellow was Thomas Johnson, the first botanist to climb Snowdon, who left a vivid account of an excursion around the River Medway, with a modern-sounding botanical mix of good plants, beer and company! Alas killed in 1644, fighting for the King during the Civil War, Johnson revised John Gerard's famous *Herball*, which he much improved. In the Introduction, he also laid out exactly why botany is important, writing '*God, through infinite goodness and bounty, has by the medium of plants bestowed almost all food, clothing and medicines upon man.*'

The Chelsea Physic Garden, confined within just under four acres, soon grew in stature and in a few years was exchanging seeds and plants with other gardens, including some of the first **Cedars of Lebanon** (page 161) in England, which arrived from Leiden in Holland.

After falling for a while on hard times, in 1722 the garden was rescued by Sir Hans Sloane (right), later President of the Royal Society (and the inventor of drinking chocolate, page 72), who had trained there, but was now the wealthy owner of the Manor of Chelsea, now probably best-known for its Square named after him. He granted the Apothecaries the site in perpetuity for an annual lease of five pounds and appointed as Gardener the botanist and horticulturist Philip Miller (1691–1771), who over the next half century would bring international renown to the Chelsea Physic Garden. His *Dictionary of Gardening* is a standard work, running to eight editions, and we still use many of his plant names today.

Numerous new plants were now arriving, including from North America through the good offices of a noted Quaker botanist, Peter Collinson, who remarked how

Miller '*has raised the reputation of the Chelsea Garden so much that it excels all the gardens of Europe for the amazing variety of plants*'. The garden was now a true botanic garden as well as a source of medicines. One interesting ornamental plant that Miller described was **Rosy Periwinkle** (*Catharanthus roseus*) (above) from Madagascar. With attractive pink flowers but armed with a cocktail of poisonous alkaloids, it was distributed by Chelsea to become an ornamental and weed of warmer climates. Only in recent decades has its value as a treatment for childhood leukaemia been discovered.

By the end of the 18th century, the garden was being overshadowed by the rise of the Royal Botanic Gardens, Kew, although Kew did not really prosper until taken in hand by the Hookers, father-and-son Directors, from the mid-19th century (page 290). At the same time botany gradually played less of a part in medical training. The Chelsea Physic Garden thereafter had a chequered history, but the Society of Apothecaries somehow kept it going, as an adjunct to botany courses and research in London, supported by various charitable bodies.

Since 1981 it has had a board of trustees and survives as a much-appreciated hub of botanical and horticultural research and public education, as well as a centre for the training and practice of the increasingly demanded skill of botanical illustration. The garden is popular with visitors and as a place for holding prestigious events – in a setting that has now been restored to its 18th-century heyday.

FROM EDINBURGH TO THE HIMALAYAS

Scotland's handsome capital city of Edinburgh is famous for its Castle, the Royal Mile, Holyrood Palace, Greyfriars Bobby and Edinburgh rock confectionery, but many people are unaware that it also has one of the world's great botanic gardens. Edinburgh Botanic Garden (below) combines glorious grounds and glasshouses with a

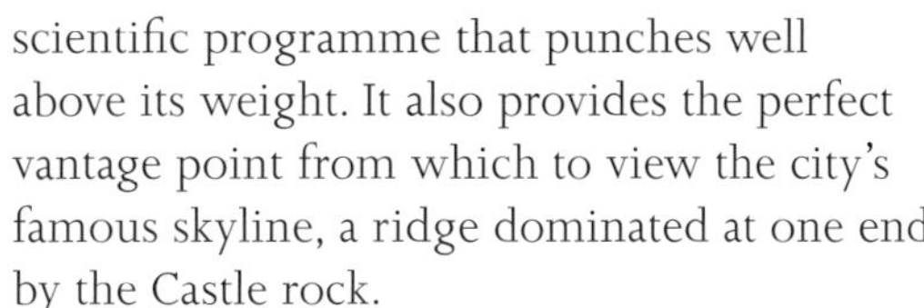

scientific programme that punches well above its weight. It also provides the perfect vantage point from which to view the city's famous skyline, a ridge dominated at one end by the Castle rock.

Founded in 1670, when times were distinctly unstable in Scotland, the Royal Botanic Gardens, Edinburgh is the second

oldest botanic garden in the United Kingdom (after Oxford), although it subsequently had to move three times from the original site near Holyrood Palace. The present 72-acre site was established in 1820, a mile outside the city centre – a good precaution as in those days Edinburgh was polluted enough to be known as 'Auld Reekie.' The modern garden comprises, with three satellite gardens at Benmore, Dawyck and Logan, the National Botanic Gardens of Scotland.

The two founders of the original Edinburgh garden, Robert Sibbald and Andrew Balfour, were doctors who wanted to grow medicinal plants, and it is appropriate that a city historically so much associated with medicine should possess an important collection of plants. Today's Botanic Garden includes an Arboretum, Woodland Garden, Chinese Hillside, Rose Garden, herbaceous borders and ten greenhouses, with extensive collections of warm temperate and tropical plants and including a fine 1834 Palm House. The garden exhibits an impressive range of coniferous trees, including **Giant Redwoods** and **Monkey Puzzles** from Chile (page 328). The Rock Garden, one of the most striking and important areas of the garden, has long been praised. In 1875, the *Gardener's Chronicle* enthused over '*the largest and most varied rock garden we have ever seen … charming beyond the power of expression*'. Since enhanced and expanded, it holds plants from all the world's continents but especially the Himalayas, through the work of Scottish plant collectors, not least the many species of **Blue Poppy** (*Mecanopsis*) and **Primula**, which thrive in the cool, moist climate.

The staff and research projects, based in the Herbarium and Library at Edinburgh, maintain close links with Nepal, Sikkim and other parts of the Himalayas – and with China, which not only has a rich native flora has but also emerged in recent years as a global centre of botanical research. On behalf of Isaac Bayley Balfour, an inspired Regius Keeper of the Royal Botanic Garden, George Forrest (1873-1932) (pictured) made seven plant-collecting expeditions to Yunnan in south-western China and adjacent territories, enduring all manner of hardship. Indefatigable in his work, during a period of anti-foreign unrest he was hunted for days through rhododendron forests by enraged monks, while at the same time noting interesting plants for when he would return! Forrest collected great numbers of new plants, including over 300 species of **Rhododendron**, which became a speciality at Edinburgh, both in botanical research and in horticulture, and he introduced hundreds of species into cultivation, not only rhododendrons, but primulas, bulbs and the popular autumn-flowering **Chinese Gentian** (*Gentiana sino-ornata*) (over page, top right).

The elegant and spacious layout of the garden reflects a long tradition of horticulture as well as pure botany, adding many species and hybrids to the private and public gardens of the UK and the world. James McNab, the garden's late 19th century Curator, who laid out the basic plan of what we see today (including the Rock Garden, although Bayley Balfour had it reconstructed

in 1908), was a talented landscape gardener and an early proponent of amenity planting and landscape restoration. To this very day, the courses in landscape architecture at Edinburgh University maintain close contact with 'The Botanics'.

The Royal Botanic Garden remains an important international centre for horticulture and well reflects the interaction between academic botany and the world of garden plants.

It is certainly one of the most beautiful of all botanic gardens.

JOSEPH PAXTON, THE WATER-LILY AND BANANAS

When you think of a leaf, you almost certainly think of something relatively small, not a giant that can grow up to three metres across and even able to bear the weight of a child. But such a leaf exists, that of the **Giant Water Lily** (*Victoria amazonica*) pictured above.

It was first discovered by Thaddeus Haenke on the Amazon in 1801, but he died before he could report this wonder of the world, and it was left to another botanical explorer, R.H. Schomburgh, to do so some thirty-six years later.

Plants & Us

What can possibly link three things – this mighty water-lily, one of the world's most economically important and popular fruits, and the roots of modern architecture? The answer: Joseph Paxton, a Victorian man of genius and imagination, with the knowledge and ability to grow and study plants, and the good fortune to have a wealthy, influential and supportive patron.

Bio-engineering is now a growth area in science, one that is increasingly turning to nature for inspiration by mimicking and learning from plant and animal materials and structures. But its origins go back a long way. In the mid-19th century, the Great Exhibition of 1851 was housed not in a hall of brick or stone but in the 'Crystal Palace', a huge glasshouse designed by a gardener. Admittedly, Joseph Paxton (1801–65) (pictured) was no ordinary gardener, also being an engineer, architect, landscape architect and botanist, as well as the co-founder of *The Gardener's Chronicle* (which still survives as *Horticulture Week*) and later also a railway investor and Liberal MP. But his real speciality was glasshouses. Two years earlier he had grown and brought to flower a **Giant Water-lily** with its colossal floating circular leaves and large handsome scented flowers that change from white to pink and last just 48 hours.

To house this great plant, Paxton (pictured) wrote, '*Nature has provided the leaf with horizontal and transverse girders and support that, I, borrowing from it, have adopted in this building*', creating a glasshouse modelled on the underside of the water-lily's own leaves. He knew these created a strong structure because he had his own daughter photographed standing on one as it floated in its tank!

Paxton took his lily-house design and expanded it from a doodle he drew on a sheet of blotting paper during a meeting, to create the innovative timber, iron and glass structure of the Crystal Palace, which was chosen against over two hundred more conventional competitive designs. At a stroke, he was at the forefront of architecture's move towards the modernist styles that would give us the skyscrapers of America and the 20th-century experiments of the Bauhaus in Germany. By using an assembly-line of iron pillars and girders and pre-cut glass panels he also anticipated modern construction techniques. As distinguished architect Norman Foster has observed, '*That really was the birth of modern architecture, of prefabrication, of soaring*

spans of glass.' In that same Great Exhibition year of 1851, Queen Victoria rightly knighted him Sir Joseph Paxton.

Paxton was Head Gardener at Chatsworth House in Derbyshire, where he created world-famous gardens and glasshouses for William Cavendish, the 6th Duke of Devonshire, who wisely appointed him when only in his early 20s. Chatsworth's 'Great Conservatory' (below) was, until the Crystal Palace, the biggest glasshouse in Britain, with room for two carriages to pass down its main thoroughfare. Cavendish was

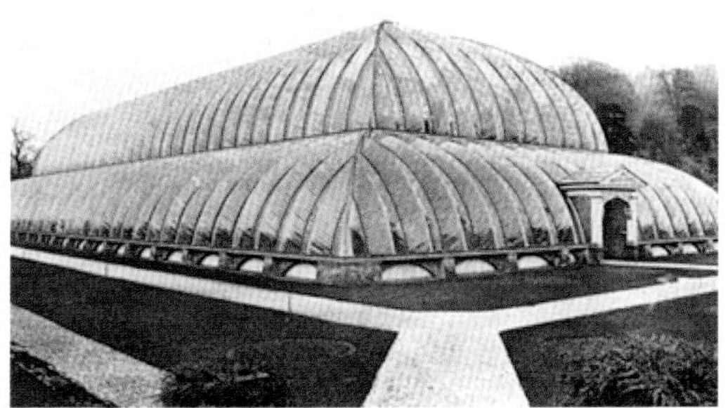

wealthy and influential, counting among his friends Charles Dickens, the Czar of Russia and now Paxton himself, whom he encouraged and supported in his numerous projects.

Paxton would prove to be one of the most important influencers of the 19th century, because he was an accomplished grower, and in 1836, in one of Chatsworth's heated glasshouses, he first harvested the familiar yellow fruits of **Banana** (*Musa*), a plant that had only recently arrived from China via Mauritius, a British colony since 1814. From there the Duke was to send propagated banana plants with a church mission to Samoa to launch a banana industry in the Pacific islands.

The rest, as we say, is history. Today the 'Cavendish' group of bananas that Paxton originally propagated comprises nearly half of the 100 million-ton global banana crop. And unlike almost everybody else in Britain, the Cavendish family, their friends and guests continue to eat their own glasshouse-grown bananas!

THE GARDENS OF HELIGAN, LOST AND FOUND

A mile or two outside the Cornish fishing village of Mevagissey on a dreary February day in 1990, two men armed themselves with machetes and set off in search of a lost garden. One of them was local landowner John Willis and the other was Tim Smit, a music industry entrepreneur who had come to live in Cornwall. Amid fallen trees and tangled masses of brambles, through vast stands of self-set **Ash**, **Sycamore** and wild thickets of **Laurel**, Tim discovered for himself a horticultural treasure trove: a vanished world of walled gardens; a vinery with scissors still hanging in place; a Head Gardener's office with a rusted kettle above the fireplace (left); a peach house with Oak trees growing through the

shattered glass and a rotting roof frame. Not only was there a sense of a beautiful and productive garden overwhelmed by nature and destroyed by neglect, but a deep melancholy, one associated with abandonment and death in war. These were The Lost Gardens of Heligan.

Heligan had been one of the great Cornish estates and had belonged to one of the important county families, the Tremaynes, ancestors of John Willis. The Tremayne family had been the squires of Heligan from 1600 until 1949 and had overseen its development from farmland to one of the finest gardens in the south-west. The kitchen gardens, replete with a pineapple pit and melon house, were a productive machine, while the grounds were full of **Rhododendrons**, **Camellia**s and botanical gems of the 19th century. It would have been quite inconceivable in 1900 that that less than a century later these celebrated gardens would have vanished from memory and from sight.

The gardens became lost not because the plants had disappeared, but because the people disappeared. Like many traditional estates, the outbreak of the First World War had signalled Heligan's decline. The evidence for this was the most poignant discovery that Tim was to make. In the crumbling Melon Yard, was found the 'Thunderbox', the gardeners' lavatory. On its wall, handwritten on the mouldy plaster, were the signatures of thirteen gardeners, dated August 1914. Of these thirteen men, sadly only four survived the war. None were to return to Heligan. The First World War marked the point of decline for the gardens, from which they emerged eighty years later. It was this same profound human tragedy that inspired Tim Smit to begin the gardens' restoration.

The Lost Gardens of Heligan were to become the largest garden restoration project in Europe, and at its heart was the aim of returning the entire two acres of productive garden to a fully functioning late Victorian-Edwardian kitchen garden, tended by hand and planted with period-correct varieties of fruit and vegetables. To achieve this, it was vital to not only have the right plants but also the correct skills to cultivate them: plants and people. It is this blend of human narrative and the world of leaf, root, flower and fruit which defines The Lost Gardens of Heligan and remains central to their popularity.

The Lost Gardens may have been found in 1990, but there is much from Heligan's golden horticultural years that remains lost or needs preserving. The restoration's focus on heritage fruit and vegetables has proved ground-breaking. With the contemporary obsession with uniformity and mass-production at the expense of flavour and nutrition, many heritage varieties have been lost and many more continue to be threatened. Heligan is about preserving the past to protect the future. These heritage varieties were developed before the widespread use of industrial fertilisers and pesticides. As we look to move away from

the chemical regimens of the past hundred years, the true value of fruit and vegetable varieties of the past and how to conserve them will once again be understood.

The success of Heligan's productive gardens has never been solely about the choice of plants. Without the extraordinary skills and knowledge of a Head Gardener, orchestrating and conducting a horticultural symphony, the kitchen would be a barren place. Since the restoration, Heligan has championed appreciation and preservation of this vital expertise. The lost art of the late Victorian Head Gardeners and gardeners live on there.

The relationship between people and plants has been a profound element of life at Heligan for much of the past few hundred years. The legacy of the Tremaynes' love of botany and gardens, for example, is

demonstrated by the National Collection of historic **Rhododendrons** and **Camellias** to be found at Heligan. Today this bond is perhaps most evident in the 350,000 visitors that come to the gardens every year. The Lost Gardens of Heligan were recently voted the UK's favourite garden, a great honour for this very special place, but also a resounding affirmation of the stories these gardens tell.

A NEW EDEN IN CORNWALL

One of the very first visitors to the Eden Project was co-author Liz Cowley, just after the opening in 2001. She vividly remembers being astonished by her first sight of its two huge Biomes, now home to over a million plants and around 7,000 different plant species.

So how did it all begin? In the words of the co-founder, Sir Tim Smit: *'In the late 1990s a small group gathered in pubs and offices to talk about an idea – to create a place like nothing anyone had ever seen before; a place that explored our place in nature, a place that demonstrated what could be done if people who wanted to make a difference got together.'*

Tim Smit was certainly no novice at creating drama. Trained as an anthropologist, he had made a career in the pop music world, as a songwriter and producer earning seven platinum and gold discs. He was more than familiar putting on a show and pulling in the punters. Having moved to Cornwall, he caught the public imagination by restoring the nearby Lost Gardens of Heligan, and became fascinated by how to get people really interested in plants by weaving human stories around them – tales of adventure, emotion and derring-do. At Eden he thought that there was an even bigger story to be told; of the plants that shaped the world as we know it and of our total dependence on, and connection to, the natural environment.

His small team bought an exhausted, 160-year-old, steep-sided china clay quarry 60 metres deep, and with no soil, to new life. There they planned a huge diversity of plants,

Plants & Us

because they wanted to showcase our dependence on the living world and take the presentation of botany and plants in a radical new direction. And because they wanted to say, 'I'm glad I did,' rather than, 'I wish I had.'

Money was raised (eventually £80 million), fledgling teams grew thousands of plants, mapped them on to the site and started planning the stories. The Visitor Centre opened in 2000 to let the public watch the construction and share the adventure. The whole site opened on 17 March, St Patrick's Day, 2001.

The concept of the Eden Project was unique: to create in the middle of one of England's poorest counties an attraction of drama, daring and difference – that would draw people from afar – whether plant enthusiasts or not. Tim Smit's career in show business and the vision of architect Nicholas Grimshaw resulted in something truly different, made possible by the modern geodesic structures and the lightweight plastic covering of what was then the world's largest conservatories complex.

The Eden Project is an educational charity. Its mission: to connect people to the living world, working towards a better future. Eden pays homage to the green things and the soil that supports and nurtures them. Plants are our lifeblood. From blue jeans to coffee beans, plants feed, clothe and heal us. They colour the fabric of our lives and, along with animals, fungi and the microbial world, supply us with clean water, fertile soil, rich biodiversity, a stable climate and the very air we breathe – our life support system.

Just over twenty years later in a deep crater in Cornwall, two covered Biomes nestle into a south-facing cliff face. The Tropical Biome is the largest rainforest 'in captivity', with **Banana plants**, **Coffee**, **Rubber** and **Bamboos**. The Mediterranean Biome, its little sister, features warm temperate plants like **Olives** and **Grape** vines, while the scimitar-shaped Outdoor gardens display temperate plants like **Tea**, **Lavender**, **Hops**, **Hemp** and **Sunflowers.** At the base of the crater is a large stage, which sits at the end of one of the longest blue herbaceous borders in the UK, with the other end leading to the Core building, an educational centre the size of a spaceship with the structure of a sunflower, which houses 'Invisible Worlds', a permanent exhibition exploring the interconnectedness of life and the environment at all scales. An all-year programme of exhibitions and story-telling breathes further life, colour and vibrancy into the site – a living theatre of plants and people.

The 15-hectare Eden site has proved to be a valuable focus and shop window for public and media interest in plants. It is a place of pilgrimage for gardeners and non-gardeners alike, and every year attracts over a million visitors of all ages and interests, with a further two and a half million to its website. It has had a huge positive impact on tourism in the county and is an important driver in the local economy, estimated to have injected two billion pounds into Cornwall's economy.

Today the Eden Project is literally full of life, with stories of interconnections and

new ideas. Its mission continues to grow and the Project shares, and works on, solutions to address some of Earth's most pressing challenges. Ideas are rooted in a deep understanding of and respect for plants and nature and our interdependencies with the natural world. Conservation is important, but it's not enough. Eden explores ways of regenerating lost landscapes and making them sustainable through an inspired holistic combination of creative, social and economic approaches. The first step, which is where it all began, is to help people to understand the value of the natural world.

The concept is spreading, Eden Project North will open in Morecambe Bay in Lancashire in 2024 and, working with like-minded organisations, Eden Project International, established in 2017, aims to set up Eden Projects on all the inhabited continents. These new Edens will focus on the global challenges that face specific localities and regions, such as soil, water, food and biodiversity. Eden Project International is currently working on projects in the UK, China and Australia.

Eden has successfully re-invented the traditional Botanic Garden and presented the ancient science and practice of botany as Rock 'n' Roll!

The build

• 2,000 rock anchors (some 11metres long) stabilised the pit sides.
• 83,000 tonnes of fabricated soil were made in 18 months.
• 1.8 million tonnes of earth were shifted in 6 months.

Building lean-to greenhouses on an uneven surface that changed shape was tricky. Bubbles were used as they can settle perfectly on to any shaped surface. The bubbles were made up of hexagons, copying insects' eyes and honeycombs , producing maximum efficiency with minimal resources. The 'skin' is made from three layers of ethylene tetrafluoroethylene (ETFE), that is not only transparent but light, non-stick, self-cleaning and transmits UV light.

Sustain ... ability plus

Eden promotes cyclic systems and renewable energies. The project:

• Uses 100% renewable electricity and is building a geothermal plant that aims to export enough renewable electricity and heat to more than wipe out its carbon footprint.
• Uses composted domestic green waste in its Outdoor Gardens.
• Recycles rainwater and groundwater which is used to flush the toilets and water the plants.
• Recycles 100% of its food 'waste', either by composting on site or anaerobic digestion by a specialist company.
• Works with others worldwide and encourages people to make changes in their everyday lives to look after the planet that looks after them.
• Believes nothing is waste until it is wasted.

MISSOURI BOTANICAL GARDEN

If you mention St Louis, Missouri, to most Americans, they'll probably think of the huge 'Gateway Arch' that celebrates the jumping-off point westwards of the settlers in their covered waggons. They may not mention a world-beating botanical garden - started by an Englishman.

Missouri has played a key role in the history of botany, and today the research and conservation projects of the city's botanical garden extend worldwide. Situated just below where the Missouri joins the mighty Mississippi, St Louis was the start and finish of Meriwether Lewis and William Clark's(top) 1804-1806 expedition, sent by President Jefferson to explore territory in the West which the USA had acquired from France as part of the 1803 Louisiana Purchase. As Christian Lamb rightly notes of Lewis and Clark in her book of notable collectors *To the Ends of the Earth*, '*their plant collection was not large but much of it was new to science*', not least those two garden favourites, **Bitter Root** (*Lewisia rediviva*) and **Clarkia** (*Clarkia pulchella*), by which the two men are commemorated.

Half a century later, in 1859, a wealthy, but rather unlikely, St Louis businessman and philanthropist, Henry Shaw, (pictured) founded a garden in St Louis that has become the globally renowned Missouri Botanical Garden. Covering 79 acres it is still known locally as Shaw's Garden. Shaw was actually born in Sheffield in England, but made his fortune selling vital hardware and other goods to the settlers heading out from St Louis, the 'Gateway to the West'. Shaw then retired at forty – with enough money to travel back to Europe. In Britain he was much impressed by the Royal Botanic Gardens, Kew, and also by Thomas Paxton's Crystal Palace and his glasshouses at Chatsworth (page 295). He resolved to use this knowledge to create an outstanding botanical garden for his adopted city.

Today's Missouri Botanical Garden, which holds 17,500 different plants, includes the 14-acre Seiwa-en Japanese garden laid out in the 1970s, set around a 4-acre lake, with traditional buildings and bridges, bamboos, bonsai and a dry gravel area, a grove of **Dawn Cypress** (*Metasequioa glyptostroboides*), a Chinese Garden, spring-flowering English Woodland Garden, Herb Garden, Biblical Garden and two formal Rose Gardens; and Shaw's own Orangery, the oldest in America, known as the Linnean House and recently returned to its original role of overwintering Citrus fruits and other tender plants. Special collections include an expanding assemblage of rare or endangered

species, over 2,000 **Orchids**, many from Latin America, some 850 tropical **Aroids**('arum lilies') and tropical **Waterlilies** and their artificial crosses, including the rare, yellow-flowered **Nymphaea** 'St Louis' (top left).

Missouri combines, in best botanic garden tradition, a mixture of scientific research, horticulture, plant and habitat conservation, education and outreach, and public recreation, including an annual orchid show. It is a global centre for plant taxonomy research, the preparation of regional, multi-volume Floras and the maintenance of Tropicos and other related botanical databases. A key project is the 30-volume *Flora of North America*, which when complete, will name, describe and provide chromosome numbers and geographical data for all the mosses, liverworts, ferns, conifers and flowering plants of the American continent north from Mexico – gathering and publishing the data in one place for the first time.

The Botanical Garden's laboratories, Herbarium of 8 million species and 250,000 volume Library maintain close links with institutes and colleagues in Latin America and China, as well as those in North America, Europe and Africa. The Garden also maintains another property at Gray Summit, 40 miles south (and just off the old Route 66!), the Shaw Nature Reserve. This 2,400-acre (nearly 10 km^2) site includes an Arboretum, a native Wildflower Garden, native deciduous woodland, 400 acres of restored tallgrass prairie and a small historic house.

The Garden's most famous and distinctive building is the Climatron, 175 feet in diameter and 70 feet tall, which provides tropical rainforest conditions. When it opened in 1960, it was the first greenhouse enclosed within a geodesic dome, the first constructed from Perspex panels and the first one air-conditioned for climate control. The

original structure deteriorated, but in 1990 it re-opened with strengthened glass panels. Today it houses over 1,400 plant species, including tropical crops, shrubs and trees, familiar house plants grown to full size, and a rotational exhibit of the garden's orchid collection, all set among lush greenery, rocky outcrops, a water-lily pool and running water. Some of the mature **Cycads** (palm-like relatives of the conifers) were exhibited at the 1904 St Louis World's Fair, an event depicted in one of Judy Garland's films, 'Meet me in St Louis'.

The Climatron glasshouse model has been copied elsewhere, from a pair of small replica houses in the botanic garden of Jibou in North west Romania (built not long after) to the giant domes of The Eden Project in Cornwall (page 300) and the ones for the huge 'Noah's Ark' park (below), linking animals and plants, in South Africa. And the Climatron is now as much a St Louis icon as the soaring Gateway Arch.

BOTANY AND 'THE BIG APPLE'

Plants probably don't spring to mind when people think of New York City. Yet this great hub of arts, commerce and finance possesses two botanical gardens, one in the Bronx, the other in Brooklyn, along with a vibrant local culture of some 550 community gardens, and pockets of wild plants and habitats in the mosaic of coasts, islands and rivers on which the city is built. Both botanical gardens are scientific institutions but their ornamental plant collections, especially, are a significant public amenity and an urban 'shop window' for plants.

The Bronx, New York's most northern borough, racially and culturally diverse, is famously a centre for Latin and African American music and the birthplace of 'hip hop'. It includes some of the city's poorest districts but also University buildings and the open spaces of Bronx Park. Occupying 250 acres (100 hectares) in the park, the New York Botanical Garden was established in 1891 as a collaboration between the Torrey Botanical Club, Columbia University and New York City. Notable members of the original board included steel industrialist and philanthropist Andrew Carnegie, financier J.P. Morgan and railroad magnate Cornelius Vanderbilt! (pictured).

At the heart of the Garden is an impressive glasshouse range, the Conservatory, opened in 1902 and originally modelled on the Palm House at the Royal Botanic Gardens, Kew, and Joseph Paxton's Crystal Palace (page 286), and extensively renovated as the Enid A. Haupt Conservatory in 1997. It contains a series of tropical ecosystems ranging across rainforest to desert and mountain habitats, exhibiting numerous species that include palms, cacti and an annual spring orchid show. A successful compromise between elegant Victorian design and modern architecture and technology, the Conservatory is an iconic building for both New York Botanic Garden and the city which it serves.

The garden has numerous plant collections, including a 37-acre (15 hectares) conifer Arboretum and an Alpine Garden. Alongside historical layouts such as the Peggy Rockefeller Rose Garden, are more contemporary gardens, such as the Herb Garden designed by the English garden designer Penelope Hobhouse (right). Particularly striking is the Seasonal Walk, intended to provide colour throughout the year, redesigned in 2014 by influential

Dutch designer Piet Oudolf with his trademark naturalistic planting of blocks of prairie grasses, perennials and bulbs, echoing the meadow and prairie planting he had earlier used in the High Line linear park on Manhattan's West Side.

A remarkable feature of the Botanical Garden is the Thain Family Forest, a 50-acre (20-hectare) stand of old-growth forest – a relict island of native vegetation analogous to the rainforest within the Singapore Botanic Gardens – which covered the area before the 17th century, when Dutch and other European settlers established 'New Amsterdam'. The city became New York only after it was (perhaps foolishly) handed over in 1667 to Britain in exchange for the tiny island of Run in the Far East (page 132) because of its then lucrative nutmeg plantations.

The New York Botanical Garden's botanical research is supported by its laboratories, which specialize in genome sequencing and other molecular studies of the taxonomy and evolution of the Flowering Plants, the Herbarium of over seven million preserved plant specimens, and the Library of over half a million books and periodicals.

At the other end of the city, Brooklyn is also a place of cultural diversity and the most densely populated borough of New York. The Brooklyn Botanic Garden, (top right) was established in 1910 as a part of the Brooklyn Institute of Arts and Sciences, which has placed the emphasis of the garden on horticulture and practical projects rather than botanical research. Much of the 52-acre (21- hectare) site, adjacent to the borough's hilly Prospect Park but also to city blocks, is planted as an Arboretum with trees and shrubs of both botanical and horticultural interest arranged in family groupings

There are a number of specialised gardens, including a conservation garden of native flora, a Boulder Garden of level scree and boulders, a Fragrance Garden (with signs in braille for the benefit of blind visitors), a garden of plants mentioned in the works of Shakespeare (page 358), a Rose Garden and a Water Garden. The climate-controlled Steinhardt Conservatory

displays tropical, warm temperate and desert plants, and also includes the C.V. Starr Bonsai Museum.

Japan features strongly in the Botanic Garden. There are two Japanese Gardens, a Hill-and-Pond garden first opened in 1915 and later combined with a meandering 'strolling garden', and one of raked sand and carefully grouped stones, a copy of the 'dry landscape' Zen temple garden of Ryoan-ji in Kyoto, Japan. The Botanic Garden's many **Cherry Trees** were originally gifted by Japan after the First World War and the Cherry Esplanade is now the focus of a traditional

spring Cherry Blossom Festival (page 152).

Brooklyn Botanical Garden has always existed deep in the heart of the local community, with a strong education mission. The Children's Garden, opened as long ago as 1914 and designed 'to introduce city children to the world of plants', is today run as a community garden widely regarded as a model for similar shared areas of garden plots worldwide. The Botanic Garden offers a broad range of courses for children and adults in practical horticulture, field studies and conservation, and runs a Community Greening programme, including promotion of an annual 'Greenest Block in Brooklyn' competition.

Thus, for well over a century, New York's two botanical gardens have well complemented one another to offer a variety of plant information, experiences and community outreach, and furthermore, a welcome haven of peace in a bustling city for visitors of all ages.

KIRSTENBOSCH, SOUTH AFRICA'S BOTANY PARADISE

To protect the new Dutch colony of Cape Town, a hedge of **Wild Almond** (*Brabejum stellatifolium*) was planted in 1660. Some of 'Van Riebeck's Hedge' survives – the only hedge in the world to be declared a Heritage Site! A century later, J.F. Kirsten, the owner of adjacent land called it his 'forest' or 'bosch', and it became Kirstenbosch – which still contains part of the hedge. With the Cape now British, in 1895 the land, on the lower slopes of Table Mountain, was bought by Cecil Rhodes, but remained an overgrown wasteland.

Rhodes bequeathed the land to the Cape Colony in 1902, and a year later a botanist from Cambridge University arrived. Professor Henry Harold Pearson, appointed Chair of Botany of the South African College, went round Kirstenbosch in a cart and realized its potential. He campaigned vigorously and the land was eventually set aside in 1913 as a botanic garden, but with such a tiny budget that Pearson had at first to work without pay. He toiled away for a decade to rescue the neglected site, making full use of its dramatic mountain setting to lay out a garden in the naturalistic English style (page 286). His strong belief was that the emphasis of the new garden should be to preserve the rich and important native flora of South Africa, especially the unique flora of the Cape region. Pearson died in 1916, perhaps of overwork, his epitaph in the garden reading, '*If ye seek his monument, look around*'.

Pearson's very first planting in the new Garden was the Cycad Amphitheatre, laid out to display these palm-like relatives of the conifers. Cycads (right) are a speciality of the South African flora, notably the genus *Encephalartos*, with its huge cones, of which Kirstenbosch grows 24 of the 25 known species, including a lonely male plant of *Encephalartos woodii*, the only specimen ever found. Other important collections include species of **Protea** or **Sugarbush** (*Protea*), both restricted to South Africa and Australia, and **Heaths** (*Erica*), the latter displaying a truly astonishing diversity of floral form and colour in southern Africa.

As well as these and other plantings, including a rockery and a *kopje* or knoll with species of the mostly southern African genus *Pelargonium* (so-called 'Geraniums'), a large Conservatory exhibits plants from the different regions of South Africa, including savanna, the Cape 'fynbos' Mediterranean-type shrubland and the semi-desert Karoo. Kirstenbosch is a centre

for botanical research and maintains a large collection of dried plant specimens in the Herbarium.

A number of distinguished botanists have been associated with the garden. A new chapter began after 1990, when the conservatist-botanist Professor Brian Huntley (below) arrived to head up Kirstenbosch, now called the South African National Biodiversity Institute. A visionary, he first of all wanted to see a change in the environmental priorities in South Africa, pointing out that, '*While millions of rands are spent every year on rescuing the rhino and the elephant, little is being done to tackle the daunting challenges of our environment's Third World destiny.*'

Even more significant was his mission to broaden interest in plants in an historically racially divided country. He realized that plants and gardens were traditionally of most interest to a white, middle-class audience. He was also acutely aware that black communities were both physically and mentally isolated from the idea of such a garden, stating in 1997, '*It simply wasn't in their culture to go round gardens. Children who have grown up in townships, particularly, with no exposure to natural landscapes, could not be expected to view our soil, our atmosphere, water, plants and animals as our richest assets. We needed to bring Kirstenbosch to a much wider audience, with a whole programme of education, upliftment and enjoyment.*' He did just that.

The results were soon obvious, with a thriving mixed-race attendance of 500,000 visitors a year and with children enjoying

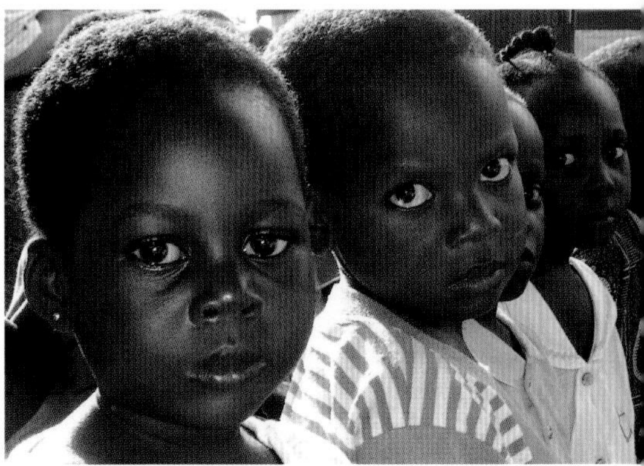

a spectacular 'outdoor classroom', school buses from the townships booked up months in advance, and a flourishing garden shop, restaurant and Visitors' Centre. Every Sunday evening in summer there is a concert, performed by local artists and international stars.

There are trails for hikers and mountaineers up the slopes of Table Mountain, one of them being 'Smuts' Track', named after South African statesman Jan Smuts (1870–1950), who was a keen amateur botanist and used it often as a route up to the summit.

Kirstenbosch has won many botany and tourism awards, not least in 2008 and 2018 Gold Medals at London's famous Chelsea Flower Show for the most creative display, together with the special cup awarded by the President of the Royal Horticultural Society (page 315).

GLASNEVIN AND IRISH BOTANY

If you asked people on both sides of the Atlantic which plants they associated with Ireland, they would probably first mention the green grass that makes it the 'Emerald Isle' – and then the potato, whose 1845 devastating blight caused famine, death and mass emigration (page102). They would

perhaps not associate Ireland with botanical research. They would be wrong.

It is not only the larger, wealthy, botanic gardens that have influenced the display and study of plants. The National Botanic Gardens of Ireland (above and top), which occupy 48 acres in the northern Dublin suburb of Glasnevin, are not only popular with visitors, but have also made a substantial contribution to botany and horticulture.

Even before the gardens arrived, the then village of Glasnevin had links with a group of influential 18th-century garden enthusiasts and writers. English statesman and writer Joseph Addison, who with Irish writer Richard Steele founded '*The Spectator*' in 1711, had a fondness for Glasnevin. Two of Addison's friends, the poet Thomas Tickell and Dr Patrick Delany, Dean of Down, had properties there with informally landscaped grounds, most radical for the time. Mrs Delany too was a plant lover – now remembered for her flower pictures, today in the British Museum, which she created from cut-out coloured paper. Thomas Tickell's land beside the little Tolka river would later be the site for the National Botanic Gardens.

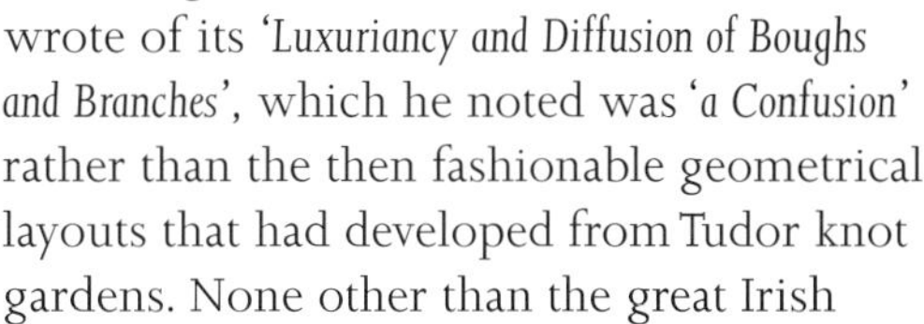

Describing his own London garden, Addison wrote of its '*Luxuriancy and Diffusion of Boughs and Branches*', which he noted was '*a Confusion*' rather than the then fashionable geometrical layouts that had developed from Tudor knot gardens. None other than the great Irish writer Jonathan Swift (right)noted how in the garden '*nature is preserv'd in every part, sometimes adorn'd, but nere debauch'd by art*'. Addison influenced another friend, the poet Alexander Pope, who wrote that "*All gardening is landscape painting*". Pope's circle included Delaney, Swift and the landscape architect William Kent, setting the scene for the English parks and gardens that revolutionized 18th century landscapes (page 288).

In 1795, with the financial support of the Irish parliament (abolished in 1800), the Dublin Society established their botanic garden at Glasnevin, under the charge of Dr Walter Wade, a physician, enthusiastic botanist and author of books on the flora of Co. Dublin and rare Irish plants. Both Wade and the Society intended for the gardens to promote practical botany in the service of medicine and agriculture, with a wide selection of plants soon established both outside and under glass. An early feature was a rockery, and peat was brought in to allow plants such as heathers to grow in the lime-rich soil. A succession of able Curators (Directors since 1966) has since made additions and improvements and ensured that the gardens have occupied the site to the present day.

One of the greatest of these, David Moore, was an early supporter of the Rev. Miles Berkeley, who in 1846 described the fungus later named *Phytophthera infestans*, the cause of the Potato Blight that led to the miseries of the Great Famine. Moore noted bleakly in a letter to Berkeley, '*Our potato crop is lost … throughout Ireland*.' Amazingly, both men were lambasted by the British and Irish botanical establishments. Moore was forced by his superiors in the Royal Dublin Society - who for some reason believed that the disease was caused by electricity in the atmosphere - to conduct worthless experiments with copper wires, whereas his pleas for the funding to research its true botanical nature and treatment fell on deaf ears.

The mid-19th century ushered in an age of glasshouse construction, following

the pioneering work of Joseph Paxton at Chatsworth House (page 295). At Glasnevin, the Famine years of the 1840s coincided with the installation of first of the Curvilinear Range of glasshouses, designed by Dublin ironmaster William Turner, also responsible for the palm house in Belfast Botanic Garden and the Great Palm House at Kew. The glasshouses at Glasnevin have enabled the cultivation of, for example, important collections of mature **Cycads** (palm-like relatives of the conifers), **Bamboos**, **Orchids and Ferns**, including a venerable **King Fern** (*Todea barbata*) (below),a tree-fern thought to be some 400 years old, and other plants from

Australia.

David Moore encouraged experimental horticulture such as growing orchids from seed and introducing tender species for outdoor cultivation, a relic of which is two **Chusan Palms** (*Trachycarpus fortunei*) (next page, top left) planted in 1870. His son became the

next Curator and between them they assured eighty-four years of continuity. Frederick Moore greatly expanded the numbers of orchids, which remain a Glasnevin speciality. Their joint efforts and those of their successors created gardens that display a wide range of plants from Ireland, Europe and around the world, including alpines on

the Rock Garden, a large selection of dwarf conifers, and an Arboretum with a fine collection of **Maples** (*Acer*), **Oaks** (*Quercus*) and **Pines** (*Pinus*). The flower-loving public was not ignored and the long, curved Herbaceous Walk with a selection of what gardeners call 'border plants', are justly famous. There is also a collection of autumn-flowering **Michaelmas-daisies** to provide late colour.

Horticulture – including training in the subject – has always been at the heart of Glasnevin's work, and the gardens have contributed many important flowers to Irish and British gardens. That suburban stalwart, the giant tufted **Pampas Grass**, (*Cortaderia selloana*) came from Argentina to Glasnevin in 1840, flowering there for the first time in Europe. Other striking newcomers to be distributed by Glasnevin included two large richly scented lilies, the **Giant Himalayan Lily** (*Cardiocrinum giganteum*), up to 3.5 metres tall and the largest of all lilies, and the white or pale pink **Natal Lily** (*Crinum moorei*). Perhaps the best-known plant associated with the gardens is **Chilean Potato Bush** (*Solanum crispum* 'Glasnevin'), a scrambling shrub covered with bluish-violet, yellow-centred flowers.

Recent years have seen increased public funding, enabling new planting, glasshouse restoration and the development of a modern herbarium and library.

Glasnevin is a beautiful, tranquil place, but with a strong practical and economic purpose that would have pleased its Royal Dublin Society founders.

FRANCE'S GARDEN OF BAMBOOS

On a hot day in the rocky hills of southern France, what better place to visit than a cool, lush, shady garden? Situated in a picturesque river valley near the town of Anduze, in the foothills of the Cévennes in SW France, lies one of Europe's most beautiful and unusual Botanic Gardens. Established in 1856 by a skilled amateur botanist, Eugène Mazel, whose family had made money in the silk and spice trade, the 34-hectare Bambouseraie bamboo park is still run by the family who bought it a few years after his death in 1890. The site is designed around a collection of 200 species and numerous garden cultivars of bamboos, reed- or cane-like woody grasses of tropical and warm temperate regions (page 249).

The bamboos of the Bambouseraie grow in clumps and thickets which create their own sheltered microclimate. A meandering network of paths and canals gently leads the visitor around this cool green setting. These are bordered by the groves of **Giant Timber Bamboo** (*Phyllostachys reticulata*) and other tall Phyllostachys species from China and Japan. In among the bamboos are numerous exotic trees, shrubs and flowers, mostly from Asia, including fine specimens of **Handkerchief Tree** (*Davidia involucrata*), **Maidenhair Tre**e (*Ginkgo biloba*), **Dawn Cypress** (*Metasequoia glyptostroboides*) and one of the largest specimens in Europe of the **Japanese Blue Oak** (*Quercus glauca*). Other trees include European natives such as huge individuals of **Oriental Plane** (*Platanus orientalis*) and **Pedunculate Oak** (*Quercus robor*); and, from the USA, a **Bull Bay** (*Magnolia grandiflora*) 26 metres tall and an avenue of **Coastal Redwoods** (*Sequoia sempervirens*). The bamboos range in size from 10 centimetres tall, through shrub-sized specimens to giants up to 25 metres tall.

The site incorporates a complete Japanese garden with clipped coniferous trees, elegant dwarf Japanese maples and a

wooden temple and bridge, created around a long, irregular pond-like canal, and a small bamboo-built Laotian village, complete with banana and sugar cane plants and pot-bellied pigs. There are pots of Bonsai trees, glasshouses with orchids and other flowers, and a maze of densely packed smaller Japanese bamboos. But, above all, thousands of giant bamboo stems rise up in their great shady groves, just as they do in the wild, the leaves gently swishing in the breeze. The Bambouseraie is both a relaxing and a unique learning experience where the visitor is immersed in the world of bamboo, including presentation of its economic uses and commissioned artwork and sculptures, as if one were actually in a garden in South-east Asia.

China, Japan and other countries in the Far East, as well as the USA, have their traditional and sometimes ancient bamboo gardens, but the Bambouseraie certainly holds one of the world's largest and most diverse collections, and one that is unique in Europe.

BRITAIN'S TWO GREAT FLOWER SHOWS

If you want to experience 'Plants on parade' in a spectacular way, you cannot do better than visit one of the world's great flower shows. America has two, in Philadelphia and Boston, Australians love their one in Melbourne, and in Europe, enthusiasts would probably vote that Holland's Keukendorf, known as 'The Garden of Europe', should take the prize.

But Great Britain boasts two world-beaters – the Chelsea Flower Show in late May and the Hampton Court Garden Festival in early July. In 2020, both were sadly cancelled because of the Covid pandemic, but they will re-open in the future.

The forerunner of Chelsea was created as far back as 1862 and was called the 'Royal Horticultural Society Great Spring Show', held in London's Kensington. But in 1912 the show moved to the grounds of the Royal Hospital, Chelsea, designed by Sir Christopher Wren and the home of the famous red-coated military veterans known as the 'Chelsea Pensioners'.

The term 'Royal' turned out to be most appropriate. In 1937, King George VI and Queen Elizabeth celebrated their coronation year, and a huge Empire Exhibition was staged at Chelsea with plants from all over the British Empire. Then Queen Elizabeth II was crowned in 1953 and that year most of the Royal Family attended the Chelsea

Flower Show - except the Queen because of pressure of work. But she has been there most years ever since, and Prince Charles and other members of the Royal family are regular attendees (like Princess Catherine - top right). In 2019 Princess Catherine co-designed a Show Garden entitled 'Back to Nature', which emphasized the benefits that gardens bring to happy childhoods and mental wellbeing. Celebrities of stage, screen, music and the arts home in on Chelsea, especially on the opening day, not least to be photographed among the exhibits. The Chelsea Pensioners too are very photogenic!

Over the years there have been many highlights, and it would be invidious to list the gardens which have made the greatest impact. But at least one clearly stood out. In 2020 the public were invited to name the Garden of the Decade – an award won by a garden inspired by the Yorkshire Dales, featuring a stone cottage, drystone walls, a stream and both garden flowers and a wildflower meadow. This echoed trends in recent years for more natural, environment-friendly exhibits and Show Gardens that emphasize native biodiversity such as that of flowery meadows (page 324), and the use of sustainable materials for propagation, planting and construction.

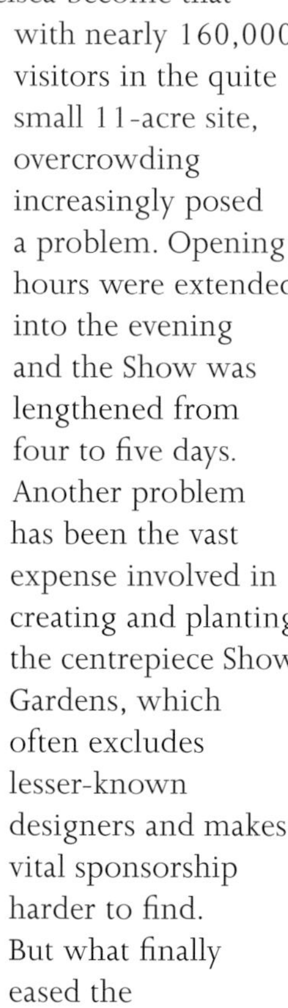

So popular did Chelsea become that with nearly 160,000 visitors in the quite small 11-acre site, overcrowding increasingly posed a problem. Opening hours were extended into the evening and the Show was lengthened from four to five days. Another problem has been the vast expense involved in creating and planting the centrepiece Show Gardens, which often excludes lesser-known designers and makes vital sponsorship harder to find. But what finally eased the overcrowding was the opening in 1990 of a second London flower show, sited in the grounds of another historic building, Hampton Court Palace, once the home of Cardinal Wolsey and Henry VIII. The show at Hampton Court started, curiously, as a sponsorship promotion to expand passenger numbers on the Network SouthEast railway. Many visitors arrived on special trains from Waterloo Station, where the staff wore celebratory Carnations.

With a larger area and extensive avenues and lawns, Hampton Court could handle 300,000 visitors, twice the numbers of Chelsea, and in 1993 the Royal Horticultural Society became fully involved, with the show renamed The Hampton Court Garden Festival in 2019. Hampton Court has proved a huge success with a gardening-obsessed British public. It has a far less fashionable and 'elitist' feel than Chelsea – which is in part a relic of the 'Season', when rich people paraded at races and regattas – and also it unashamedly embraces commerce, the show being an opportunity for growers, nurseries and seed companies to exhibit and popularise the latest products of the plant breeder's art. And it is later in the year than Chelsea, so more flowers are in bloom.

Both flower shows enjoy a week of prime-time TV coverage, although Hampton Court is more national than international, whereas Chelsea has a global reach of an outstanding 1.6 billion viewers.

An astonishing audience!

ALLOTMENTS IN WAR AND PEACE

Posters exhorting the public to 'Dig for Victory' are a memorable image of the Home Front in World War II. With food often scarce, allotments or, in America, community gardens – plots allocated to those without land to grow vegetables – came into their own, along with other so-called 'victory gardens' which sprang up in gardens, on private land and in public spaces, from railway embankments to botanic gardens, London parks and the White House lawn.

Constance Spry, famous for promoting flower arranging in Britain (and who arranged magnificent floral displays at the coronation of Queen Elizabeth), observed in the 1950s: '*Allotments really took hold of us during the 1914 -18 war and many learned for the first time the healing that comes through working in the soil and the joy and elation that is to be found in the miracle of growing a plant from a seed.*' She was writing

Anthony Hannaford

in the heyday of allotments, during and following the Second World War, when one and a half million were under cultivation. Now reduced to some 300,000 in all, yet with an ever-increasing demand, they look set to remain a significant element of UK gardening life.

Allotments provide many benefits, although their principal purpose is to give families and individuals the wherewithal to produce plentiful, good quality, home-grown food. They emerged from the 16th century onward, as the Enclosure Acts fenced common land and increasingly deprived country people access and landowners would allocate plots to the poor and landless. As expanding urban sprawl in the 19th century created a largely landless population, allotments were established through the 1908 Small Holdings and Allotments Act and subsequent legislation.

An allotment is no mere vegetable patch. It requires hard but enjoyable work, yields a cornucopia of vegetables, soft fruits and flowers, saves money, provides healthy exercise and fresh air, and opportunities to exchange seeds, plants and ideas with other gardeners. Allotments are often home to old and rare vegetable varieties, thus conserving crop plant genetic diversity, and a refuge for rare 'arable wildflowers'. The food produced is fresh and flavoursome – few foods taste as good as freshly dug new potatoes – and composting recycles garden and kitchen rubbish and reduces the use of peat. Herbicides and pesticides are much frowned upon, and the non-intensive cultivation allows wildlife to flourish. An allotment site, with its individual plots, boundaries, hedges and spare corners is a sustainable ecosystem which reduces 'air miles'. Some plots have chickens, and there may be a wildflower meadow and beehives.

Research by Sheffield University has shown how, when compared with arable land, allotment soil has 32% more carbon and 25% more nitrogen and is much less compacted. Food yield on allotments is up to 11 times higher, with no deterioration of soil quality. Governments should support allotments more, as did Mikhail Gorbachov

(pictured) in the closing years of the Soviet Union when his *perestroika* (restructuring) reforms promoted them as a significant contributor to the national food supply.

Allotments in Britain have again come to the fore. The Coronavirus lockdown of 2020 and possible food shortages, together with much greater public awareness of growing environmental issues, has greatly revived interest in home-grown produce, as well as self-sufficiency and allotments. 'Dig for Victory' has perhaps returned!

The sad story of the Diggers

Allotments in England are a symbol of both community spirit and of freedom, individuality and self-sufficiency, with a dash of old-fashioned rural radicalism. In April 1649, in a key event in the history of the allotment movement, a group of landless people occupied St George's Hill near Weybridge in Surrey. The Diggers, one of several radical political and religious groups to emerge from the English Civil War, cleared land, built small cottages and planted beans, parsnips and carrots in the sandy heathland soil. Local landowners complained to the government – the Commonwealth that had replaced Charles I – and, despite the intervention of the fair-minded Sir Thomas Fairfax, the commander of the New Model Army, ordered the soldiers to drive the Diggers away and destroy all that they had achieved. The story of their doomed peaceful struggle for land, and the idea that the Earth is a resource to be shared wisely for the common good, rings down the years as an inspiration to conservationists. St George's Hill is today an affluent London suburb and home to a prestigious golf course.

Lionel de Rothschild, of the great banking family, and an expert on gardens, was asked to address members of the City Horticultural Society, before they left for their commuter trains. Most of them had allotments or tiny suburban gardens. So they were somewhat surprised by one piece of advice. '*No garden, however small, should contain less than two acres of rough woodland.*'

PUBLIC PARKS, GRASSY URBAN BLESSINGS

Public parks - an absolute blessing for those living in crowded cities who have no garden, for those who own dogs, and for anyone wanting to exercise in the fresh air. But they were a long time coming, not until the late 16th century – with one of the first created in Spain, Seville's La Alameda de Hércules (below).

Today, of course, they are not only widespread, but designed with all kinds of facilities to increase our enjoyment and health with well-spaced trees, gardens, ponds and play, sports and picnic areas. Above all, park visitors benefit from grass, short to make walking and running easier and reduce insects, which is managed by mowing – made possible since Edwin Budding's invention of the lawn mower in 1830 (page 255).

Britain was the birthplace of the Industrial Revolution, with workers leaving the countryside and pouring into overcrowded cities and towns that became smoky slums from the start. No wonder no less than 27,000 public parks were laid out in Britain to try to give the populace some healthy outlet. Their popularity increased after Sir John Lubbock, Liberal MP, polymath and friend of Charles Darwin, guided The Bank Holiday Act of 1871 through Parliament and on public holidays city dwellers flocked to parks.

Older famous parks had grander origins. London's Hyde Park (below)was named

Anthony Hannaford

after a village that King Henry VIII annexed for his royal hunting ground. St James's Park and Regent's Park were laid out by the great John Nash, the renowned architect of the Regency period, famous for Buckingham Palace and Regent's Street. Joseph Paxton, best-known for his vast greenhouses for Chatworth and the Great Exhibition (page 295), created Princes Park in Toxteth, a suburb of Liverpool - which was then nearly as rich a city as London. Across the Mersey, in nearby Birkenhead in 1847, Paxton laid out an even grander park (top right), the

first in the world to be publicly funded. Such was the appeal of its design that it was soon widely imitated.

Curiously, in North America, it was rural cemeteries at first that were widely used for recreation. But soon dedicated parks were being laid out, like Lincoln Park in Chicago, Mission Bay Park in San Diego, and of

course, Central Park (above)in New York City, probably the most visited park in the world. Frederick Law Olmsted came to England in 1850 to visit Birkenhead Park, and was much influenced by Paxton's ideas when he designed Central Park.

Today, public parks remain open, grassy urban 'green lungs', with space to walk, run, ride horses or bicycles, play sports, picnic, paint, enjoy bird-watching or just watch the world go by. When there is no more room for big traditional parks, there are 'linear parks' created on abandoned urban railway lines, the most famous being the High Line Park (top) on New York's Lower West Side, Chicago's 606 park or small so-called 'pocket parks', as in Glendale, California. You could say that Dublin's St Stephen's Green, opened to the public in 1880 within an existing Georgian square, was an early version of such a compressed urban haven.

Even if mostly small, parks have made a big difference to urban living.

Anthony Hannaford

GIVERNY, MONET'S 'BEAUTIFUL MASTERPIECE'

When most of us look out of the window of a train, we often see little more than the boring backs of houses, apartment blocks or track-side rubbish and graffiti. By chance, in 1883, Claude Monet looked out and saw just the house he wanted to live in. He would make it famous forever.

The village of Giverny is very old, dating back to Roman rule in Gaul. The house that Monet had seen, and at first, rented, was a farmhouse complete with a kitchen garden and an orchard. He became more and more attached to it, eventually buying it in 1890. He began to transform the gardens, and with

200,000 flowers and a specially dug water-lily pond, filled by diverting a branch of the nearby River Epte.

Monet was one of the great French Impressionists, who had shocked the art establishment with their novel and vibrant use of colour and light. In particular Monet, who loved experimenting with the way that light changed the same scene painted at different times of the day, as with his studies of Rouen Cathedral and Westminster Bridge, and he was equally adept at urban scenes and his beloved French countryside.

But never has a painter and his own house and garden been so strongly linked. The pond, with its **Waterlilies** (*Nymphaea*), **Weeping Willows**, and its little Japanese bridge with its two trailing **Wisteria** (*Wisteria floribunda* and *W.chinensis*), are now familiar to the whole world through a series of wonderful paintings, each recording different light and weather conditions, sometimes caught from the bank or from a rowing boat filled with canvasses ready to be painted.

Monet even built an especially long studio for some of his Nymphéas series – huge, panoramic views dozens of feet across.

It is curious to realize that some of these beautiful and peaceful canvasses were painted against a background of trains steaming past with troops and ammunition for the 1914-18 front, close enough for him to hear the 'thudding of the guns.'

Monet's house is carefully preserved, complete with the Japanese prints that he collected, a charming kitchen and that magnificent garden and lily-pond. Hundreds of thousands of art-lovers come to pay their respects each year. However great his paintings were, Monet always insisted, '*My garden is my most beautiful masterpiece*'.

Everyone should be very glad that Claude Monet, by chance, glanced up to look out of the train window and was not engrossed in a book!

SISSINGHURST – A MARRIAGE OF TWO GREAT TALENTS

Chance played a major role in the story of Sissinghurst in Kent, one of the most famously romantic gardens in the world. If Vita Sackville-West had not fallen for, first the charms of Harold Nicolson, and second, for a derelict castle and wasteland in Sissinghurst, this glorious garden would certainly have been lost to us forever. Their marriage in 1913 led to a great half-century collaboration of visionary planting (Vita) and extraordinary design talent (Harold) and produced a stunning combination of abundance and restraint. Unusually the garden is divided into separate rooms and features 'one-colour areas', the most famous being the 'White Garden', where the lack of any other colour not only produces a rare feeling of tranquillity, but also persuades the eye to look more closely at the structure of the plants.

As Vita said herself in an article in the journal of the Royal Horticultural Society: *'I could never have done it myself. Fortunately I had, through marriage, the ideal collaborator… He had a natural taste for symmetry, and an ingenuity for forcing focal points or long-distance views where everything seemed against him, a capacity I totally lacked.'*

Both saw the garden as another house, creating room after room of intimate spaces (in Harold's words, *'a succession of privacies'*), each surrounded by walls or high hedges, and each embracing a formality of shape with an exuberant freedom of planting. And both were prolific writers and diarists, so the history of the garden and its creation have been kept for posterity, from the time that the land was little more than a wilderness of weeds.

Their treasure trove of writing was certainly not confined to diaries. A novelist, poet and essayist of distinction, Vita wrote numerous works throughout her life, the most famous of which are the novels *The Edwardians* and *All Passion Spent*. She also contributed for fourteen years to a weekly gardening column in the *Observer* newspaper, describing her horticultural failures as well as her successes and building up a legion of avid readers.

Both were as unconventional in their private lives as they were in their garden, indulging in extramarital, homosexual affairs – Vita, famously, with Virginia Woolf and Violet Trefusis. However the marriage of Vita and Harold remained strong.

But for the chance of these two eccentric and highly charismatic personalities coming together, working alongside each other and having the means to pursue their dream, there would be no Sissinghurst. Indeed, even Harold himself had initial doubts about the scale of the project. However, he also added the telling phrase: *'We like it.'*

How supremely fortunate for the world's gardeners and plant lovers that they did!

FLOWERY MEADOWS OLD AND NEW

Anthony Hannaford

Few sights in the countryside are as beautiful and uplifting as a meadow bright with wildflowers, but today such places are all too rare. A century ago, Britain was full of them. The English, especially, love flowery meadows, which have inspired poets, prose writers and artists since Chaucer and Shakespeare and are deeply engrained in the national conscience. Now people increasingly want to enjoy them in public spaces and their gardens.

In the past nobody actually ever planted wildflower meadows. Over centuries of farm husbandry, they simply evolved from native grassland, probably once restricted to steep slopes, riverbanks and woodland glades, to become the motor of the rural economy. They yielded a range of economic benefits – grazing, hay, meat, hides and wool, milk, butter and cheese, as well as honey, medicinal herbs and wild greens – and less obvious ecological 'goods and services' such as carbon storage and slower water run-off. They also sheltered the useful insects that pollinate crops and fruit trees and prey upon pests. These benefits continue, but with today's lack of traditional non-intensive management, biodiversity-rich 'High Nature Value' grassland has become one of the most threatened temperate ecosystems, surviving mostly in the mountains of Eurasia. But, these Alpine meadows too are threatened by modern farming, and by climate change.

In the UK, since the Second World War, 97% of these iconic grasslands have sadly disappeared from the countryside. They survive in isolated pockets, usually in nature reserves rather than on farms. Modern intensive farming did for them by the mass use of industrial fertilizers and by cutting the grass too early in the season before the wildflowers have bloomed and set seed, then fermenting and storing it as silage. Their decline begun once tractors started to replace horses, which required only plentiful grazing and hay for fuel. Old permanent pastures as well – always grazed, not mown – less flowery but with their own special plants, were replaced by short-term leys of fast-growing **Ryegrass** (*Lolium perenne*) (1) and **White Clover** (*Trifolium. repens*) (2). Some wildflowers, including the much-loved **Cowslip** (*Primula veris*) (3), are more typical of pastures than hay-meadows.

Only recently, when most of the old meadows have gone, are they more widely appreciated, even showcased. They have frequently featured as an element in garden

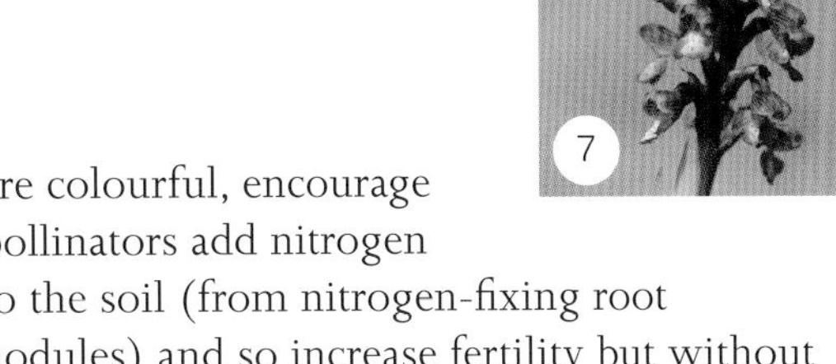

designs, not least at the Chelsea Flower Show, where they've made a considerable impact. The intimate mix of grasses and flowers both looks beautiful and is a habitat for bees, butterflies and other insects, so that even the smallest patch can make a useful contribution to conservation.

Some so-called wildflower meadows are sown with colourful annuals, but rather these are imitations of arable fields and are readily invaded by coarse weeds. Most, but by no means all, native meadow wildflowers are longer-lived perennials that can compete in a dense sward, and it is these that are best included in a garden meadow. They form a varied selection, including **Clovers**, **Buttercups**, **Scabious**, **Knapweeds** and members of the **Mint** and **Sage** and the **Dandelion** and daisy families. Many bulbs, including **Daffodils** (*Narcissus pseudonarcissus*) (4)and, in damper spots, **Snake's-head Fritillary** (*Fritillaria meleagris*) (5) will also naturalize well among the grass. **Clovers** and related leguminous plants are particularly valuable to include, as they are colourful, encourage pollinators add nitrogen to the soil (from nitrogen-fixing root nodules) and so increase fertility but without over-enrichment.

Provided a site does not have a rich soil, which tilts the balance towards more aggressive species, a flowery meadow can be established from seed and transplants (such as seedlings grown as 'plugs' in compartmented trays). Sowing the annual, semi-parasitic **Yellow Rattle** (*Rhinanthus minor*) (6) will help to reduce the vigour of the grasses and allow the flowers to establish better. One should try to find seed from as local a source as possible and good suppliers can advise with this. For too long, much supposedly native wildflower seed came in from abroad, often robust agricultural versions of widespread plants that look wrong and may cause genetic problems when they cross with native populations.

An exemplary wildflower meadow,

and one of the world's most famous, is that established and nurtured by HRH The Prince of Wales since the 1980s in the grounds of Highgrove, his Gloucestershire home. Although integral to the garden landscape and planted with exotic bulbs such as **Alliums**, **Camassias** and **Tulips**, it is a true native meadow. The floral diversity has

steadily increased – to include seven different orchids – helped by careful maintenance and an annual seed collection to repair and expand the site. The sward is cut, in stages, in late July and early August, to ensure that the grasses and wildflowers can set seed. The Prince, who keeps a personal eye on his meadow, is particularly proud of a colony of rare **Green-winged Orchids** (*Anacamptis morio*) (7) which arrived of their own accord – a tribute to the health and vitality of a well-managed habitat.

To encourage the establishment of more such flowery meadows, in 2012 Prince Charles convened an alliance of conservation partners, led by Plantlife, to establish a nationwide network of Coronation Meadows marking the 60 years since the coronation of his mother, Queen Elizabeth. In 2016, the 90th Coronation Meadow was initiated in London's Green Park to celebrate her 90th birthday.

Flowery meadows, once feared lost forever, are thankfully having a deserved renaissance. They may no longer have practical value on farms but will always be needed to give us pleasure and boost our mental well-being while an providing an invaluable food source for our increasingly diminishing insect population. But one hurdle will remain - can farmers afford them?

DEREK JARMAN AND HIS SHINGLE BEACH GARDEN

Britain is a nation of gardeners. The English especially have always loved their traditional cottage gardens where varied and colourful flowers grow together informally in profusion, many of them self-seeding to create their own patterns. Although the flowers are often old-fashioned, there's always scope for experiment and novelty in the selection of plants and in garden layout.

One of the most talked-about and innovative of all cottage gardens was created not by a conventional garden designer of the old school but by a radical, avant-garde film maker, stage designer and gay activist who died in 1994. A 'Renaissance Man' who was a painter and writer too, Derek Jarman had been interested in gardens since childhood and, when in 1986 he purchased the black-painted timber Prospect Cottage on the shingle promontory of Dungeness in Kent, he set about creating his own vision of a Paradise Garden. Loosely resembling a normal cottage garden, it was

planned to be wild, anarchic, free and with no true boundary. The garden has never been allowed a fence – being technically within a nature conservation site, though almost in the shadow of a nuclear power station – but Jarman added structure by incorporating assorted driftwood and flotsam, and he encouraged robust clumps of **Sea Kale** (*Crambe maritima*) (below), a member of the cabbage family or Brassicaceae, with thick,

crinkled greyish leaves and dense clusters of scented white flowers. Dungeness holds one of its largest British populations – and it is also a fashionable and peculiarly English spring vegetable. He selected some hardy garden plants (alas most of the roses died in the salty winds) but also made full use of this and other native shingle plants, notably **Yellow Horned-poppy** (*Glaucium flavum*) (top left) and other wild poppies (page 50), and established weeds such as

Red Valerian (*Centranthus ruber*) (right), from the hills of the Mediterranean but quite at home among the hot dry pebbles and cobbles of the English seaside.

This colourful garden was a refuge, comfort and inspiration for its creator, who was sadly diagnosed HIV-positive soon after he bought the cottage and knew he had but a short time to enjoy his own little house and garden. It remains a place of pilgrimage for his admirers, gardeners and artists and has much influenced modern garden design and use of materials in gardens, even helping to inspire nurserywoman and gardener Beth Chatto to create her own gravel garden.

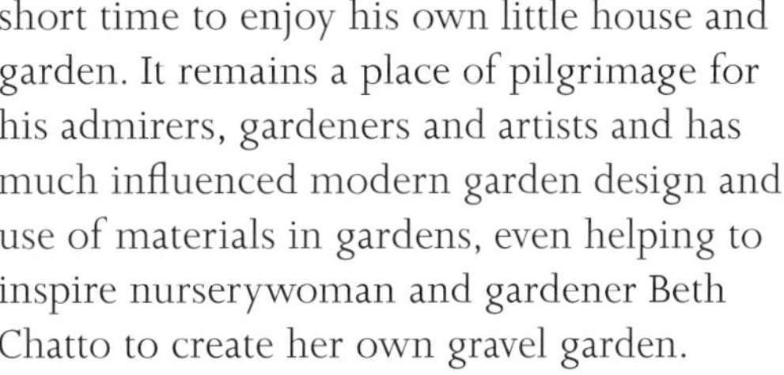

In the Kent seaside town of Folkestone the disused railway line along the old harbour mole has been landscaped into a long shingle garden, echoing both nearby Dungeness and Jarman's garden. Dominated by native plant life but by no means exclusively so, the tufted grasses, sea kale and variety of white, pink, red, yellow and blue wildflowers blend ornament, local authenticity, biodiversity conservation and municipal order into an intriguing contemporary mix! And, after the death of Jarman's partner in 2018, a crowd-funding campaign saved Prospect Cottage and its shingle garden for posterity. An arts charity, Creative Folkestone, now owns and maintains the site, a most unusual gardening legacy that does not detract from, but enhances, conventional English informal planting.

Plants & Us

ANCIENT CONIFERS – ORNAMENTS AND SURVIVORS

Imagine what we'd say if our friends announced that they'd seen a dinosaur at the bottom of their garden! But in plant terms, that's exactly what has happened with the discovery of trees closely resembling the ones that dinosaurs lived with and ate.

The massive Australian bushfires of 2019–2020 did incalculable damage to forests, wildlife and human communities. Amid the destruction, an inspiring image was a tall grove of ancient coniferous trees deep within a precipitous gorge, vivid green against the scorched scrub and forest. The trees had been headline news in 1994 when this new species, **Wollemi Pine** (*Wollemia nobilis*), was first discovered in the Wollemi National Park in the Blue Mountains of New South Wales, near Sydney. Up to 40 metres tall, with distinctive knobbly bark, slender crowns, long flat leaves and large spiky cones, they closely resemble fossils of 200 million years ago from the age of dinosaurs.

The discovery caused a stir far beyond botanical circles, not least because the Wollemi Pine turned out to be a lost relative of a 'dinosaur' in the same family – one already a feature of some UK suburban landscapes. **Monkey Puzzle** (*Araucaria araucana*) (top)has become associated with Victorian houses, gardens and parks, an evergreen cliché of leafy suburbs and old-fashioned vistas. Preferring damp temperate climates and widely planted in the UK and along the west coast of North America, it grows to 40 m tall, with a straight trunk and domed mass of spiky-leaved branches. Native to the lower slopes of the Andes of central and southern Chile, where it is the national tree, and western Argentina, it grows wild *en masse* and no longer looks gawky and misplaced but is magnificent. Alas, the once extensive Monkey Puzzle forests have been extensively damaged by logging (happily banned since 1990), fires, grazing and replacement by non-native trees. The Pehuenche native people, for whom the trees are sacred, still depend on them for their nuts and timber.

The Pacific region from Australia to Chile, around its rim and on islands like Taiwan and New Caledonia, holds much of Earth's diversity of rare conifers. Several of these special trees now feature prominently in parks and gardens worldwide. Some of them have been known to science for centuries, such as **Maidenhair Tree** or the **Ginkgo** (*Ginkgo biloba*) (next page top), a beautiful tree with long-stalked, fan-shaped leaves that is largely extinct in the wild but had survived around ancient Chinese

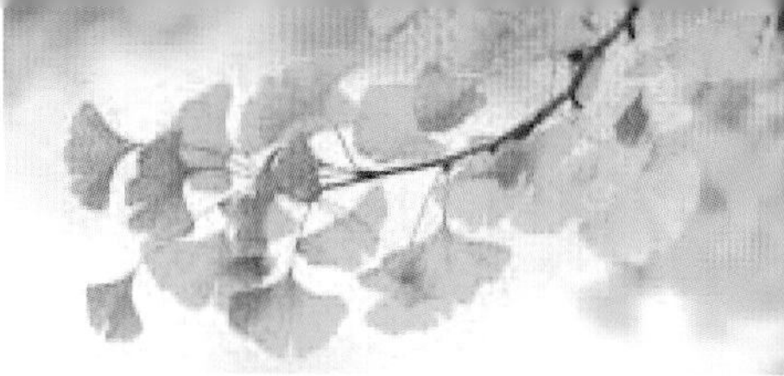

and temples.

Others have turned up only in the last 100 years. In 1944 Chinese botanists discovered a few groves of a coniferous tree which, like Wollemi Pine, was close to previously known fossils. Named in 1948 only after World War II had ended and scientists could visit (and collect and distribute seeds), **Dawn Cypress** (*Metasequioa glyptostroboides*) (top right) , is like a diminutive **Giant Sequoia**. It is now widely planted in gardens, streets and parks, including Strawberry Fields, the area of New York's Central Park dedicated to the assassinated Beatle, John Lennon.

The Wollemi Pine, Monkey Puzzle and some other ancient relict conifers are all in the Araucariceae, a southern hemisphere family that is a good example of a plant distribution broken up millions of years ago by continental drift. **Norfolk Island Pine** (*Araucaria heterophylla*) (middle right), Christmas tree-like with spaced regular whorls of branches, is native only to the island of that name between Australia and New Zealand – but is a familiar sight for tourists as a tall specimen tree planted in Mediterranean gardens. At the northern end of New Zealand's North Island, New Zealand **Kauri** or **Kauri Pine** (*Agathis australis*) (bottom right), survives from once extensive forests perhaps covering over 12,000 square kilometres. Amazingly, old growth Kauri forest, the trees up to 50 metres tall with trunks that can grow as massive as those of Giant Sequoia, was still being clear-felled up until the late 1960s. Now the Kauri forest is protected not only for the great trees and their rich habitat but also as an efficient carbon store, estimated to capture nearly 1,000 tonnes per hectare, one of the highest levels known on Earth.

Sadly, all these trees face uncontrolled logging and also forest fires, an increasing feature of a warming planet. Australian bushfires, started by lightning, devastated half a million hectares, but the Wollemi Pines were saved – just two were lost – by dropping water and retardant from the air, after which firefighters descended into the gorge to set up an irrigation system. The remote and sheltered habitat provides the trees with a degree of safety from natural events – they must have survived bushfires for countless millennia – and also greedy, and thoroughly unscrupulous plant collectors. Finding the invasive soil-borne water mould, *Phytophthora cinnamomi* on some of the pines, perhaps introduced on the clothes or equipment of well-meaning visitors, shows how wise conservationists have been to withhold the precise locality from the public.

Such ancient conifers are among the most remarkable and fascinating of living plants and provide vital evidence for scientists studying evolution and plant geography. And our lives would be the poorer without them out there 'on parade'.

WALKING STICKS, AND KEEPING THE PACE

In Greek legend, the Sphinx devoured all who approached the city of Thebes and were unable to answer her question. '*What creature walks on four legs in the morning, two at noon, and three in the evening?*' In Sophocles's 5th century BC play, 'Oedipus the King', Oedipus correctly answers: '*Anthropos*', a man – who crawls on all fours as a baby and walks upright as an adult, but in old age leans on a third leg, a stick. The angry Sphinx threw herself off a cliff and Thebes rewarded Oedipus with marriage to Jocasta, his mother and the widow of the father he had inadvertently killed, thus setting off the tragedy at the heart of the play.

Who first used walking sticks? Probably our earliest ancestors as an aid to balance in advancing years (though their life expectancy was much shorter) or following an injury, and more often as a useful companion on rocky, slippery or uneven terrain. After all, even gorillas have been seen using sticks to walk with!

But the concept of the walking stick purely as an aid to balance falls far short of their role in human history. Walking sticks were also symbols of leadership and authority, and the wielding of a stick to command attention or preface a momentous message goes back to antiquity. In the biblical Book of Exodus, Moses is said to have waved his staff or stick to part the Red Sea waters and save his people; and his brother Aaron, too, had a famous rod, with which he performed miracles. Benjamin Franklin so valued his ornate stick that he left it to his good friend President George Washington.

Now generally seen as purely walking aids, this was certainly not their sole purpose through the centuries. In the 17th century, the walking stick replaced the sword as part of the upper-class dress code, and sticks became fashion items with intricate designs. In 1700, London even issued licenses for gentlemen to carry walking sticks correctly to ensure etiquette!

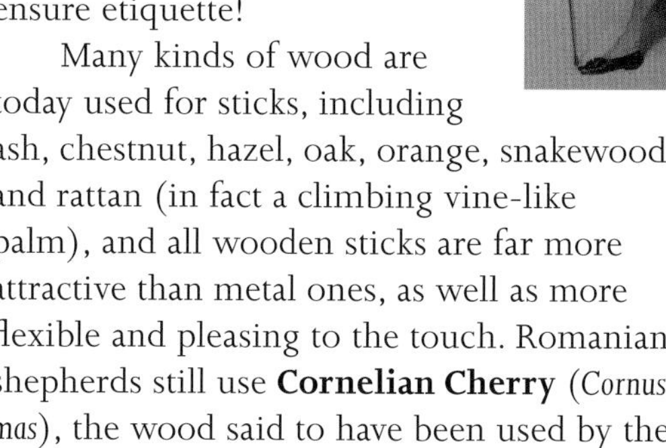

Many kinds of wood are today used for sticks, including ash, chestnut, hazel, oak, orange, snakewood and rattan (in fact a climbing vine-like palm), and all wooden sticks are far more attractive than metal ones, as well as more flexible and pleasing to the touch. Romanian shepherds still use **Cornelian Cherry** (*Cornus mas*), the wood said to have been used by the heroes of ancient Greece and Rome to make the shafts of their spears and javelins.

In the military, sticks or canes have been used as symbols of authority for centuries, with Roman centurions carrying vine staffs. British army soldiers and Royal Marines used to carry 'swagger sticks' when going off duty, a practice briefly followed by the US Marines (and, unsurprisingly, General George Patton). British officers had their canes, with cavalry

officers appropriately sporting riding crops. Officers in Irish regiments, including the Irish Guards, carried **Blackthorn** (*Prunus spinosa*) sticks based on the old Irish weapon, the shillelagh or countryman's cudgel.

A unique version of the walking stick is the 'pace stick', carried by British drill instructors. This opens up to measure the various pace lengths the drilling soldiers should march.

Curiously, among foreigners this has only been taken up by the Australian Federal Police, the Royal Danish army, and the Army of Pakistan.

FRIENDS ACROSS THE STREET

Of course, most of us like to have friendly neighbours – and keep in touch with them. But how strange and wonderful that trees can feel and do the same! One species in particular seems to like to reach out to friends across the street.

If you visit the beautiful old city of Burgos in northern Spain in winter, when the leaves are off the trees, you will see how the **Plane Trees** (*Platanus acerifolia*) have reached over and linked branches both down the street, the Paseo El Espolón, and also across it.

While trees and plants often link up and communicate through their roots underground (page124), it is very unusual and dramatic to see a parade of them doing that above our heads.

Do they find comfort and security in touch and communication?

BARK, TANNIN AND LEATHER

The legionaries of Republican and Imperial Rome, dominant and largely undefeated for half a millennium, consumed leather as much as they did iron. As Professor Barrie Juniper of Oxford University has perceptively remarked: '*The grim efficiency of the legion was based in no small part on the sophistication of the Latin tanning industry.*'

Indeed, leather is one of the most important materials for our history and society. After all, how many of us don't wear leather shoes or boots? Or belts or jackets? Or never sit in a leather chair? Leather is simply something we take for granted, without ever thinking about it. And, surprisingly, its production, or 'tanning', is utterly dependent on plants.

The tanning of animal skins and hides (the latter from cattle and horses) to manufacture leather goes way back into our prehistory. The traditional curing process relies on the 'tannins' present in plants, which help to make them unpalatable to grazing or browsing animals. Complex polyphenolic chemicals with a bitter and astringent taste, tannins combine with the collagen proteins in the skins and hides, altering their structure to make the material more flexible, durable and resistant to decomposition by bacteria and fungi.

Leather making may have begun in Asia but was developed in the Middle East. The ancient Egyptians tanned leather with the bark and pods of **Red Acacia** (*Acacia seyal*) (above), which contain up to 20% tannin. Today, another Acacia species, **Black Wattle** (*Acacia mearnsii*), native to Australia, but now grown from southern Africa to Kenya, provides a global source of tannin. Other trees and shrubs include the wood of **Sweet Chestnut** (*Castanea sativa*) and a of species of **Quebraco** (*Schinopsis*) from Argentina and Paraguay, now much depleted through over-exploitation. The leaves of **Mediterranean Sumac** or **Tanner's Sumac** (*Rhus coriaria*), are used in making Moroccan, Spanish and other high-quality leathers. Tannin extracted from a number of other trees, including mangroves, is widely used elsewhere.

Above all, oaks have been a major source of tannin. For example, the particularly large acorns and woody, shaggy-scaled acorn-cups of **Mount Tabor Oak** (*Quercus ithaburensis*), native from Syria to Palestine, together with **Valonia Oak** (subspecies *macrolepis*), its variant in Turkey, the Balkans and Southern Italy, were an important crop in the eastern Mediterranean region from ancient times. The bark of other Mediterranean and European oak species, both deciduous and

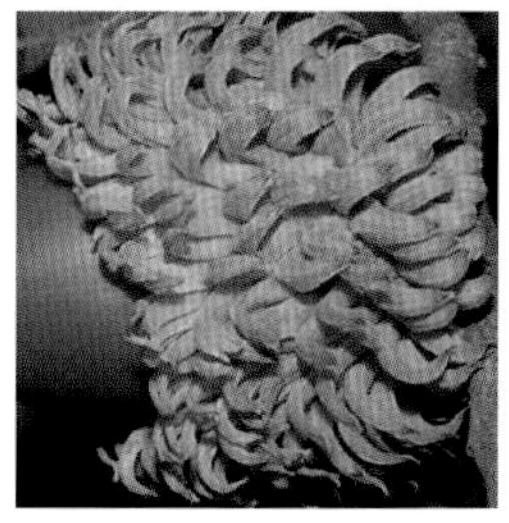

evergreen, has also been used in tanning. The **English Oak** (*Quercus robur*) and the similar, related **Sessile Oak** (*Quercus petraea*) yielded much more than the timber for which they are famed, with the largest boom in bark production being during the period 1780–1850. The wars against France and later in the British colonies necessitated much leather equipment for men and horses and large numbers of boots and shoes on land and sea.

Tanning was a time-consuming, unpleasant business, usually banished to the edges of towns due to foul smells and the pollution of water courses. Hides

and skins were soaked, cleaned, dehaired, stretched and softened with a variety of unpleasant substances including urine, dog or pigeon dung, brains and lime before the actual tanning with bark – not a job for the fainthearted! High quality and specialized leathers are still prepared and tanned with oak bark along traditional lines – a process which may take a year to complete – though today's tan-yard is more mechanized and certainly more hygienic! Tanning mostly now involves the use of chemicals like chromium sulphate, which produces the softer leather suitable for clothes, furnishings and items such as handbags, as well as the 'uppers' of leather shoes.

Leather, an ingenious and successful combining of animal and plant products, provided pre-industrial societies with saddles and harnesses for horses, blacksmiths' and other artisans' aprons and other hard-wearing clothing. It was from earliest times adopted by armies, as it made possible the development of efficient soldiers' kit – shields, helmets, armour, jerkins, scabbards, the quivers and wrist guards of the archer, boots and sandals. (Ironically, Napoleon's Grande Armée invaded Russia in 1812 shod with boots of Northampton leather!)

For civilians as well as soldiers, from the past to the present, leather has provided footwear, belts, coats, baggage, wineskins, jugs and mugs, and canopies, tents, sails – even boats. In 1976–77, explorer and historian Tim Severin and his crew sailed an Irish curragh (pictured) of forty-nine traditionally tanned ox hides stretched over a wooden frame, laced together with almost two miles of leather thongs, from the Dingle peninsula in SW Ireland, via Iceland to Newfoundland. They thus showed how St Brendan, the Irish monk and legendary 6th century Atlantic voyager, could indeed have sailed to America via Iceland.

Leather has come a long way since the unsavoury tan-yards of past centuries, but it remains one of the most persistent and valuable influences of plants on human society.

Of course, there are many ways that plants have influenced our lives other than feeding, clothing and healing us. For thousands of years, they also fulfilled another basic function – providing a roof to keep out the elements from where we live and work, and they did it with thatching.

Thatching is the craft of building a roof with locally available dry vegetation like straw, reeds or other grasses, sedge, flax, rushes, heather, broom, raffia or palm fronds. Indeed, for most of history it was the only way to roof a dwelling. Thatch was light in weight, could cover uneven surfaces, repel rainwater and snow, provide insulation from cold and heat, and use cheap, locally available plants. Indeed, thatch could be, and still is, found all over the world in temperate and tropical regions, from the most ancient times in the Americas, Asia and Africa. In Europe, straw became a key material in Neolithic times when cereals were first being grown.

In Britain, thatch was the only widespread material for roofs until the mid-1800s, when it became gradually possible to transport heavy Welsh slate by canals and then harness the power of the new steam engines. It survived longer in Ireland, from where it has largely disappeared in recent years. More recently, short-stemmed wheat varieties replaced the old tall wheats (depicted vividly in Pieter Breughal the Elder's famous 1565 painting 'The Harvesters') (above) and another new machine, the combine harvester, affected thatching because it cut the straw too short. This made 'Norfolk' reed, the long semi-rigid stems of **Common Reed** (*Phragmites australis*), more popular. So, for a long while, in spite of some grand buildings with thatching, a thatched building became associated with poverty. Now, because people are looking for a 'rustic' look, by contrast thatch tends to reflect affluence, and there are around 60,000 thatched buildings in Britain – alongside a revival in the numbers of skilled thatchers, using either Norfolk reed, mostly imported today from eastern Europe, or specially grown long 'heritage' straw from old wheat varieties.

The relatively common family name of Thatcher in the UK, including a rather famous Prime Minister, Margaret Thatcher, is testament to how thriving the industry once was. Long may it continue to be.

SINGAPORE: THE RAINFOREST THAT BECAME A GARDEN CITY

Tropical rainforests are vulnerable yet vital to the integrity of Earth's biodiversity and climate. We hear daily of how these once extensive forests of the Old and New World Tropics are being cleared for farming or building, never to be replaced. But it is unusual for this special ecosystem, albeit a small fragment, to thrive deep within a city, like Singapore. This technologically advanced, wealthy, island city-state at the tip of the Malay peninsula has been wisely planned as a 'Garden City', and at its heart the rainforest is an integral part of the 82-hectare Singapore Botanic Gardens. Along with Tijuca Forest in Rio de Janeiro, Brazil, this is the only rainforest to lie within a city.

Sir Thomas Stamford Raffles, who founded the city in 1819 as a trading post, and after whom the world-famous Raffles Hotel is named, established a small garden for investigating tropical crops. It soon closed, but in 1859 the present Singapore Botanic Gardens site was established in a pocket of surviving rainforest and adjacent abandoned plantations. The colonial administration took over the Gardens in 1874, appointed a supervisor and three years later took delivery of rubber tree seedlings from South America via the Royal Botanic Gardens, Kew (page 291).

The first Director, H. N. Ridley (1855–1956) arrived in 1888, just as the age of the motor car and its appetite for rubber tyres was dawning. Known as 'Rubber Ridley', he both adopted the technique of the rubber-tapper's 'herringbone' cuts in the bark and researched the growing conditions to make young trees become quickly productive. Most important, he tirelessly promoted rubber planting in Malaya, thereby jump-starting the trade that once dominated the global rubber industry. On his 100th birthday, he remarked, "*It is a great delight for me to have lived to see Malaya so prosperous, and the gardens the best tropical gardens in the world.*"

From the mid-1920s, under the Directorship of R. E. Holttum (1895–1990) the Gardens expanded horticulture and orchid hybridization, making Singapore a centre for commercial orchid growing and cut flowers. Since 1981 its National Flower of Singapore is the **Singapore Orchid** (*Vanda* 'Miss Joachim'), a late 19th century hybrid bred by an Armenian resident. The National Orchid Garden, with over 1000 species and 2000 hybrids of orchids, remains one of the Gardens' special attractions. Another notable collection is the Ginger Garden, devoted to members of the Zingiberaceae plant family, which include **Ginger** (*Zingiber officinale*) itself (see p. 179) and **Turmeric** (*Curcuma*), source of the pungent yellow spice and dye.

Despite these triumphs, during the 1930s the colonial authorities questioned the value of the Gardens. Partly to address this perception, E. J. H. Corner (1906-96, another long-lived botanist!), Assistant Director before World War II and during the difficult period of Japanese occupation in 1942–45, applied his wide botanical knowledge to writing *The Wayside Trees of Malaya* (1940), in two volumes and 800 pages – a forerunner of modern studies of the great richness of the trees and forests of Malaysia. Corner ingeniously trained macaque monkeys to collect fruits for him to study, from high up in the trees!

After Singapore gained its independence from Britain in 1965, the government embarked on a policy of tree planting and making the new state into a green and attractive garden city. Singapore Botanic Gardens has since been closely involved in tree propagation and horticultural training, as well as in botanical research and publication, and it is an integral part of the state's National Parks Board. It is a UNESCO World Heritage Site and a major tourist attraction.

The Botanic Gardens are now dwarfed, but not botanically superceded, by the larger, 250-hectare (100-acre) 'Gardens by the Bay' nature park by the island's Marina

Reservoir. This beautifully landscaped site, which annually attracts over 50 million visits, includes a 'World of Plants' biodiversity and conservation display and four Heritage Gardens illustrating the economic plants associated with the history and multicultural traditions of Singapore. Dominating the Gardens is the world-renowned Supertree Grove, 18 tree-like steel towers 25–50 metres tall that are themselves planted with climbing plants, orchids, bromeliads and ferns to form vertical gardens. The 'trees' also generate solar power, collect rainwater, provide air venting ducts for a Flower Dome – the largest glasshouse in the world – and a Cloud Forest glass-covered biome on the site, and give shade and shelter to visitors. Several are connected by high aerial walkways and the structures are strikingly illuminated after dark. Garden waste is recycled to power a steam turbine to generate electricity to cool the biomes.

Singapore may have lost most of its original rainforest, but in compensation it has gained a prestigious tropical Botanic Garden and a Garden City that is a global model for green planning and the creative use of plants in architectural landscaping.

The world's largest flower

Sir Thomas Stamford Raffles (1781-1826), statesman, administrator, zoologist and botanist, is commemorated by Singapore's Raffles Hotel and in the name of the world's largest flower, **Rafflesia** (*Rafflesia arnoldii*). This parasitic plant, one of some 30 related South-East Asian species, lives out of sight – and without stems, leaves or roots – deep in the tissues of a rainforest vine. The 5-petalled, flower, red and dotted with white warts, which can be a metre or more across and weigh ten kilos, has a strange beauty but a foul smell, having evolved to resemble a piece of carrion to attract flies!

Singapore Sling

Raffles Hotel is famous as a luxury haunt of writers, film stars and royalty, and for

its exotic cocktail, Singapore Sling, said to have been created 'before 1915' by barman Ngiam Tong Boon in the legendary Long Bar, now sadly moved and rebuilt. Recipes and opinions vary on this most botanical of long drinks, but the original was said to mix:

30 ml Gin – juniper berries and other 'botanicals'

15 ml Cherry Heering – sour cherries and spices

7.5 ml Bénédictine – 27 herbs, fruits and spices, of which six are a trade secret

7.5 ml Cointreau – sweet and bitter oranges, with a secret recipe

120 ml fresh Sarawak pineapple juice

15 ml lime juice

10 ml Grenadine syrup – pomegranate

Dash of Angostura bitters – gentian root and other herbs and spices

All shaken together and garnished with a slice of pineapple and a cherry. Delicious!

SAVING ANIMALS AND PLANTS - A NEW NOAH'S ARK

It is obvious that, in order to survive, animals need a healthy Plant Kingdom. At a most basic level, without grass, for example, there would be neither cattle, sheep, goats and horses, nor chickens, giraffes, zebras, deer, wildebeest or rhinos. And without fruit, many fewer birds, monkeys or bats. Every living thing relies on plants for food, even the carnivores, which are ultimately dependent on the plants that their prey eats.

However, it may be much less obvious that plants will not survive without a healthy Animal Kingdom. Pollination of flowers first springs to mind, not just by insects, notably bees, but by a host of birds such as the hummingbirds of the Americas and the sunbirds of the Old World, reptiles, bats and over a hundred other mammals, from possums to lemurs (in all, more than 1,400 species of vertebrate are known to pollinate flowers). At the same time, a huge number of plant species depend on birds and animals eating their fleshy fruits, nuts and seeds, and so are dispersed far from the parent plant. Some seeds will not even germinate unless they have passed through a bird's digestive tract.

There are examples from all over the world of the vital interaction between animals and plants. As environmental campaigner George Monbiot argues so well in his book *Feral* – a plea for more wilderness in the form of 'rewilding' – the presence or loss of 'keystone' larger animal species is particularly critical. In America's Yellowstone Park, the biodiversity and the vegetation itself were greatly improved after 1995 by, amazingly, the re-introduction of wolves. This reduced the excessive deer numbers and caused the deer to avoid lingering in valleys and along rivers, thus allowing bankside willow, aspen and other vegetation to regenerate, with the enhancement of the whole aquatic habitat. Even bears increased in numbers, feeding on both the larger number of berries and remains of carcasses. Human culling of deer had previously not worked. In British Columbia, the forests flourish if populations of the salmon that

swim up the rivers to spawn are healthy and not over-fished. The salmon are eaten by 100,000 bears and their remains in the bears' droppings fertilize and improve the forests with marine-derived nitrogen and other soil nutrients. A virtuous circle.

In southern Africa there will soon be a huge, exciting and pioneering venture which aims to promote and actively help animal survival on Earth, and therefore that of plants, in what will be the world's most advanced wildlife conservation park. Whilst animal species top the list, of necessity this means preserving areas of natural habitats plus all their inhabitants, with the interdependence of plants and animals a key emphasis for study.

The new conservation park, named 'Noah's Ark', in KwaZulu-Natal, South Africa, will cover an area of 100 square kilometres, adjacent to iSimangaliso Wetland Park, a UNESCO World Heritage Site.

Work has begun preparing the area, which was carefully selected for its stable climate, well suited to animals from tropical and sub-tropical regions around the world. These will roam freely within the protection of high security systems and a programme of empowering indigenous communities to manage their lands, with anti-poaching a top priority. The plan is enthusiastically supported by the local population, headed by the Royal House of the Zulus and the leader of the region, Nkosi Tembe.

The area will provide a safe, protected habitat for animals, which includes a 20–30 square kilometre visitor and science compound. The Ark is intended to draw in children and adults to connect with nature and survival.

A Visitor Centre will present Noah's Ark objectives and achievements. As with other modern natural history museums, the Centre will use interactive displays, multi-sensory activities and lifelike animal holograms to instil a sense of awe, wonder and respect for

'Nature's Kingdom'.

The project's *You are Noah* books, inviting *everyone* to take a role as Noah, are following the development of the Ark as TV tie-Ins to Sky TV 's 'Noah's Ark' series. The founders of the Noah's Ark project, Richard and Hein Prinsloo Curson, have appeared on ITV's 'Good Morning Britain' and in many South African media to stress that this modern-day Ark is intended to save all endangered species from yet another mass extinction (as when the Cretaceous dinosaurs disappeared from the face of the Earth). Taking the lead for many more projects like this to follow, species will be given sanctuary and returned to wildernesses, more than a third of the planet, which according to the UN Convention on Biological Diversity have been designated for protection.

Expertise is being drawn on climate-controlled domes from Britain's Eden Project, on plants from Kew Gardens and South Africa's Kirstenbosch Botanical Garden among others, and on aquariums from specialist AMC Global. Yet, as nothing of this order has ever been attempted or is being attempted, the Ark will break new ground in all areas. A centre of excellence will be set up, drawing on research and scientists from

around the world, to discover all there is to know on ecosystems and how plants and animals interact as well as how to protect wildlife from industry, climate change and poaching (with security even higher than that in Jurassic Park).

The research facilities will focus on protecting endangered species, by creating carefully planned breeding programmes and housing world-class DNA and seed banks – for conservationists and ecologists to catalogue and share information on the fundamental blueprints of life – information that is required to ensure the most effective conservation measures and restoration of species to the wild.

Central to the Ark's conservation strategy are the GeoDomes inspired by the Eden Project and its magnificent Tropical and Mediterranean Biomes (page302). Noah's Ark will have fifteen GeoDomes, replicating environments across the planet, centred on three domes measuring 230m across and 90m high, or as tall as a 30-storey building. These will replicate climate

conditions in the tropical, temperate and polar zones – the polar dome obviously being the most challenging. Twelve will house climates and habitats ranging from desert to Mediterranean regions, sub-arctic and highland. Each dome will be fitted with sophisticated smart glass technology to control normal day and night cycles of the animals' natural habitats.

Each stage demands unrivalled expertise, from researching, selecting and sourcing species along with their habitats, to building and testing the structures, and finally populating them and keeping the inhabitants safe and well – and, most crucially, wild.

Among the biggest challenges, if not the biggest, will be to design, build and fill the sea aquarium. Water piped directly from the nearby Indian Ocean will create a life support system for the marine environment reproduced in the aquarium – which will be the world's largest. The Aquarium and its giant underwater observatory will reflect the 71% of the planet covered by oceans, and the 94% of life on Earth that exists within those depths.

Richard and Hein are taking positive action on this large scale to try to provide a way for everyone everywhere to become actively involved in tackling our planet's crisis.

They aim to inspire humanity to work together to fight the 'ecological war', protect the circle of life, and encourage governments world-wide to rethink their relationship with the planet and all the life upon it. Our future depends on it.

PLANTS AND THE ARTS

PROSE AND POETRY

The Secret Garden
The American wildness
Two fascinating plant biographies
Enid Blyton and Nature study
Plants and the English landscape
Plants in poetry
Wordsworth and his Daffodils
Shakespeare and his botany
Ovid's Tales of people becoming plants
John Clare, the botanist poet

THE SECRET GARDEN

Surely one of the most enchanting stories ever written for children must be *The Secret Garden*, written by Frances Hodgson Burnett in 1911, giving thousands of us the dream of being in such a place – a hidden sanctuary, and in the case of the heroine, Mary, a haven from her troubles.

An only and unwanted child, totally neglected by her parents, Mary is sent back to England from India at ten years old after their deaths from cholera. She first lives with a vicar and then with Archibald Craven in his isolated manor on a bleak moor in Yorkshire.

An extremely damaged child, she is befriended by Craven's maid, Martha, who tells her that his wife, Lillian, used to love being in the private walled garden outside, but died suddenly after a tragic accident – after which Craven locked it up and threw away the key in despair.

This immediately arouses Mary's curiosity and she then becomes determined to find the key – which she eventually does with the help of a friendly robin seen pecking at the grass as if desperate to find something.

Asking Martha for garden tools, her twelve-year-old brother brings some to the house, and from then on her health and happiness are transformed – as, in time, is the walled garden.

One night, woken by pitiful wails, she discovers Colin, the bed-ridden son of Mr Craven. She begins to visit him regularly, telling him about the secret garden, which arouses his curiosity to such an extent that it becomes her dream to take him there in his wheelchair, his first venture outside for years. Soon their secret trips to the equally secret garden create a marked improvement to the boy's health, and at last he learns to walk again.

Eventually, returning from a long trip abroad, Craven is amazed to find not only his now mobile son in the secret garden, but a stunning sanctuary of plants. Just as the garden is transformed, so is he, and in due course the relationship with his son and Mary.

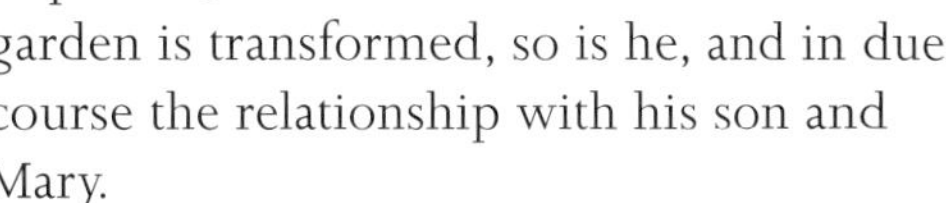

The Secret Garden is of course a novel, but real life stories abound of gardens making a miraculous difference to people's lives.

THE AMERICAN WILDNESS

English nature writers have tended to emphasize the inhabited countryside, with farms and gardens. But the best American nature writing is, perhaps unsurprisingly, about wilderness, or about the wildness that persists even after the untouched wilderness has gone. This reflects the vastness and grandeur of the landscape and perhaps, too, the remarkable historical narrative of the ever westward-expanding 'Frontier'. A common theme among these American writers is a deep philosophical awareness of the wonder of nature and the spiritual healing it provides.

In 1845, Henry David Thoreau (1817–62)(below) built himself a wooden cabin on the shore of Walden Pond, a lake set in *'thick and lofty pine and oak woods'* near his home town of Concord, Massachusetts. His reflective, discursive account of the two years he spent there, cultivating beans and corn as in a Native American garden and always close to nature, are recorded in *Walden* (1854), a classic of American literature. A competent botanist, he noted by name the trees, shrubs and wildflowers about him; and he was no mere dreamer, for after his return to civilization he addressed himself to political and civil rights issues. His peaceful idyll in the woods – *'We need the tonic of wildness ...We can never have enough of nature'* – also much influenced the great Irish poet W.B. Yeats (over page). In his famous poem, 'The Lake Isle of Innisfree' (1890), Yeats transposes Thoreau's cabin and bean rows to Lough Gill in his native County Sligo:

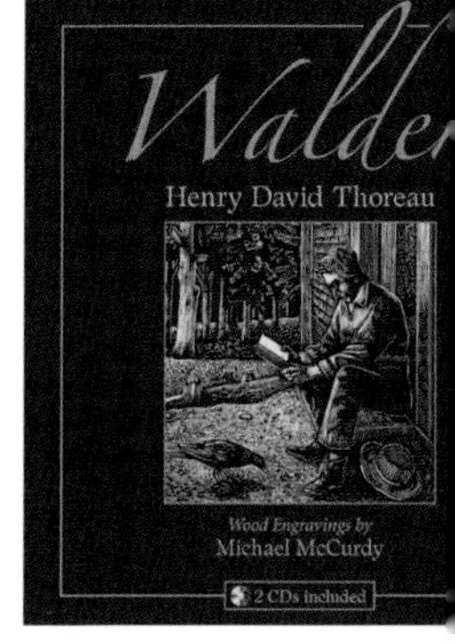

'I will arise and go now, and go to Innisfree,

And a small cabin build there, of clay
and wattles made;
Nine bean rows will I have there,
a hive for the honey bee,
And live alone in the bee-loud glade.'

John Muir (1838–1914) (top right) who hailed originally from Dunbar in Scotland, was a naturalist, author and campaigner for the protection of the American wilderness. Describing himself as 'a disciple of Thoreau' (he even built a cabin in Yosemite), in 1871 he received a visit from the leading American writer Ralph Waldo Emerson, who had been a friend and mentor to Thoreau and had himself written an important essay on 'Nature'. Offered a teaching post at Harvard by the great man, Muir apparently commented: *'I never for a moment thought of giving up God's big show for a mere profship!'*

Instead, Muir's essays and articles on the wild nature of California were widely read and he became known as the 'Father of the National Parks'. He was a co-founder of the Sierra Club conservation movement and his writing inspired Congress in 1890 to establish Yosemite as a National Park. He guided many visitors, from scientists to celebrities and in 1903 he took President Theodore Roosevelt around the Park and the two men camped out in a grove of **Giant Redwood** trees (*Sequoiodendron giganteum*). Three years later the Yosemite Valley and the Mariposa Grove, the National Park's largest Redwood stand, were transferred by Congress from state to federal control.

Aldo Leopold (1887–1948) was an expert on wildlife management and a founder of the Wilderness Society, a group whose campaigning led to the passing by Congress of the 1964 Wilderness Act. He was both a practical conservationist and fine writer, although he published sparingly. However, *A Sand County Almanac*, based on the observations of land he owned in Wisconsin and published after his death in 1949, is a classic piece of elegant nature writing which continues to inspire conservationists. Leopold, who stressed the great importance of a 'land ethic' and the moral responsibility of humans for nature, is regarded as one of the very first truly modern conservation biologists and was an early UN conservation advisor.

He nicely combined his observations with imagination. For example, noting a single large plant of the sunflower-like **Compass Plant**

(*Silphium laciniatum*) surviving in a corner of an old Wisconsin graveyard, once open prairie, Leopold reflects on what '*a thousand acres of Silphiums looked like when they tickled the bellies of the buffalo*'. And when it dies: '*With it will die the prairie epoch*'.

But probably the most influential of American nature writers was a marine biologist who emerged from the US Fish and Wildlife Service writing team. Rachel Carson (1907–1964) did not write about plants as such, apart from seaweeds, which she loved, but her wide interests covered all sorts of biological and ecological topics. She adored nature and wrote like a poet, and her books sold. *The Sea around Us* (1951) was 86 weeks in the *New York Times* best-seller list. This gem of scientific natural history is, however, overshadowed by her most significant work. First serialized in *The New Yorker* magazine, *Silent Spring*, an unanswerable indictment of the great damage wrought by the indiscriminate, sustained use of pesticides, was published in 1962. This was a seminal moment in the rise of the conservation movement and paved the way for much of the US government's subsequent environmental legislation.

By then dying of cancer, Rachel Carson was already looking ahead to her next book, writing: '*In our own lifetime we are witnessing a startling alteration of climate.*' She was, concerning the threat from climate change, as ever, years ahead of her time.

SAVIOUR OF THE EVERGLADES

The expansive subtropical swamplands of the Everglades are one of the glories of American nature and a UNESCO World Heritage Site. Extending across 1.5 million acres of southern Florida, the Everglades were designated a National Park in 1947. That same year saw the publication of *Everglades, River of Grass*, a book that has become a classic of environmental literature, which celebrates the ecology and history of this special wilderness – rich in biodiversity yet lying

just outside of Miami. The author, Marjory Stoneman Douglas, who died aged 108 in 1998, had settled in Miami after the First World War, when it was a small resort only a little older than herself. A columnist and assistant editor for *The Miami Herald*, turned tireless freelance writer, she wrote short stories, plays and novels and addressed women's issues and social justice, opposed Prohibition (page 176) and supported the establishment of the local Fairchild Tropical Botanical Garden in 1936. Above all, she was a doughty campaigner for the environment. As she put it, '*It is a woman's business to be interested in the environment. It's an extended form of housekeeping.*' She dedicated most of her long life to defending the Everglades from drainage, agriculture, and proliferating tourism and real estate. For, as she begins the book, '*There are no other Everglades in the world*'. Her publisher had envisaged a book about a river, but she revealed a much more complex situation. Lake Okeechobee overflows south-west to produce a slow-moving river 60 miles wide and supporting a mosaic of habitats: 'grass' or **Sawgrass**

(*Cladium mariscus*) swamp and islands with hardwood forest, stands of **Slash Pines** (*Pinus*

elliottii) and old-growth **Swamp Cypresses** (*Taxodium distichum*), mangroves, estuarine flats and seagrass meadows (page 117). The Everglades are a refuge for manatees, Florida panthers and American crocodiles – and the water source for Miami. Even after the book was published, Marjory Stoneman Douglas fronted the opposition to aggressive sugarcane growers, a proposed airport, and canal construction and increased diversion of water by the US Army Corps of Engineers. Her determination, and the half million copies sold of *Everglades, River of Grass*, saved the Everglades for posterity.

On Marjory Stoneman Douglas's 90th birthday, the high school in Parkland, Florida (where notoriously a 2018 mass shooting killed seventeen), was named in her honour, and in 1993 President Clinton awarded her the Presidential Medal of Freedom

The Presidential Medal of Freedom is the highest U.S. civilian decoration. The only other biologist recipient was Rachel Carson.

TWO FASCINATING PLANT BIOGRAPHIES

For obvious reasons plants rarely feature as either heroes or villains in works of fiction (except, perhaps, as poisons). Nevertheless, at least two 20th-century short nature stories concern wild plants, one from England, the other from North America.

Henry Williamson (above) is famous for his books about animals, especially the best-selling *Tarka the Otter* and *Salar the Salmon*. But '*A Weed's Tale*', which he included in his 1923 collection of short stories, *The Peregrine's Saga*, is a rare nature story devoted to the life of a plant. It is also one of his best. Set in Georgeham, the North Devon village where Williamson made his home after the First World War, it tells of a battered plant of **Wood Dock** or **Blood-veined Dock** (*Rumex sanguineus*) that grows from the mud beneath the iron boot scraper of the elderly widower 'Uncle Joe'. The old fellow persistently hacks and mutilates '*thaccy dirty weed*' as it tries to re-grow and he seems to have killed it. Then he himself dies – but the dock survives and a last burst of energy '*made it send upwards, out of its roots, a green tower, builded slowly from materials sent from the base... During its span of life, it had toiled hard to make seeds; and they were made.*'

Ernie, a village child who appears from time to time in Williamson's stories, plucks and plays with the dock's mature seeding stem, using it as a toy sword, and then discards it on a recently turned heap of soil in the churchyard. The seeds sprout and '*as though in faithful and compassionate memory, a score of young plants*' establishes themselves on the neglected grave of the old man. Beautifully observed, it is a simple, almost biblical parable, with perhaps a nod to Jesus's short account of the Mustard Seed in St Matthew's gospel (p. 218). The boot scraper can still be seen outside Uncle Joe's former cottage and Wood Docks continue to grow in the churchyard close to Williamson's own resting place.

Another plant story, from Canada, was written by Grey Owl or Wa-sha-quon-asin, (above) a contemporary of Williamson and like him an early champion of wildlife conservation, who became something of a celebrity in the 1930s. '*The Tree*' was published in *Tales from an Empty Cabin* in 1936 and later re-issued as a short, illustrated book. Grey Owl's story, which interweaves the lives of a grizzly bear, a Blackfoot brave and, long outliving both, a great **Jack Pine** (*Pinus banksiana*), was probably based on a tree he came across during his travels as a trapper before he embraced conservation. The tree is eventually felled to clear the path of a highway cut through the mountain wilderness. It is another simple morality tale, elegantly told.

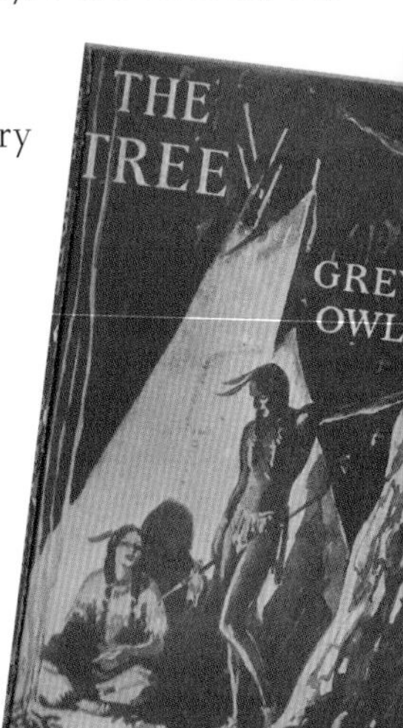

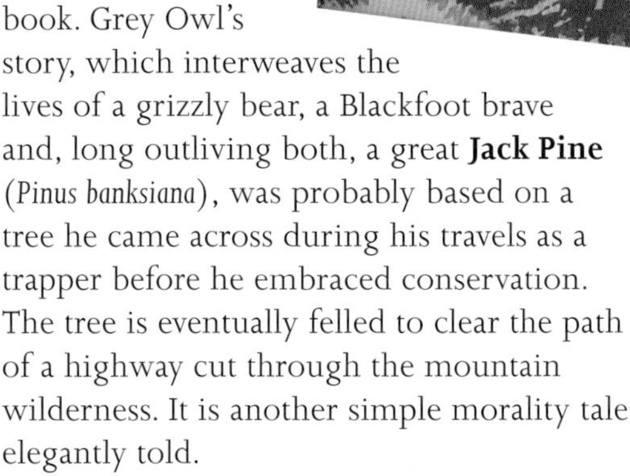

Lecturing in England in 1936, Grey Owl thrilled and inspired not only the future Queen Elizabeth and her sister Princess Margaret, but also a young David

Attenborough, now perhaps the world's most renowned and influential conservationist.

Sadly, for a while the reputation of both authors fell under a shadow: that of Williamson for a naïve flirtation with fascism in the 1930s, and that of Grey Owl when in 1938 he died of drink and it emerged he was not a Native American at all but an Englishman from Hastings in Sussex, named Archibald Belamey!

Today we remember both as great nature writers and pioneer conservationists, and it is a pity the two men never met. They would surely have got on famously.

ENID BLYTON AND NATURE STUDY

Children today are remarkably aware of the many threats to our planet and its plant and animal life. To many of them the future of the natural world is a source of considerable anxiety, even fear. At the same time, both children and adults are increasingly divorced from nature and the life of the countryside. This has led to suggestions that schools should bring natural history – which would complement laboratory and theory-based biology – into the national curriculum. Ironically, in the guise of 'nature study', it was once a regular part of primary school life that came to be sidelined as irrelevant to a modern, utilitarian education.

Older generations will have mixed views on a subject that did not appeal to everybody, or was seen to be 'girly', but many absorbed a love of nature and simple, useful information such as the names of the common trees. Of course, much depended on the knowledge and enthusiasm of individual teachers, and there were no textbooks as such, although for plants there were a few popular small guides such as the *Observer's Book of Wild Flowers*. One children's author did, however, try to fill the gap – the now deeply unfashionable Enid Blyton, in her day as successful as J.K. Rowling has been with her Harry Potter books.

Enid Blyton (1897–1968) was a publishing phenomenon, the prolific author of over 700 children's books. Despite constant criticism from teachers and librarians for her perceived limited vocabulary and poor literary merit, as well as her reactionary middle class world view, Blyton's books have sold more than 600 million copies in 90 languages (J.K. Rowling's have sold 500 million). And they continue to

sell. Children have always loved them, borrowed them and asked for them – stories of mystery and adventure, including the *Famous Five* and *Secret Seven*, of schooldays, fantasy and fairy tales, not least the adventures of *Noddy*, but also animal stories and books on natural history.

Enid Blyton knew that the best way to pass on her love of nature to children was through stories. *Enid Blyton's Book of the Year* (1941), based around a rural primary school, includes copious nature notes, but *Enid Blyton's Nature Lover's Book* (1944) goes much further. It is structured around the narrative of three children who go out on two walks each month of the year with their neighbour, Mr Meredith, aka 'Uncle Merry', and Fergus, his Scottie dog. The walks lead the children through a joyful learning experience across the seasons and habitats in and around their village, apart from in August when they visit the seaside, and they discover a wide assortment of wildflowers, birds, amphibians, reptiles, insects and mammals. *Enid Blyton's Nature Lover's Book* was clearly popular, with six reprints up until 1956, plus a 2008 facsimile edition.

The language is simple and clear but never shirks from a didactic message or basic technical terms such as plant family names like the Cruciferae or 'cross' flowered family and Labiatae or 'lip'-flowered family. Blyton captures an older countryside undamaged by modern intensive agriculture and sprawling housing estates, filled with wildflowers and birdsong that we once took for granted but have now mostly lost. Some images are timeless: January **Hazel** catkins, patches of blue **Germander Speedwell** and **Greater Stitchwort** amid April showers, followed by sheets of **Bluebells** in the woods, golden **Meadow Buttercups** in May, **Honeysuckle** by night in June, late **Harebells** in September, flowering **Ivy** in October and evergreen foliage in bare November woods. Blyton was happy to let children pick wildflowers, a good way to engage their interest and enthusiasm.

Blyton had a mission – to promote nature study in schools. The *Nature Lover's book* (1949), which combines illustrations and stories in 'education through story-telling', was nothing less than a simple biology course for 5- to 7-year-olds. An accompanying textbook for teachers, by L.J.F. Brimble, botanist and Editor of the prestigious journal *Nature*, covers everything from plant and animal biology and birds, butterflies and pond-life to folklore and life on the farm.

The key message in Enid Blyton's *Nature Lover's Book* comes after the last walk, on a snowy Christmas Day. By the Christmas tree, John, the youngest child, shyly thanks Uncle Merry, '*The biggest present you've given us is the key of the countryside, Uncle!*'; who replies, '*Once you've got it, you never, never lose it!*'

A question many people have asked another John, one of the authors of this book, John Akeroyd, is '*Where did you first learn about plants and flowers?*' The answer is '*in the nature books of Enid Blyton*', especially that *Nature Lover's Book*, one they rarely expect to hear!

Incredibly, people still tend to look down on Enid Blyton, obviously unaware that she wrote over 600 books!

PLANTS AND THE ENGLISH LANDSCAPE

England enjoys a long tradition of writing about nature and the countryside, farming and gardening. The farmer who writes or the gardener who creates both 'by pen and spade' are a special element in the fabric of English literature, which has nature writing deep in its soul. Charles Darwin (pictured) himself was a talented nature writer and deserves to be more highly regarded as one of the great Victorian men of letters. (Just as many forget that he was as much a botanist as a zoologist).

English writers and artists have frequently been absorbed by topography and landscape, especially in traditionally farmed countryside. This represents the opposite of wildness and wilderness - though equally rich in plant and animal life - and indeed contemporary nature writing has gone a stage further by finding inspiration in nature-rich urban and suburban landscapes. This passion for the land even influenced the 18th century Agricultural Revolution, for which English landowners have often been given credit, by promoting crops such as **Clover** (page 245). Their achievement was as much as anything to write about what they were doing. Even a political writer like journalist and agitator William Cobbett, who in *Rural Rides* (1830) assessed English farming while venting strong opinions, clearly revelled in the countryside through which he travelled.

By contrast, American nature writing (page 344) is much more about wilderness, past and present, in that spacious, varied and, for a long time, unexplored continent.

Perhaps the best-known of all English nature writers was an 18th-century clergyman, Gilbert White, author of *The Natural History and Antiquities of Selborne* (1789), the Hampshire village where he inherited the family home and was four times curate. This meticulous, if rambling, record of observations he made in the garden and adjacent countryside is legendary, especially with regard to birds, about which he was an expert. But he had much to say about plants, being a keen gardener and botanist who possessed two editions of the *Gardeners Dictionary* by Philip Miller, curator of the Chelsea Physic Garden (page 293). His wide range of correspondents included Sir Joseph Banks, the greatest botanist of the age and advisor to George III, who built up the collections at Kew (page 289). He grew fruit trees and experimented with new crops like potatoes and melons. He employed various helpers, not least one Goody Hampton as a 'weeding woman'. A fortnight before his death he was harvesting early cucumbers.

White, who always drew upon his own observations out in the field, was remarkably aware of what a century or more later we would call 'ecology'. One comment especially has a modern resonance: '*Trees are great promoters of lakes and rivers... for, since the woods and forests have been grubbed and cleared, all bodies of water are much diminished; so that some streams, that were very*

considerable a century ago, will not now drive a common mill.' White was a forerunner to the era of the great Victorian naturalists and natural scientists, Charles Darwin himself acknowledging him as an early influence. *The Natural History and Antiquities of Selborne*, like the Bible and Shakespeare, has never been out of print.

Even in fiction, nature can be important. Thomas Hardy created powerful images of nature as a background to his novels, especially his evocation of Egdon Heath, a fictional landscape, but one modelled on the biodiversity-rich heaths of southern Dorset. He provides both detail and a sense of place, as in *Tess of the D'Urbervilles* (1891): *'The lane they followed was so solitary that the hazel nuts had remained on the boughs till they slipped from their shells, and the blackberries hung in heavy clusters.'*

The novels and short stories of D.H. Lawrence are noted for their perceptive view of human relationships, but he ought to be remembered too as a nature writer, especially good at describing flowers. Like the poet William Wordsworth, Lawrence loved **Lesser Celandine** (*Ranunculus ficaria*) (top). He often mentions celandines, realizing how their 'little suns' define the early spring landscape on an often cold, sunny day. In *Sons and Lovers*, the main character Paul Morel, (based on Lawrence) remarks, 'I *saw a sloe bush in flower and a lot of celandines. I'm glad it's spring.*' And later on, describing an Easter excursion, '*Celandines and violets were out. Everybody was tip-top full of happiness.*'

In the late 19th century, the Wiltshire-born writer Richard Jefferies wrote detailed descriptive essays about the farm and countryside in which he grew up, and later about the south London suburbs to which he moved so as to be closer to his publisher. His main interest was birds, but he loved wildflowers and knew how well they evoke the country scene. In his 1883 essay '*The Pageant of Summer*' he describes the brilliant blue flowers of **Birdseye** or **Germander Speedwell** (*Veronica chaamedrys*) on a grassy bank in May: '*The violet and cowslip, bluebell and rose, are known to thousands; the veronica is overlooked. ... brightly blue and surrounded by greenest grass, embedded in and all the more blue for the shadow of the grass ...*' Jefferies had a great influence on both the poet Edward Thomas and the novelist and essayist Henry Williamson (page 348) - and on countless readers who love the English countryside.

Jefferies never quite mastered novel writing, despite fine descriptive passages. However, in *After London* (1885) he produced a remarkable piece of 'green science fiction', imagining a post-apocalypse England lapsed into medieval barbarism, in which London has become a decayed swamp of ruins and poisonous water and air. He vividly describes how nature was reclaiming civilization, first by general regrowth and 'rewilding' of the landscape, followed by encroachment of scrub, woods and marshes that obliterated former farmland and settlements. Alas, Jefferies died of tuberculosis aged just 38.

W.H. Hudson, a contemporary but who lived until 1922, was a better writer, certainly of novels, and had wider experience. He grew up on the pampas of Argentina, which he described in his memoir *Far away and long ago* (1918), but lived in London from 1869. He set his novels in South America, notably *Green Mansions* (1904), about a man who encounters Rima, a sprite-like girl who lives amongst nature, eating only plants, in the Guyana forest. The story is a gentle parable and plea to save tropical rainforests, an advanced idea for the time (as is Rima's vegan diet)! Hudson found his greatest success with books on birds and the English countryside. He and Jefferies are buried in the same graveyard in Worthing, Sussex.

Leaving aside the 'New Nature Writing' genre, which is a rapidly evolving subject in itself, in recent decades two influential writers have achieved commercial success by tackling plants and nature from very different directions. Richard Mabey, who has an arts rather than science background, shot to fame in 1972 with *Food for Free* and has since written books on plants, natural history and the countryside, including *Flora Britannica* (1996), a classic compendium of UK botanical information. His essays are his very best work, and nobody writes more eloquently on subjects like weeds or the wild hidden corners of suburbia. Oliver Rackham, on the other hand, was an academic botanist specializing in woodland historical ecology, who did more than anybody to explain the English countryside – and why landscapes, trees, other plants and human settlements look the way they do. He and others like him can read the countryside like a book and then communicate to others.

Both Rackham, who died in 2018, and Mabey have shown how each plant tells a story and has its own special influence on us all.

PLANTS IN POETRY

It is hardly surprising that so many poets have found inspiration in plants, but what is surprising is the contrast between those who simply celebrated their beauty or referred to them in love poems and those who have used them to evoke sadness and tragedy, loss and death. Here are extracts mentioning plants from some of our favourites, or we think most moving.

This first poem laments the terrible loss of 850,000 young British men in the first World War, while others rue the passing of time and fading faculties.

In Memoriam
Edward Thomas
The flowers left thick at nightfall in the wood
This Eastertide call into mind the men,
Now far from home, who, with their sweethearts, should
Have gathered them and will do never again.

Cover me over
Richard Eberhart
Cover me over, clover;
Cover me over, grass.
The mellow day is over
And there is night to pass.

The Old Oak Tree
W.H. Davies
I sit beneath your leaves, old oak,
You mighty one of all the trees;
Within whose hollow trunk a man
Could stable his big horse with ease.

The nymph's reply to the shepherd
Walter Raleigh
The flowers do fade, and wanton fields
To wayward winter reckoning yields;
A honey tongue, a heart of gall,
Is fancy's spring, but sorrow's fall.

To the Virgins, to Make Much of Time
Robert Herrick
Gather ye rosebuds while ye may,
Old Time is still a-flying;
And this same flower that smiles today
Tomorrow will be dying.

Song of Autolycus
William Shakespeare
When daffodils begin to peer,
With heigh! The doxy over the dale,
Why, then comes in the sweet of the year;
For the red blood reigns in the winter's pale.

Virtue
George Herbert
Sweet rose, whose hue angry and brave
Bids the rash gazer wipe his eye;
Thy root is ever in its grave,
And thou must die

To Autumn
John Keats
Season of mists and mellow fruitfulness,
Close bosom-friend of the maturing sun;
Conspiring with him how to load and bless
With fruit the vines that round the
thatch-eves run;

The Passionate Shepherd to his love
Christopher Marlowe
Come live with me and be my love,
And we will all the pleasures prove,
That valleys, groves, hills, and fields,
Woods, or steepy mountain yields.

And I will make thee beds of Roses
And a thousand fragrant posies,
A cap of flowers, and a kirtle
Embroidered all with leaves of Myrtle;

But could youth last and love still breed,
Had joys no date nor age no need,
Then these delights my mind might move
To live with thee and be thy love.

The Trees

Philip Larkin
The trees are coming into leaf
Like something almost being said;
The recent buds relax and spread,
Their greenness is a kind of grief.

Nothing Gold Can Stay
Robert Frost
Nature's first green is gold,
Her hardest hue to hold.
Her early leaf's a flower;
But only so an hour.
Then leaf subsides to leaf.
So Eden sank to grief,
So dawn goes down to day.
Nothing gold can stay.

It is not growing like a tree
Ben Jonson
It is not growing like a tree

In bulk doth make Man better be;
Or standing long an oak, three hundred year,
To fall a log at last, dry, bald, and sere:
A lily of a day
Is fairer far in May,
Although it fall and die that night –
It was the plant and flower of light.
In small proportions we just beauties see;
and in short measures life may perfect be.

To a snowdrop
William Wordsworth
Lone Flower, hemmed in with snows and white as they
But hardier far, once more I see thee bend
Thy forehead, as if fearful to offend,
Like an unbidden guest. Though day by day,
Storms, sallying from the mountain-tops, waylay
The rising sun, and on the plains descend;
Yet art thou welcome, welcome as a friend.

A Red, Red Rose

Robert Burns
O my Luve is like a red, red rose
That's newly sprung in June;
O my Luve is like the melody
That's sweetly played in tune.

The lady of Shalott
Alfred Lord Tennyson
On either side the river lie
Long fields of barley and of rye,
That clothe the wold and meet the sky;
And thro' the field the road runs by
To many-tower'd Camelot;

The Sugar plum tree
Eugene Field
The fruit that it bears is so wondrously sweet
(As those who have tasted it say)
That good little children have only to eat
Of that fruit to be happy next day.

The Child's Song in Spring
Edith Nesbit
The Silver Birch is a dainty lady,
She wears a satin gown;
The elm tree makes the old churchyard shady,
She will not live in town.
The poplar's gentle and tall,
But the plane tree's kind to the poor dull city-
I love him best of all!

I know a bank whereon the wild thyme blows
William Shakespeare
I know a bank whereon the wild thyme blows.

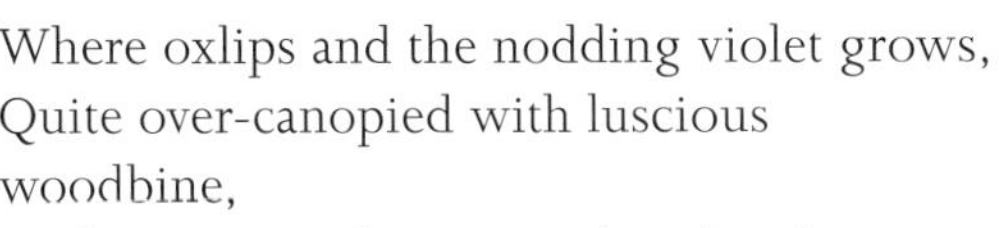

Where oxlips and the nodding violet grows,
Quite over-canopied with luscious woodbine,
With sweet musk-roses and with eglantine:

Pencil and Paint
Eleanor Farjeon
Winter has a pencil
For pictures clear and neat,
She traces the black tree-tops

Upon a snowy sheet.
But autumn has a palette
And a painting-brush instead,
And daubs the leaves for pleasure
With yellow, brown, and red.

WORDSWORTH AND HIS DAFFODILS

One wildflower above all others inspired a famous poem. 'I wandered lonely as a cloud', often referred to simply as 'Daffodils', by William Wordsworth, is a classic piece of 19th-century Romantic poetry that beautifully evokes the well-loved golden-yellow flower often seen as 'the harbinger of Spring'. Most people have come across the opening lines:

'I wandered lonely as a cloud
That floats on high o'er vales and hills,
When all at once I saw a crowd,
A host of golden daffodils;
Beside the lake, beneath the trees,
Fluttering and dancing in the breeze.'

Wordsworth and his sister Dorothy had discovered them during an April walk along the edge of Ullswater in the Lake District. As she wrote in her diary, 'there was a long belt of them along the shore, about the breadth of a country turnpike road. I never saw daffodils so beautiful.'

Wild Daffodils (*Narcissus pseudonarcissus*), sometimes found in similar great crowds in open woods and pastures, are smaller, more elegant plants than the garden Daffodils. They were not even Wordsworth's favourite wildflower, which was the diminutive, buttercup-like **Lesser Celandine** (*Ranunculus ficaria*) (next page, top), another golden flower of early spring. But that 'host' of

Daffodils clearly left their mark on his soul, and that of his beloved sister, and will be remembered wherever people read poetry. Wordsworth's deep affinity with nature, and his appreciation of how it soothes the emotions and enhances the imagination, were a major influence on both his fellow Romantics and the public – and today we also appreciate how important nature and plants can be to mental health (page 35).

Daffodils still flower beside Ullswater each springtime.

SHAKESPEARE AND HIS BOTANY

Most people would, like the authors, consider William Shakespeare to be one of the greatest writers of all time, and a huge influence on the English language. But how many of us have noticed his numerous allusions to plants, and his obvious interest and love of them? In her fascinating book, *A Shakespearean Botanical*, Margaret Willes points out his plethora of allusions to plants, from **Aconite** to **Wormwood** and his evident knowledge and enthusiasm for the plant kingdom. The Bard read many books and it is thought that he was friends with the botanist John Gerard, who, like Shakespeare, was a protégé of Queen Elizabeth's First Minister Lord Burghley, and whose illustrated *'The Herball or Generall Historie of Plantes'* was a best-seller.

Plants and flowers appeared in most of his famous plays and poetry. Some, admittedly, no longer spring to mind for the layman or feature in today's garden centres, but a huge number that Shakespeare referred to would still be entirely familiar to us today.

Here are just a few of his plant allusions:

'O mickle is the powerful grace that lies
in herbs and plants, stones and their true qualities,
for nought so vile that on the earth does live
but to the earth some special god doth give.'
Romeo and Juliet

'I am withered like an old apple-john.'
Henry IV

"Macbeth shall never vanquished be, until Great Birnam wood to high Dunsinane hill shall come against him."
Macbeth

'When daisies white and
violets blue
and lady-smocks, and Silver
white,
and cuckoo buds of yellow hue
do paint the meadows with
delight...'
Love's labour lost

'Go, bind thou up young dangling apricots
which, like unruly children, make their sire
stoop with oppression of their prodigal weight.'
Richard II

Plants & Us

*'When roasted crabs hiss in the bowl,
then nightly sings the staring owl.'*
Love's labour lost
(Shakespeare was referring to crab apples.)

Daffodils, that come before the swallow dares, and take the winds of March with beauty'
The Winter's Tale

*'I know a bank whereon the wild thyme blows
where oxslips and the nodding violet grows,
quite overcanopied with luscious woodbine,
with sweet musk roses and with eglantine.'*
A Midsummer night's dream

*'Kate, like a hazel-twig is straight
and slender, and as brown in hue
as hazel-nuts, and sweeter than the kernels.'*
The taming of the shrew

'Did her steal into the pleachèd bower, where honeysuckles, ripened by the sun, forbid the sun to enter.'
Much ado about nothing

*'To guild refined gold, to paint the lily
To throw a perfume on the violet, is wasteful and ridiculous excess'.*
King John

*'Let the sky rain potatoes, let it thunder
to the tune of Greensleeves'.*
The merry wives of Windsor

*'Let him that is a true-born gentleman,
from off this briar pluck a white rose with me.*

*'Let him that is not coward nor no flatterer
pluck a red rose from off this thorn with me.'*
Henry IV

*'There's rosemary, that's for remembrance.
Pray, love, remember.'*
Hamlet

'Thy sugared tongue to bitter wormwood taste.'
The Rape of Lucretia

Shakespeare's works are full of plants, including Aconites, Anenomes, Apricots, Berries, Bladder-wracks (a seaweed), Cabbages, Carnations, Carrots, Daffodils, Daisies, Roses, Lilies, Marjoram, Rosemary, Rue, Lavender, Mint, Savory, Marigolds, Primroses, Violets, Oxslips, Crow-flowers, Pumpkins, Potatoes, Nettles, Orchids and Nuts.

Thyme Hazel Honeysuckle Rosemary

OVID'S TALES OF PEOPLE BECOMING PLANTS

Publius Ovidius Naso, better known as Ovid (43BC–17 AD), was one of the greatest poets of ancient Rome. His most widely read work, the 15-book *Metamorphosis* or 'Transformations', brings together numerous myths from Rome, Greece and elsewhere: '*I want to speak about bodies changed into new forms.*' These stories are often familiar, and would certainly have been to Ovid's readers then, but he tells them beautifully.

A feature of *Metamorphosis* is the plentiful references to plants, especially trees. These tales of transformation are set outdoors among Nature and many concern people at times of passion, stress or death being turned into plants. A few examples:

Perhaps the best-known of the stories is that of Narcissus, a beautiful youth loved by the nymph Echo and by other women, and men. A youth whom he had scorned prays to Nemesis, goddess of vengeance, who condemns Narcissus to endless unrequited love. He falls in love with his own reflection in a clear woodland pool, eventually fading away and dying. Mourners find no body, only a transformed Narcissus, now 'a flower with a circle of yellow petals round a yellow centre'. This is probably the elegant, scented Poet's Narcissus or **Pheasant's Eye** (*Narcissus poeticus*), which is still widespread in the wild in damp places in the hills of southern Europe and is also a popular garden bulb.

Another funeral story is of a thicket of Cornel or **Cornelian Cherry** (*Cornus mas*) that grew up on the funeral mound of one of the sons of King Priam of Troy, Polydorus, who had been killed on the orders of a treacherous king of Thrace. The spears of the assassins had shafts of the hard Cornel wood, as did those of Theseus and other ancient heroes mentioned in Metamorphosis and other poems of Antiquity.

One story, set in Babylon, became the famous 'play-in-a-play' performed in Shakespeare's 'A Midsummer Night's Dream.' The lovers Pyramus and Thisbe lose contact during a nocturnal tryst at an old tomb under a mulberry tree. Pyramus finds Thisbe's scarf, bloodied by an angry lion that had recently caught its prey. Fearing her dead, he kills himself with his sword, whereupon Thisbe finds his body and kills herself too. The dark purple fruits of the **Mulberry Tree** (*Morus nigra*), coloured evermore, says Ovid, by the blood of the hapless lovers, readily stain clothes even today.

A particularly poignant story is that of Baucis and Philemon, an old married peasant couple. They give shelter to two strangers, travellers turned away by wealthier neighbours. The couple share freely their

simple food and wine. Ovid lovingly evokes the details of their humble home, with many references to plants: the roof of '*thatch and reeds from the marsh*', a bowl for washing and drinking cups of **Beech** wood, a couch of **Willow** wood with '*a mattress, stuffed with soft sedge grass*', a table '*wiped with stalks of fresh mint*' on which Baucis serves a meal that includes endives and radishes, nuts, figs and dates, plums, apples and grapes. As Philemon refills the cups, he notices how the flask of wine remains full. For the visitors are gods, Jupiter and Mercury no less.

Immediately the old couple apologize for their rough country fare and try to catch their only goose – but the bird runs to the gods, who spare its life.

Then they tell the couple that they must leave and come with them up the nearby mountain, as they will destroy the town which denied them hospitality. Struggling up on their sticks, Baucis and Philemon look back to see that only their own home has survived. It is now a fine temple and they will be its guardians. But they ask the gods for one more favour: that neither will outlive the other. And when they die, they are indeed united – transformed into an intertwined pair of trees, an **Oak** (*Quercus*) and a **Lime** (*Tilia*).

Alas, Ovid managed to upset Rome's Emperor Augustus and shortly after – despite flattery towards the Emperor near the end of *Metamorphosis* – he was banished. He died far away, in exile in Tomi, today the Romanian port of Constanta on the Black Sea. Ovid is now the National Poet of Romania and his sad face adorns labels on bottles of a dessert wine, *Lacrima lui Ovidiu* or 'Ovid's Tear'.

JOHN CLARE, THE BOTANIST POET

'Ragwort, thou humble flower with tattered leaves
I love to see thee come and litter gold ...
Thy waste of shining blossoms richly shields
The sun tanned sward in splendid hues that burn
So bright and glaring that the very light
Of the rich sunshine doth to paleness turn
& seems but very shadows in thy sight.'
– 'The Ragwort' by John Clare

A perfect image of the golden flowers of **Ragwort** (*Senecio jacobaea*) brightening dry brown summer pasture. Few poets have written so much, so well and so knowledgably about plants as John Clare. Born in 1793 in Helpston, a small, then remote, village in Northamponshire, he received little formal education but was steeped in the sights, sounds, life and work of the countryside. Unlike England's other 19th century Romantic poets, he was humbly born and eked out a living as a gardener, labourer and tenant farmer, later helped by friends and patrons. Clare's poetry didn't just mention nature, birds and plant life in passing or as a poetic convention but evoked or described them in detail gleaned from his own observations.

Although he left school

at 11, Clare continued to read poetry and built upon the knowledge he absorbed of folk ballad – he was a talented fiddler – and local dialect. This enabled him to develop his own special, imaginative, unfettered use of language, even to coin words like 'crumping', the sound of a footfall in fresh snow. As a countryman he could identify all the common wildflowers, but he was clearly a competent amateur botanist, once sending specimens of the rare, purple-flowered **Pasque-flower** (*Pulsatilla vulgaris*), which survives today in pastures near Helpston, as a gift to his publisher.

His arrival on the London literary world in 1820 was greeted by readers and fellow writers, who saw him as the 'Peasant Poet', but success was hard to maintain and his books of poetry did not sell as well as he had hoped. He drank too much and suffered physical and mental illness, along with the strain of supporting a wife and seven children while living in poverty. A great sadness for him was how the 18th century Enclosure Acts – whereby the law granted former common land to the gentry and church for agricultural improvement – swept away the unfenced pastures and heaths of rural England – and an older way of life, which he mourned all his days. Unafraid of social comment, Clare presents a balanced picture of hardship, times of jollity and love, and nature's richness and beauty in the English rural scene of two centuries ago. His poem about Ragwort shows how even such a common, pestilential weed of farmland could inspire him to rapture. He would have understood our modern word, 'biodiversity.'

As his depression and erratic behaviour increased, in 1837 his supportive publisher arranged for him to enter an asylum in Epping Forest in Essex, but he yearned for home and four years later he escaped and walked back to Helpston. Later that year he was declared insane and he would remain in the Northampton Asylum, still writing, until his death in 1864. In the early 20th century, with an increased interest in English nature writing (page 351) and rural life, Clare's work and reputation underwent a revival.

In recent decades he has attracted even more interest and his poems will always be special to those who love nature, wildflowers and birds.

Books by John Clare include *Poems Descriptive of Rural Life, Village Mistrel, The Shepherd's Calendar* and *Rural Muse.*

ART, ARCHITECTURE AND DECORATION

Progress and its influence on plant art
Plants as persuaders
Plant symbolism in art
Antipodean art
Plants at a price
The intrepid Marianne North
Without doubt, Redouté
Watch for wayside weeds.
Plants on other materials
Wood and carving
William Morris and his flowery wallpaper
Bears' britches and Greek Columns
Royal Albert and Porcelain

Plants & Us

PROGRESS AND ITS INFLUENCE ON PLANT ART

Plant painting long influenced the world, but it was also influenced by sheer 'progress', especially in the Victorian era.

Some progress involved the painters' basic tools of the trade – paints which were now in convenient tubes, broad and square-ended brushes, easels which were light and portable and various new photographic aids, like *camera obscura*, *camera lucida* and the mirror lens.

All of these enabled artists to work outside and cope with rapidly changing light conditions, as we see with Monet and the other French Impressionists and Britain's J.M.W. Turner. Turner himself reflected the effects of progress in his railway scene, 'Rain, Speed and Steam' and also his memorable 'Fighting Temeraire', with the Trafalgar veteran warship being towed off to be scrapped by a 'modern' steam tug.

Indeed, steam power offered radically improved transport and played a major role in transforming how far a painter could travel. Gauguin could never have visited Van Gogh but for the train, and Marianne North's magnificent collection of 890 paintings from all over the world, now exhibited at Kew, (page367) was only possible because of her travels on steamships.

Many of the exotic foreign plants featured in paintings were also only possible to keep and to paint because of the new heated orangeries and conservatories like those built by Sir Joseph Paxton at Chatsworth (page295).

PLANTS AS PERSUADERS

The popularity of plants and their everyday connection with life means that since the 19th century they have provided useful imagery to persuade people to do new things and explore new horizons. The British railway companies commissioned attractive landscape posters to encourage the newly well-off to leave the crowded and polluted industrial cities and visit the countryside.

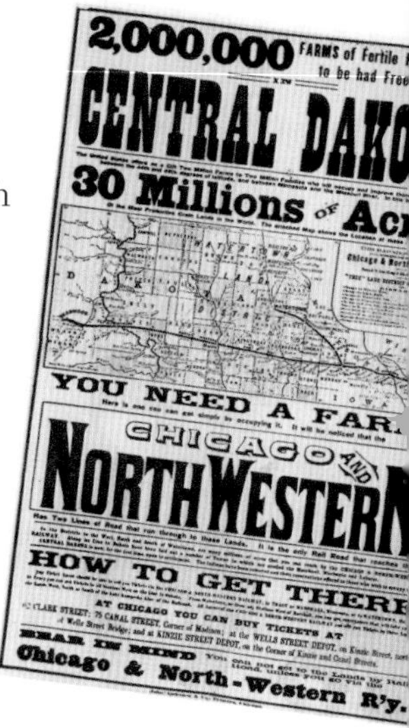

The American railroad companies, keen to create markets for their lines, and to sell to farmers the millions of acres they had been granted, created posters aimed at both America and Europe to promote agricultural possibilities.

Meanwhile, the new international travel companies like Thomas Cook featured palms and other exotic trees and plants in their extensive publicity.

Less pleasant, but one of the most powerful pieces of visual propaganda was William Hogarth's 'Gin Lane' (page 46). He was not to feature the barley and juniper in gin, but rather the chaos and depravity created by the 'Gin Craze'.

The horrors of war were often most powerfully depicted by illustrating what war could do to the beautiful countryside – perhaps most poignantly portrayed by Paul Nash, commissioned as a war artist, with his scarred battlefield of 1917, 'Menin Road',

with only the bare stumps of the trees and a few dockweeds remaining.

The Second World War produced excellent propaganda posters in Britain like 'Dig for Victory' and others featuring the 'Land Girls' of the Women's Land Army – the rural equivalent of America's industrial 'Rosie the Riveter'.

PLANT SYMBOLISM IN ART

One of the strongest influences on the art of the world is the use of the symbolism of plants and flowers. In Greek and Roman society, flowers were used to focus on the passing nature of life, with flowers scattered on bodies before they were cremated. Paintings later reflected these transitory thoughts, but there were all kinds of other symbolic uses – unmistakable to the observer.

Daisies and **Lilies** were symbols of purity. Adopted by the Catholic Church, the Lily features in hundreds of Renaissance paintings and also of several of the 'Annunciata', when an angel announces to Mary that she is going to give birth to Jesus, painted by Piero de la Francesco, Filippo Lippi, Leonardo da Vinci and Jan van Eyck. When **Carnations** and **Pinks** appear in paintings it meant an impending marriage. **Sunflowers** hinted at Royal favour or patronage. The **Acorn** started as a Nordic and Celtic symbol of fertility and immortality, but soon appeared elsewhere. Raphael painted his client, Pope Julius X, on a seat decorated with acorns, the symbol of that Pope's powerful family.

In the East, the **Bamboo** is one of the three 'trees of good omen' – with the **Pine** and the **Plum**. In Japan, the **Peach** blossom is the symbol of virginity, like the **Lily** in the West, while in China the **Peach** fruit is an emblem of immortality. One painting, 'Ophelia' by the Pre-Raphaelite John Millais, managed to include all sorts of flower symbolism. The **Rose** refers to Ophelia's brother calling her 'the rose of Mary'. The **Poppy** represents death, the **Daisy** purity and **Pansies** stand for thinking, **Violets** for faithfulness and **Forget-me-nots** are self-explanatory.

It's difficult to work out how or why such characteristics were assigned to flowers and plants, but there are certainly a lot of them. The **Rose**, of course, for love. **Aloe**, healing and protection, **Azalea**, femininity, strength and beauty, **Carnation**, love and femininity, **Daisy**, innocence and purity, **Fern**, health, luck and protection, **Gardenia,** trust, clarity and purity, **Lavender**, relaxation and comfort, **Orchid**, admiration and love, **Peony**, compassion and good relationships, **Rosemary,** remembrance, love and fidelity, **Sage**, health, purity and wisdom, **Sunflower,** happiness, adoration and loyalty, **Tulip,** unconditional love.

Some might seem obvious in their connotations: **Cactus,** protection and endurance, **Monstera,** respect, **Money Tree**, wealth, **Venus Flytrap,** strength and courage.

But these are probably unlikely to feature in paintings, being unable to evoke the same emotions!

PLANT ART AT A PRICE

Flowers have been an important subject for artists throughout history. In Ancient Egypt, the **Lotus**, symbolizing the sun, was often used in papyrus paintings, amulets and ceramics. In the Middle Ages and the Renaissance, floral patterns were used in the background. Japanese **Cherry Blossom** and other motifs influenced wallpaper designs. Flowers were also the focal points in the still life paintings by Renaissance artists of the 15th and 16th century; and by Dutch artists like Jan Davidsz de Heen and Ambrosius Bosschaert in the 17th century. The 19th century Impressionists like Manet, Monet and Renoir painted wonderful still life flowers, but also often worked *en plein air*, leading to many famous paintings in which flowers, plants and trees were captured beautifully. Flowers were also represented in 20th century art movements like Modernism and Pop Art, with Georgia O'Keefe and Andy Warhol.

Pictures of flowers and plants, as with other artworks, have sold for enormous prices. The most ironic of these must be two paintings by Vincent van Gogh. In March 1987, 'Sunflowers', one of his most famous works was sold for $40 million. A few months later, his 'Irises' sold for $53.9 million, then the most expensive painting ever sold. It is now only the 25th most expensive painting sold. It is incredibly sad to remember that during his lifetime, impoverished Vincent sold just one picture – for a few centimes – and a week before he died.

Plants & Us

THE INTREPID MARIANNE NORTH

Before the age of photography or mass travel, one intrepid woman brought hundreds of images of plants to a British public which was avid to find out about the wonders of an exotic world. Not only was Marianne North (1830 -1890) a prodigious painter of plants, but also an astonishingly brave one. To travel round the globe alone in her middle age meant all sorts of obstacles and dangers – rugged terrain, unpleasant insects and animals, searing heat, torrential rain, possible food poisoning and lack of doctors – yet nothing deterred her.

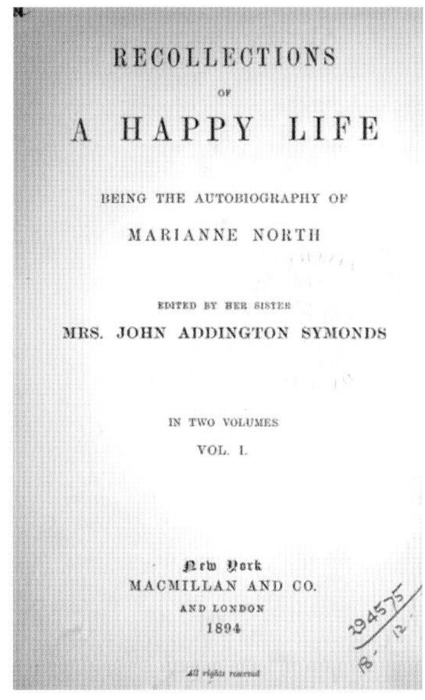

RECOLLECTIONS
OF
A HAPPY LIFE

BEING THE AUTOBIOGRAPHY OF
MARIANNE NORTH

EDITED BY HER SISTER
MRS. JOHN ADDINGTON SYMONDS

IN TWO VOLUMES
VOL. I.

New York
MACMILLAN AND CO.
AND LONDON
1894

All rights reserved

What makes her story even more surprising was that she had a comfortable and genteel upbringing. Her father, Frederick North, was the Member of Parliament for Hastings and her mother's father was also an MP.

At first, she travelled with her father, but on his death carried on alone – visiting and painting in Sicily, the United States, Canada, Jamaica, Tenerife, Japan, Brazil, Chile, Borneo, Java, Ceylon, India, Australia, New Zealand, South Africa and the Seychelles.

She liked to paint trees, plants and flowers in their natural habitats, 'Plants in their homes', as she put it. She also painted a huge variety, 727 genera and over 1,000 species, some of which were previously undiscovered. Indeed, several plants have even been named after her: **Giant Crinum Lily** (*Crinum northianum*) (pictured), now *Crinum asiaticum*), **Miss North's Pitcher-plant** (*Nepenthes northiana*) from limestone rock walls in Borneo, and **Çapucin** (Creole name) *Northia seychellana* from the Seychelles. On her travels she also began to see the wasteful destruction of plants, bitterly mourning the removal of groves of California's **Giant Redwoods** and similarly precious trees in Australia.

Having created an astonishing 832 paintings, she offered to pay for a special building to house them at the Royal Botanic Gardens, Kew, an offer that the Director, Sir Joseph Hooker, great botanist and explorer as he was, readily agreed to. This is now the much-visited Marianne North Gallery. She personally arranged all the paintings – including ones of animals, birds and landscapes as well as plants – and then painted the frieze and the decoration around the doors. Her wish was for Hooker's close friend Charles Darwin to open the Gallery, but he sadly passed away just before its opening in 1882.

After her death in 1890, her sister took over the manuscript of Marianne's book and published it. It was called *Recollections of a happy life*. For plant lovers, her life was also a very influential one.

'WITHOUT DOUBT, REDOUTÉ'

If asked 'Who was the greatest ever botanical artist?', many plant lovers might probably say Pierre-Joseph Redouté, if familiar with his outstanding paintings – and may well have reproductions of his work in their homes, as do countless houses throughout the world. They might also agree with his deserved soubriquet 'The Raphael of flowers.'

The son and grandson of painters, the Belgian Redouté first became enthusiastic

about painting flowers in Holland which had a long tradition of importing species like **Tulips** (page 124), **Narcissi**, **Anenomes, Lilies** and **Hyacynths**, and attracting artists who loved painting them.

When he came to Paris, he was mentored by a book lover and amateur botanist, Charles-Louis L'Héritier de Brutelle, who introduced him to his aristocratic circle – and crucially to Queen Marie-Antoinette, for whom he became the official painter. He also taught painting, and one friend said, '*In spite of his rather uncouth appearance, he counted all the prettiest women in Paris among his pupils.*'

In 1788, Redouté and L'Héritier rushed to England carrying plant specimens of botanist Joseph Dombey to save them from falling into the hands of either France or Spain. His visit meant that Redouté was able to meet Sir Joseph Banks and to study botany for a year at the Royal Botanic Gardens at Kew (page 289). He also met the Italian engraver Francesco Bartolozzi and became familiar with his 'stipple engraving', using delicate dots, vital to Redouté's later colour etchings.

But soon back in France all hell was to break loose, with the French Revolution and 'The Reign of Terror'. Many of his well-connected clients were among the 30,000 men and women executed, above all his main patron Queen Marie-Antoinette, who with her head shorn, was ignominiously dragged off in 1793 by the mob in a dung cart to the guillotine. His world could well have ended. But somehow his engaging personality and supreme skill rose above the atrocities and attracted new clients – and eventually Josephine, soon to become Napoleon's Empress.

Josephine was unusual – the daughter of a sugar planter on the island of Martinique. Lively and with a great aesthetic sense, Napoleon fell for her in seconds.

Her husband had been guillotined and she had waited in prison for the same fate, only

saved by Robespierre, chief proponent of the 'Terror' being executed himself. Redouté was to create the same relationship with Josephine that he had with Marie-Antoinette. At her chateau, Malmaison, she had a superb collection of roses – which Redouté celebrated with perhaps his most famous work, the three-volume folio '*Les Roses*'.

His life also coincided with a period when people were passionate about books illustrating plants – and to these Redouté contributed over two thousand published plates, ensuring his widespread fame. Luckily, he lived at a time when such books of plant and flower illustrations were becoming more and more popular, and his income was supplemented by private commissions, a salary from the art-loving Josephine and his painting classes, well-attended due to his genial personality.

Josephine, unable to provide an heir for Napoleon, lost her position and died. But patronage continued from her successor Empress Marie-Louise, (pictured), and then later, Queen Maria Amalia, the wife of King Louis Philippe. A critic wrote '*What other painter can point to two Queens and two Empresses as his pupils?*'

Others marvelled at the contrast between his marvellous and delicate art and his appearance. '*A thick-set figure with elephantine limbs, a head as heavy and flat as a Dutch cheese, thick lips, dull voice, crooked fingers and hands like a blacksmith!*'

Pierre-Joseph Redouté died in June 1840, aged 80, completing a painting of a lily. The art and plant world are influenced by him to this day. And there are not many painters, or indeed, people, who have led quite such full lives, or whom – surviving times of grotesque horror – have given the world such beauty.

Plants & Us

WATCH FOR WAYSIDE WEEDS

When one of the authors, John Akeroyd, was at school he studied both Botany and Art. One classmate asked him why he was doing a 'silly combination of A-Levels', at which point the art master intervened, firmly addressing the critic: 'In an Italian Renaissance studio, everybody would have studied Botany as well as Art!'

You would probably have to be both an artist and a botanist to notice how some of the world's great artists have lovingly depicted humble weeds in their paintings.

John Nash was an artist who had been interested in botany since school and thereafter kept an observant eye on plants. His masterful and moving portrayal of a shell-blasted First World War landscape, '*The Menin Road*', (page 365) shows both shredded stumps of trees and, quietly present in the foreground, reddish-brown plants of **Broad-leaved Dock** (*Rumex obtusifolius*). This ubiquitous farmyard and roadside weed usually forms great clumps, whereas these are mere scraps, diminished by shellfire like the trees, though just about surviving. This dock, re-growing from root fragment and well adapted to disturbed soil, was one of the many weeds, mostly quick-growing annuals such as **Poppies** (page50), that

a visiting Kew botanist recorded in 1917 on the Somme battlefield a year after the fighting, and soon to become the symbol of the fallen that we wear on Remembrance Day.

Docks can also be seen a century earlier as a detail in the sketches and paintings of John Constable (1776–1837), who meticulously observed nature and the rural scene. For example, he painted 'Study of Dock Leaves' (1828), but was especially expert at depicting burdocks, as in a small painting of probably **Lesser Burdock** (*Arctium*

minus), from the 1820s, 'Plants growing near a wall'. He made many studies of this typical wayside plant, notable for its burrs that adhere to clothes and animal fur (page 139), showing its somewhat greyish leaves. Burdock also appears as a significant detail in the foreground of Constable's most famous painting, 'The Hay Wain' (1821).

Norwich artist John Crome also drew and painted burdock, which appears with other weeds – most instantly recognizable – in 'Mousehold Heath, Norwich' (c.1818), though 'Dock Leaves' (1813) is clearly burdock! Both artists sketched out of doors and well knew how these commonplace weeds vividly bring to life larger studio paintings like 'The Hay Wain'. Such brilliant evocation of a scene from a now vanished world is probably why this work has been voted the Britain's second most popular painting, only losing out to J.M.W Turner's 'The Fighting Temeraire'.

An artist of the previous generation, George Stubbs (1724 - 1806) is famous for his astonishingly accurate portraits of horses, cattle and other animals. One of his series of similar horse paintings, 'Mares and Foals in a River Landscape' (c. 1762–8) has a leafy and flowering burdock in the foreground. It has been suggested that it may refer to the name of one of the horses, but above all it adds authenticity to the natural setting of the animals. A dog portrait, of a 'Brown and White Norfolk or Water Spaniel' (1778), has two beautifully executed white-flowered

aquatic 'waterweeds', **Flowering Rush** (*Butomus umbellatus*) and **Arrowhead** (*Sagittaria sagittifolia*), nicely reflecting the name of this now extinct breed. Both plants would have been more widespread in 18th-century England and Flowering Rush was familiar enough to be called 'Pride-of-the-Thames'.

Perhaps the most beautiful, and famous, historical depiction of workaday weeds is Albrecht Dürer's 1503 watercolour '*Das Grosse Rasenstück*' or 'The Large Piece of Turf', described by Richard Mabey as 'painting's discovery of ecology'. It is certainly one remarkable Renaissance man's inquisitive view of the natural world about him, at a time when plants and flowers were beginning to attract the skilled attention of both early plant taxonomists and botanical artists, as John Akeroyd's art master pointed out. Among the wildflowers clearly shown below among the various grasses – all identifiable – are the basal leaf rosettes of **Daisy** (*Bellis perennis*) and **Broad-leaved Plantain** (*Plantago major*), the leaves and

furled seed-heads of **Dandelions** (*Taraxacum*) and the basal leaves of **Burnet-saxifrage** (*Pimpinella saxifraga*)

Dürer observed and displayed the elements that make up a grassy space – pointing the way forward to how scientists, artists and all of us since would view plants and flowers in the future.

WOOD AND CARVING

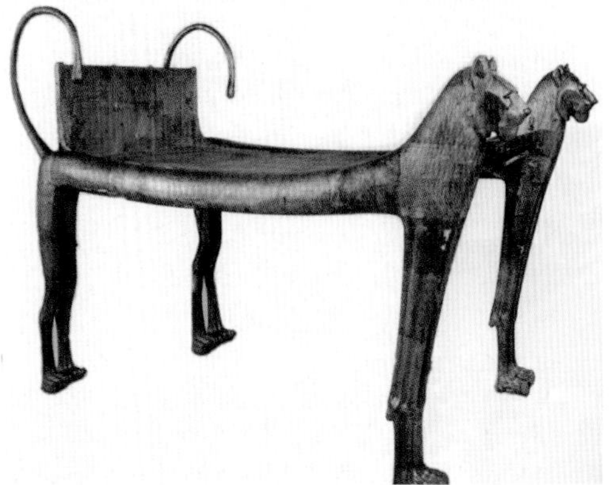

Carving objects from wood – for practical or artistic purposes – understandably goes back a very long way. Wood, in all its varied forms, was and is a wonderful material, and mankind turned to it for many vital uses – tools, boats and weapons. But it was not long before the artistic possibilities became obvious. In the Cairo Museum there is a superb statue of a man carved from **Sycamore Fig** (*Ficus sycomorus*) dating back to 4,000 BC. Indeed, Egypt boasts some of the oldest and finest surviving wood carving, partly because of its dry climate. The carvers used **Sycamore Fig** and **Tamarisk** trees, and the hard, strong wood of native species of **Acacia.** The Bible tells us that this was the wood (shittim) from which the Israelites built the elaborately carved Ark of the Covenant after they had fled from Egypt. Said to contain stones carved with the Ten Commandments, it was later lost during one of their many wars.

Egypt's lack of forests meant that they had to import the wood of **Cedar**, **Aleppo Pine**, **Box** and **Oak**. Not just portrayals of Kings and Gods were carved from wood, but also furniture - beds and chairs with heads of animals featuring the same detail. The Egyptian tradition continued for millennia, thousands of years before the birth of Christ, who himself, as we know, was a carpenter, giving this noble profession extra status.

While the Far East and Islam also embraced such artistic wood carving, we are most familiar with it through Christianity. Many of the very early carvings have not survived due to damp European conditions, but the Gothic Period of the 12th–15th centuries culminated in fabulous carving

of choir stalls, rood screens, pulpits, lecterns and roofs in England, France and the Germanic countries. Colour was used throughout and there were detailed designs of foliage – particularly oak, maple and vine.

In Britain the puritanical attitudes of the Reformation put a temporary stop to such ornate splendour, but the Renaissance brought it back. But it is surprising that while many of us could think of the names of many of the painters of the age, most would be hard-pressed to name one carving hero – except Grinling Gibbons (1648–1721). His talent was discovered by John Evelyn, the famous diarist and

passionate advocate of trees and wood, who with Sir Christopher Wren introduced him to King Charles II.

Gibbons was to become known as the 'King's Carver', and worked directly for three monarchs, Charles II, James II and William III. Carving in wood, his depiction of foliage was so delicate that someone said that his pot of carved flowers above the door of his London house *'would tremble from the motion of passing coaches'*. And Prime Minister Horace Walpole wrote, *'Nobody before Gibbons gave wood the loose and airy*

lightness of flowers.' Gibbon's carving genius, mostly in **Lime** (*Tilia*) wood, can be seen at Windsor Castle, Hampton Court and St Paul's Cathedral, together with many great churches and house in Britain and abroad.

It is a sad fact that *Encyclopaedia Britannica* was right when it said, *'Of late years, carving has gone out of fashion. The work is necessarily slow and requires substantial skill, making it expensive.'*

Regretably, not the first wonderful skill to become a victim of 'progress'.

WILLIAM MORRIS AND HIS FLOWERY WALLPAPER

In his lifetime, William Morris (1834–96) was best known as a poet. He could have been known for so many things, because he was a true 'polymath' and one of the great figures of cultural Britain. He was also a painter, a translator, a designer, a novelist, a poet, a creator of stained-glass windows, the main founder of The Society for the Protection of Ancient Buildings, a close associate of the Pre-Raphaelites, a founder of the Socialist League and an early Marxist.

He was deeply attracted to Medieval and Romantic themes and imagery and to John Ruskin's writing on art and architecture. But we now mostly remember William Morris for his use of plants and flowers in his unique designs for wallpaper, furnishing fabrics, carpets, tapestries and embroidery.

In the 1860s the British wallpaper market was booming and Morris decided to focus on this. 'Trellis' in 1862 was the first of 50 ground-breaking designs, all featuring exuberant flowers, scrolling foliage and plants. They are clearly based on plants and their structures but are stylised and fanciful rather than conventionally realistic.

Ever a lover of nature, for his printing he resorted to plant-based inks, too, using indigo, walnut shells and roots, and madder as well as cochineal and kermes, the latter derived from small plant-eating insects. Morris did much to revive the use of blue indigo dye, extracted from **Indigo** (*Indigofora tinctoria*), and also red dye, extracted

from **Madder** (*Rubia tinctoria*), both of which from the mid-19th century had been largely replaced by synthetic aniline dyes.

His complex printing technique culminated in no less than 68 separate hand-carved wooden printing blocks for his 1880 wallpaper design for St James's Palace. This royal commission was joined in 1887 by Queen Victoria's request to design wallpaper for Balmoral Castle, all adding to his 'Morrisonian' reputation in rich and aristocratic circles.

Not everyone liked his style, notably Oscar Wilde. Nor were his expensive designs on a grand scale suitable for 'ordinary' houses. Curiously, Morris himself, now rich, regarded his wallpapers as 'makeshift' decoration, preferring, perhaps rather snobbishly and despite his socialism, even more expensive woven textiles.

But his influence on interior decorating was huge and his work was copied for years with cheaper paper 'in the Morris style'.

In 1940 Arthur Sanderson & Sons bought the Morris wallpaper business, acquiring the printing blocks, logbooks and existing stock. Thereafter, scholarly interest in William Morris's work introduced his designs to a new generation, creating renewed enthusiasm for his work and a broader interest in the elaborate, organic floral designs of the Victorian period.

Already well-known for their English chintz patterns, Sanderson included examples of Morris's floral designs in their machine-printed wallpaper ranges throughout the 1960s and 1970s. Changing values led to a greater focus on authenticity and the Morris & Co. trademark was reinstated in the early 1990s to promote the reproduction of the original patterns in authentic colourways.

As both a very successful man in many fields, and especially when he applied plant

images to wall surfaces, William Morris has had a huge and enduring influence on art and society. One could do worse than follow his perceptive principle to '*have nothing in your houses that you do not know to be useful or believe to be beautiful*'.

But how may of us manage that?

BEAR'S BRITCHES AND GREEK COLUMNS

At the end of 2020, in the final days of his presidency, Donald Trump issued one of his last executive orders. Noting how US federal architecture was characterised '*by beautiful and beloved buildings of largely, though not exclusively, classical design*', he suggested that from now on this traditional influence should set the style for new public buildings. It must rank as one of the few treasured items of American life that Donald Trump did not seem to want to tear down!

In America, the UK and other counties, over more than two centuries the grand architectural model of ancient Greece and Rome proved popular for civic buildings, among both rulers and the ruled. Classical Greek architecture can be grouped into three main types or 'orders', which are mainly characterized by their columns. The earliest order was the rather squat Doric, followed by the slender Ionic and lastly by the Corinthian, similar to Ionian but on a grander scale and much more ornate, with elegant, fluted columns and capitals decorated by leaves and scrolls. The order takes its name from the ancient city of Corinth in southern Greece, but was much adopted and enhanced by the Romans. Whereas columns were essential structural elements in Greek buildings, the Romans employed arches and relied less on columns, which were more for ornament.

The Corinthian order was reputedly first created during the 5th century BC, when the architect and sculptor Callimachus spotted a plant of **Acanthus** or **Bear's Britches** (*Acanthus mollis*) growing up inside a votive basket left on a young woman's tomb. He copied the large, deeply cut, somewhat spiny leaves, by skillful drilling and undercutting of the stone to incorporate two rows of stylized leaves on the capitals of the columns. This leaf motif has endured for more than two millennia and has been widely influential in all branches of art and design.

Acanthus, a robust leafy perennial plant, with tall spikes of 2-lipped white flowers emerging from under spiny purplish leaf-like bracts, is still widespread on waysides and waste ground in the Mediterranean region, often growing around the ancient buildings it influenced, either as a weed or because it provides the custodians with greenery, flowers and ground cover and requires no maintenance. Many of the gardeners who have admired its stately appearance live to regret its invasive tendencies. It is the national plant of Greece.

The Corinthian order adorns numerous Greek and Roman buildings. Perhaps the finest example is the great columns of the Greco-Roman temple of Olympian Zeus in Athens. This design even spread to northern India, to where Greek influence remained in the centuries following Alexander the Great's campaigns in Asia. It extended into the Byzantine architecture of the Eastern Roman Empire and into the Middle Ages. Following the Renaissance, when architects defined the classical orders, Acanthus foliage became a standard element in Neoclassical architecture, for example in the Corinthian columns of the Bank of England, the National Gallery and Somerset House in London, and the Capitol, Supreme Court and Library of Congress in Washington and the New York Stock Exchange.

The leaves of this wayside plant have probably been copied more than any other and we see them every day. They feature across a range of artistic styles and periods, whether in Baroque furniture, through details such as decorative ironwork, wooden picture frames and surrounds of mirrors, or in the fabric designs of William Morris and Sandersons.

ROYAL ALBERT AND PORCELAIN

One of the most popular artistic displays of plants and flowers is on porcelain, or what we usually call 'china'. And given that floral patterns are so attractive, that's hardly surprising. Nor is it any mystery that we call it 'China', because it was that country which invented it and made it famous. What *is* surprising is just how old china manufacturing is, beginning as long ago as 1,600 BC during the Shang dynasty. Gradually the introduction of a special clay called kaolin, derived from the decomposed feldspar minerals in granite rocks, achieved the whiteness and translucency that came to be called 'Chinese Porcelain', named after the old Italian *porcellana* or cowrie shell.

By the time of the Ming dynasty (1368–1544), fine porcelain, especially that made in the city of Jingdezhen, was being

exported to Asia and Europe along the Silk Road, later by sea, and in England, this high-quality porcelain found its way to the tables of royalty and the gentry. However, soon more ordinary people in England would call tableware 'china'. Hundreds of tons of cheaper plates, cups and saucers were brought over in the holds of the ships of the East India Company which carried light tea cargoes. The china was merely to ballast the ships and to give them stability, while making a little extra money.

Then Portuguese traders brought samples of kaolin (above) to Europe, and in Saxony near Colditz a secret kaolin source was found and mined. In 1712, the secrets of the elaborate Chinese porcelain making processes were revealed by a Jesuit priest. For all her efforts to keep her most precious products secret, China, as with tea, was often a victim of 'industrial espionage' (page 70). The Chinese monopoly in porcelain-making was ended, and soon the German name Meissen came to the fore, based on the town near Dresden in Saxony. In England, fifty years later, Thomas Frye took out a patent on porcelain containing bone ash, which made the product much stronger. 'Bone china', later perfected by Josiah Spode and Josiah Wedgwood, was traditionally two parts bone ash, one part kaolin and one part feldspar-rich china stone. William Cooksworthy then found deposits of kaolin in Cornwall and set up a factory in Plymouth. If you visit the Cornish town of St Austell, you can see the extraordinary, almost mountainous landscape of the waste created by English China Clays. Some china stone is still being extracted and exported. One of the old china clay pits is now home to the Eden Project (page 300).

Among the many leading British porcelain companies that feature the ever-popular decorative motifs of flowers and plants is Royal Albert, which proudly bills itself as 'fanatics about florals'. The company started in 1896 in 'The Potteries' of Stoke-on-Trent and was not named after Queen Victoria's beloved consort, but rather celebrated the 1895 birth of her grandson, the second son of King George V and Queen Mary, later to reign as King George VI. Royal Albert prided itself on being English and from the start specialised in floral designs. It is not surprising that 'Old Country Roses', featuring England's national flower, is still one of its most successful collections.

All the items are cast from fine bone china, finished by hand, which then has the floral pattern applied by transfers, with clear glaze baked on and a banding or details of 24 carat gold. For over a hundred years, Royal Albert has inspired the thought that by sipping a cup of tea from beautifully made bone china with a floral design, you can escape for a few moments to a charming world, filled with romance and nostalgia. Sold globally, its customers clearly agree. Few companies would attract enough interest in their products to have 100,000 followers on their Instagram account!

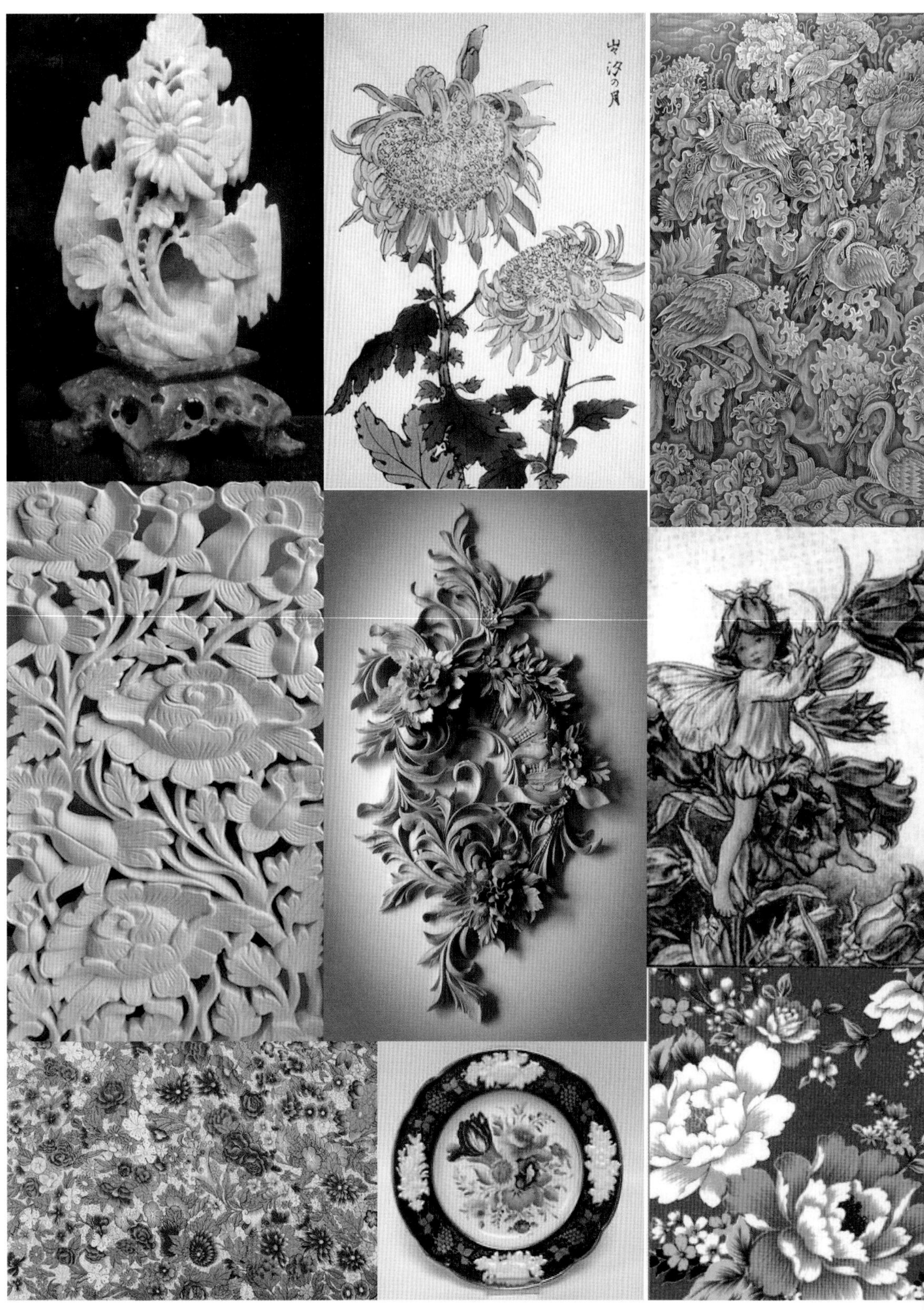

SCREEN, STAGE AND SOUND STUDIOS

SPAGHETTI – THE TREE THAT NEVER WAS

In the 1950s, Panorama was one of the BBC's flagship programmes, its anchor presenter being the portly and portentous Richard Dimbleby, whose sonorous tones had led us through the first televised royal wedding in 1953. It was in black and white, but the world watched entranced as young Queen Elizabeth and Prince Philip were married in Westminster Abbey.

Thus the British public was familiar with Dimbleby and his distinguished style

of delivery, and expected Panorama to cover important matters all over the world.

In 1957, the viewers of Panorama watched Dimbleby in Switzerland, where the camera followed him as he strolled through an orchard of trees festooned with strands of spaghetti.

Apparently, Dimbleby told us solemnly, the annual spaghetti harvest was going well enough, but when he interviewed the farmers they grumbled about the prices they could obtain. For listeners, the voice-over explained that the reason was a matter of

volume, 'Cultivation in Switzerland isn't on anything like the scale of the Italian spaghetti farms. Many of you will have seen the huge spaghetti plantations in the Po Valley.' So this was obviously a serious economic and social crisis, to which Dimbleby listened sympathetically.

Hundreds of viewers failed to notice the irony in Dimbleby's sign-off: 'And that's all from Panorama on this first day of April', and some called in to find out how to grow spaghetti at home. A spokesman for the BBC advised them to 'place a sprig of spaghetti in a tin of tomato sauce and hope for the best'.

In fairness to such viewers, it must be pointed out that in 1957 most British people didn't travel abroad and spaghetti was then regarded as rather exotic and foreign. So perhaps the stuff really did grow on trees?

Richard Dimbleby didn't seem to suffer too much in public esteem from his momentary lapse into the frivolous – with one of the best April Fool's jokes ever!

GARDENING ON OUR SCREENS

Gardening, of course, is now a huge and lucrative industry. Books had once been the main source of information about plants and gardening, but with the arrival of television, which expanded greatly during the 1950s and 60s, this changed radically and the new inspiration became TV gardening programmes, despite no colour. Then and now, these usually follow a magazine format, with cultivation tips, spotlights on groups of flowers, fruits and vegetables and visits to beautiful or historic gardens.

In recent years the emphasis has increasingly been on garden design, and this has generated its own genre of 'house and garden' TV. The key to TV gardening, and thus the success and impact of the various programmes, has always been the presenters, and the degree to which they are engaging, charismatic, likeable and informative. Viewers love to debate their relative merits and foibles!

The 'Godfather' of TV gardening in the UK was Percy Thrower. This unassuming, knowledgeable man (top right), a household name on radio and TV for many years, never forgot that he was first and foremost a gardener and plant-lover rather than a presenter. He began on radio and in 1962 moved to the small screen, where from 1969 and with the arrival of colour television, he was the first presenter of BBC's popular hardy perennial, 'Gardeners' World'. He also appeared regularly on the iconic children's programme 'Blue Peter,' even creating a special garden at the BBC TV centre. The BBC, snobbish about 'trade', dropped Thrower in 1975 when he started doing work on TV commercials. He then built up a successful horticultural business.

The longest serving presenter of Gardeners' World, from 1979 until his sudden tragic death from a heart attack in 1996, was Geoff Hamilton, another much-loved personality. A down to earth, kindly, humorous man and very much a practical, 'hands on' gardener, he did as much as anybody to promote organic gardening in the UK and to discourage the use of peat in garden compost. He was also a magazine editor and writer.

For the last two decades, 'Gardeners' World' has been dominated by George

Montagu 'Monty' Don, often referred to as 'the nation's gardener'. Having run a successful business with his wife making costume jewellery, he was forced to change tack completely after the stock market crash of 1987, becoming a gardening writer and broadcaster. As well as fronting 'Gardeners' World' from 2003, Don has written and presented TV series on British, French, Italian, Japanese, Islamic and, most recently, American gardens, as well as 'Around the World in 80 Gardens' in 2008. Following in the footsteps of Geoff Hamilton, he has always promoted organic gardening, a policy which has really caught on. His apparently effortless, laid-back manner which still results in fine displays of trees, shrubs, flowers and vegetables makes gardening seem easy! And in a world where gardeners traditionally suffer from a scruffy or even effete image, Monty Don undoubtedly generates an aura of urbane beefcake! He has certainly added greatly to the accessibility and popularity of plants and gardening.

By contrast, the wild card in the world of plants on British TV arrived suddenly in the late 1960s. David Bellamy, (right) then a popular botany lecturer at Durham University, was brought in to comment on marine pollution. This launched his successful career promoting plants and conservation to a world far beyond academia. His huge presence and persona (both broad and tall, his 2002 autobiography was apptly subtitled *Jolly Green Giant*) was immediately apparent and this natural lecturer and communicator was soon presenting Bellamy on Botany (1972) and many other TV series. A bushy beard and distinctive voice (as comedian Lenny Henry famously mimicked, '*Gwapple me Gwapenuts!*') compounded his popular appeal.

Plants were suddenly up there with all those animals. Bellamy campaigned widely and passionately and was always prepared to speak his mind or lie down in front of the bulldozers. He even spent his 50th birthday in a Tasmanian jail for his efforts to disrupt tree felling in the island's unique temperate rainforests. In later years, he was spitefully sidelined by the BBC and some of the conservation bodies to which he had given so much, for his then often unconventional views on global warming and several other controversial topics.

But thousands of ordinary people will always remember the big-hearted David Bellamy as 'The Botanist', certainly the most charismatic television gardening presenter of his time.

TELEVISION, RECIPE FOR CHANGE

We are hearing more and more about plant-based foods and diets. Not only do such eating regimes – and well-balanced omnivorous diets – confer health benefits, but they can also help to feed an expanding world population and even contribute to a reduction in global warming. At present too many crops are simply converted into animal protein, which often involves the consumption of potential plant protein, habitat destruction and increased emissions of 'greenhouse' gases such as carbon dioxide and methane.

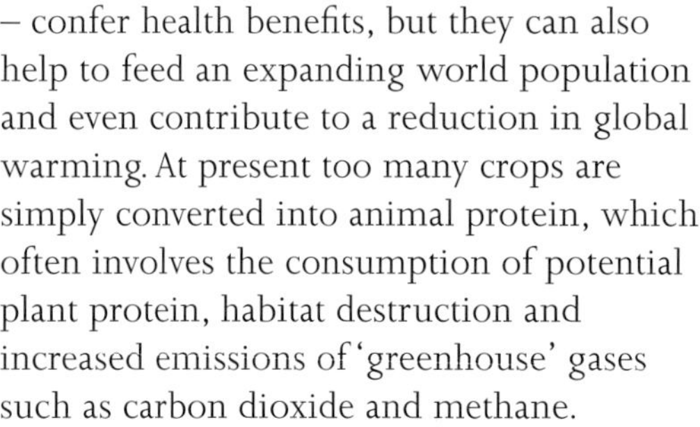

Although human society largely depends upon just a few food crops, an increasing range of cultivated and wild plants is now being eaten. The interest in using new plants in cooking was once limited by three important factors – weak transport and poor communications, not to mention reticence about untried food.

As we know, for thousands of years and all over the world, most people, unless they were rich (or perhaps sailors, soldiers or merchants), rarely travelled more than about twelve miles from their homes, whether on foot or horseback. They also grew their own food or bought it from local markets which only sold vegetables and fruit grown locally.

In bigger towns the food might have come from a little further away, perhaps even twenty or thirty miles, brought by horse - or ox-drawn wagons. We saw this with Covent Garden in London, Les Halles in Paris or Fulton Market in Chicago. Only with very high-value plants or else plant products like spices was it worth bringing them further, slowly by ship or along the Silk Road or other caravan routes from the East.

All this changed with the coming of the railways. Now food could arrive fast from many miles away, as with watercress being sent into London from Alresford, or also from Alabama to the big American cities (page 203). There was, amazingly, even a nightly 'Rhubarb Express' to the London markets from the 'Rhubarb Triangle' in Yorkshire (page 214). Railroads made Chicago the commodity centre of America, with special trains bringing food from California and other distant states.

With improved shipping in the 19th century, especially when refrigerated ships arrived, even food staples like wheat and other grains could come from different countries and, importantly, from different climates. The advent of cheap air travel then meant that food could be brought rapidly from across the world and between hemispheres, so that summer crops were available throughout the year.

Although vegetables and fruit could come from afar, it needed the element of communications to encourage people to consume them. Most people had only cooked what their mothers made, similarly servants if they did the cooking, and restaurant cooks. What changed all this? As literacy improved and printing became cheaper, so cooking and recipe books became more available. The most famous,

Plants & Us

Mrs Beeton's Book of Household Management, in fact mostly about food and cooking, was published in 1861. Most of the recipes had, in fact, been outrageously poached from the shy and retiring Eliza Acton, whom Delia Smith described as 'one of the best writers of recipes in the English language.' Today, of course, there are thousands of cookery books. Elizabeth David, in particular, had an enduring influence. Her books introduced French and Mediterranean food to a Britain recovering from rationing in the second Wotld War and its aftermath.

But the next big influence was cooks on television, introducing audiences to new plants. For instance, Fanny Cradock is credited with introducing us in 1955 to the **Avocado Pear**, Prue Leith educated us into using **Ginger** and more recently Gillian McKeith has advanced our use of **Quinoa**.

The very first of the TV chefs was, surprisingly, British, with Philip Harben and his 'Cookery' programme in 1946, followed that same year in America by James Beard's 'I love to eat'. Julia Child, so famous that she was later impersonated on film by Meryl Streep, influenced Americans to appreciate French cooking and had a programme called 'How to cook vegetables'. Anthony Bourdain encourages his fellow Americans to adopt foreign dishes, especially from the East. American cookery writer Robert Carrier found most of his fame in England in the 1970s but remained popular on both sides of the Atlantic. Among his many books was *The Gourmet Vegetarian* (1994).

More recently, Nigella Lawson loves to focus on vegetables, as does Hugh Fearnley-Whittingstall, who always promotes a strong ecological message. One of the most influential international TV chefs has to be the forceful, even belligerent, Gordon Ramsay, whose TV titles reflect his style – Hell's Kitchen', 'Kitchen Nightmares' and even 'The 'F Word'. For years he was rude about vegetarians and their food but he now includes a vegan menu at his restaurants!

Perhaps one of the greatest influencers to use plants in a healthy diet was Jamie Oliver (left)with his 2005 TV campaign to improve school cooking, 'Jamie's school dinners'. He even won moral and financial support from Prime Minister Tony Blair. One startling result was that in the schools that had pioneered his teaching, their English and science exam results actually improved.

Since 1961, when the vegetarian restaurant 'Cranks' opened in London's Carnaby Street, the vegetarian and vegan influence on cooking has continued to expand. Best-selling author Israeli-British chef Yotam Ottolenghi, while not even a vegetarian himself, wrote a weekly column in *The Guardian* called 'The New Vegetarian' and his cookbooks, TV shows and no less than six restaurants reflect his enthusiasm for plants and vegetables in cooking.

Today, more and more of us are turning to vegetable meals alongside meat-based dishes, while committed vegetarians have a greater choice than ever. The old adage – 'meat and two veg' (as an ideal meal) may have gone for ever.

That's surely no bad thing, especially as veggie meals cost less!

PLANTS IN FEATURE FILMS

While plants and flowers appear in plenty of documentaries and television programmes, we find that in feature films they show very little influence. Mythical plants appear in *The Day of The Triffids* and in *Avatar*, and there are plenty of scary movies about evil plant-like creatures threatening humans as in *The Evil Dead, Invasion of the Bodysnatchers, Little Shop of Horrors, The Happening,* and *Poltergeist*. And sometimes the mythical plants are nice, like the Ents in Lord of the Rings, or the real ones like Edelweiss in 'The Sound of Music'.

But very often the names of plants and flowers appear to be chosen casually with almost nothing to do with the plants themselves. *The Scarlet Pimpernel* is about the French Revolution, *Blue Gardenia and Blue Dahlia* are merely a featured nightclub, *A Clockwork Orange* and *Wild Strawberries* have nothing to do with fruit, nor *Steel Magnolias* with flowers, or *Camomile Lawn* with mowing. At least crop failure is why Sergeant Howie is finally encased in twigs and burned in *The Wicker Man*.

And while most such films have little to do with plants, they also did not influence anything much. One exception must be *Grapes of Wrath*, nothing to do with grapes and its title taken from 'The Battle Hymn of the Republic'. It's a stirring film starring Henry Fonda which must have drawn public attention to the ravages on agriculture of the Dust Bowl and the difficulties of reaching the Orange groves of California.

Perhaps, at least, the charming and moving film, *The Secret Garden* might get young girls interested in gardening.

PLANTS IN MUSIC

Such is the importance of plants, flowers and trees to all aspects of our lives, you might expect them to be mentioned more in classical music and opera. They do appear occasionally. In his opera 'Xerxes', Handel has the Persian king address an aria to a stately **Plane Tree** (page 3), and the most widely performed works of the Italian composer Respighi is his orchestral suite, 'The Pines of Rome' a tribute to the elegant **Umbrella Pines** (*Pinus pinea*) a feature of the Roman landscape.

Among other plants starring, mostly in minor parts at the concert hall or opera house, Puccini has the Flower Duet in 'Madame Butterfly', Verdi features 'La Dame aux Camélias', Bizet has the Flower song in

'Carmen', Mascagni a 'Cherry Duet,' while Gilbert and Sullivan extolled 'The Flowers that bloom in the Spring', and the flower duet in Delibes' 'Lakmé' was borrowed for a classic British Airways commercial – the list is long. But they have had minimal influence on society at large.

Folk, blues and other popular songs on the other hand, perhaps because they arose originally out of events in the everyday lives of ordinary people, often mention the plants that surround us. Many of these songs have become widely known and loved. In the garden, songs have been inspired, especially by flowers – **Roses** ('A red, red Rose', 'The 'Yellow Rose of Texas', 'Kiss from a Rose'),

Potatoes ('The garden where the praties grow'), even herbs ('Parsley, Sage, Rosemary and Thyme'). Out in the countryside, there were trees ('Banks of Green Willow', 'The Willow Tree', 'Bury me under the Weeping Willow'), crops or rather beer ('John Barleycorn'), but especially **Cotton** ('Pick a bale of Cotton'), which did much to fire the angst and imagery of Blues and the whimsy of Country music; also spring flowers ('The banks of the Sweet Primroses'), winter-green foliage ('The Holly and the Ivy') and wildflowers generally as a symbol of mourning. ('Where

have all the flowers gone?', by Pete Seeger, later a hit for Peter, Paul and Mary, 'The Flowers of the Forest'). This last, a lament written after the English destroyed the flower of Scottish chivalry at the Battle of Flodden in 1513.

Here are just a few popular songs that may have influenced our lives.

'The Holly and the Ivy'

Holly and ivy have long been part of Christian symbolism in Britain's churches, and were even included in a love-song written by Henry VIII. The carol we sing at Christmas reflects the fate of Jesus: *'The holly bears a berry, as red as any blood'*, and *'The holly bears a prickle, as sharp as any thorn.'* And every year we decorate our churches and houses with these evocative symbolic plants and sing that carol.

'A Red, Red Rose'

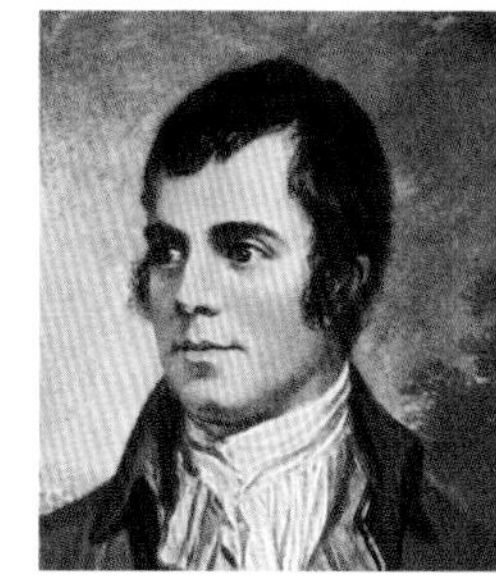

'O my Luve's like a red, red rose
That's newly sprung in June;
O my Luve's like the melodie
That's sweetly play'd in tune:

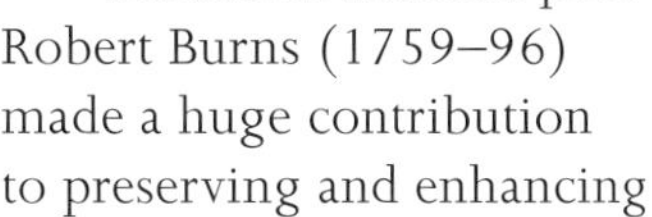

Scotland's national poet Robert Burns (1759–96) made a huge contribution to preserving and enhancing traditional Scottish songs, most famously 'Auld Lang Syne'. But another one, which he called a 'simple old Scot's song', has also become one of the best-loved songs of all time, covered by a wide range of popular and folk singers. It is perhaps the most passionate of the many songs that celebrate roses.

'Dixie'

'I wish I was in the land of cotton, old times there are not forgotten,
Look away, look away, look away, Dixie Land.
In Dixie Land where I was born in, early on a

frosty mornin',
Look away, look away, look away, Dixie Land.'

'Dixie' is one of the most popular tunes in American history. Originally created in the North as part of a 'blackface' minstrel show, during the Civil War it became the theme song of the Confederacy. Amazingly, President of the Union Abraham Lincoln thought of it as his favourite. It had many variations, and like 'Lili Marlene,' was later popular on both sides of a bitter war.

'Eating goober peas'

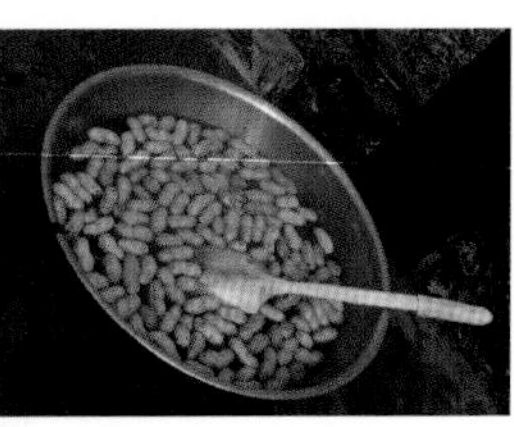

Short of food in the American Civil War, the Confederates were always at a disadvantage compared with the more industrialized Union, resorting to eating boiled **Peanuts**, or 'goober peas', named after a Mr Goober.

This song about them is still popular, especially in the South, and Ernie Ford, Burl Ives and Johnny Cash amusingly sang how hard and noisy it was to eat the peas.

'Just before the battle, the General hears a row.
He said, "The Yanks are coming, I hear their rifles now."
He turns around in wonder and what do you think he sees?
The Georgia Militia eating goober peas.'

'Someone's digging my potatoes, trampling on my vines.'

'Now my vines were all green, my potatoes red,
I thought you were my friend 'til I caught you in my bed.'

Sung in America by Muddy Waters, Big Bill Broonzy and others.

However, in Britain the BBC banned the 1954 Lonnie Donegan version because of one especially lascivious verse!

'The Rose of Alabamy'

World audiences might never have heard this 1846 slave song if, in the blockbuster film 'The Outlaw Josie Wales', the wounded young 'Abe' had not sung it to distract the potential killers of Clint Eastwood.

'Maple Leaf Rag'

In his most famous rag, Scott Joplin was probably not referring to the **Maple tree** but to the Maple Leaf Club in Sedalia, Missouri. His 'Weeping Willow Rag' was, however, referring to the tree, as were Bessie Smith and Ottilie Patterson in Blind Boy Fuller's 'Weeping Willow Blues':

'I heard the whistle blowin', the fireman ring the bell.
They're takin' away that willow tree that give me this weepin' spell.
And that's the reason I've got those weepin' willow blues.'

Jazz does not give us many songs related to plants, except, of course, those about cotton and slavery.

'Pick a bale of cotton'

This traditional slave or convict work song became a skiffle favourite, first made popular by Lead Belly, especially when the racist '*Dat nigger from Shiloh kin pick a bale o' cotton*' was removed. Singers included Harry Belafonte, Johnny Cash, Sonny Terry and Brownie McGee, and in Britain, Lonnie Donegan and also The Vipers – who took the

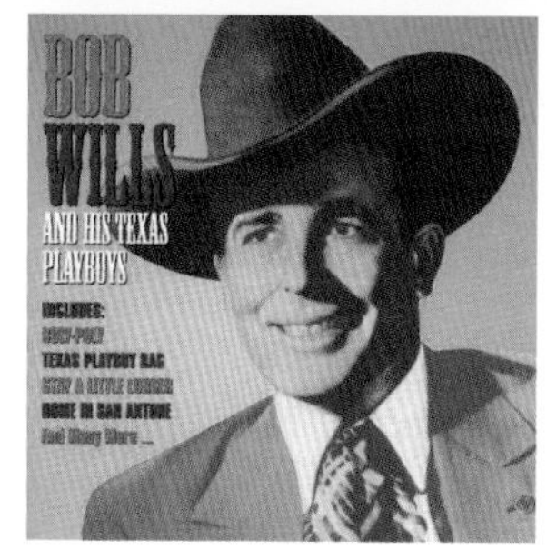

tradition of going faster and faster to the ultimate degree.

'Bury me under the Weeping Willow'

As one of the great founders of Country and Bluegrass music, the Carter Family had lived among trees and plants in Virginia all their lives. This song, about a love-sick girl, was the first they ever recorded, in 1927, earning $50 and a half cent per copy. Later, on tour with her father Johnny Cash, a very young Rosanne Cash learned how to sing it from Helen Carter in her dressing room.

'Oh, bury me under the weeping willow.
Yes, under the weeping willow tree.
So he may know where I am sleeping.
And perhaps he will weep for me.'

The Carter family's **'Wildwood Flower'** had Roses, Myrtle and Hyssop in its lyrics, but also an imaginary 'Emanita', which was probably meant to be **Death Cap** (*Amanita*), one of a group of dangerous forest mushrooms – entirely suitable for polishing off offending lovers!

'San Antonio Rose'

The signature tune of Bob Wills and his Texas Playboys, the pioneer and champion of 'Western Swing'.

'For that moonlit pass by the Alamo
And Rose, my Rose of San Antone
Deep within my heart lies a melody,
A song of old San Antone.'

It was also sung by Country stars like Merle Haggard and Patsy Cline, and even one memorable Austin night referred to by Mick Jagger – taught by Waylon Jennings to sing *'Makes me proud to be in Texas, where Bob Wills is still the King'*.

The Banana Boat Song (Day O)

A traditional Jamaican work song reflecting the growth of the Banana trade, with the dock workers loading ships all night.

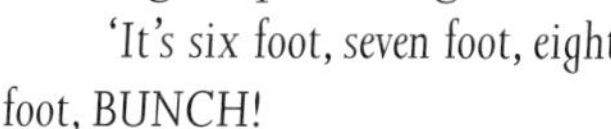

'It's six foot, seven foot, eight foot, BUNCH!
Daylight come and he wan' go home.'

It was made famous by Harry Belafonte's calypso version in 1957, but was performed by dozens of artists, and it also seemed very popular as a parody.

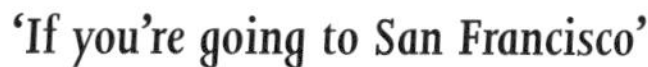

'If you're going to San Francisco'

Written by John Phillips of The Mamas & the Papas, and sung by Scott McKenzie in 1967, it was an instant hit, reaching number four in the USA charts, and number one in Britain and Europe, selling five million copies worldwide.

'If you're going to San Francisco
be sure to wear some flowers in your hair.
If you're going to San Francisco
you're gonna meet some gentle people there.'

It attracted thousands of young people to San Francisco, and in Europe was adopted as a freedom anthem against the Vietnam War and during Czechoslovakia's 1968 Prague Spring uprising against Soviet rule. It also featured in several films, including 'Frantic', 'The Rock' and 'Forrest Gump'.

'The grass is blue'

Kentucky Blue Grass (*Poa pratensis*) gave its name to the acoustic string folk music of the Appalachians. Dolly Parton, the huge Country star also famous for so many other styles in her 50-year career, has written more than 3,000 songs. This one, about denying the sad truth of a lover's rejection, won a Bluegrass Grammy.

Rivers flow backwards
Valleys are high
Mountains are level
Truth is a lie
I'm perfectly fine
And I don't miss you
The sky is green
And the grass is blue

'The green, green grass of home'

A Country song first made a hit by Porter Wagoner in 1965, it was also sung by Elvis Presley, Joan Baez and Johnny Cash and, in Britain, by Tom Jones, who made it a worldwide number one hit.

'The old home town looks the same
As I step down from the train
And there to meet me is my mamma and pappa
And down the road I look, and there runs Mary
Hair of gold and lips like cherries
It's good to touch the green, green grass of home.'

Few fans of this song know that this cheerful theme is, however, ended by the singer realising that it's a grisly dream, prior to execution and being buried under that green grass.

'Green grow the rushes, O'

A very old English folksong and carol, it is called by other names and has obvious biblical and astronomical references.

'I'll sing you twelve, O
Green grow the rushes, O
What are your twelve, O?
Twelve for the twelve Apostles'
Ending with:
'One is one and always one
And evermore shall be so.'

It is not clear why rushes were chosen for the refrain, but it is claimed that Mexicans first called Americans 'Gringos' because they heard them singing 'Green grow…."

'Parsley, Sage, Rosemary and Thyme'

'Scarborough Fair' was a 17th century ballad made popular by Simon and Garfunkel in the 1960s – notably in the soundtrack to the film 'The Graduate' – passed on to them by English folk singer and guitarist Martin Carthy (later justifiably upset when the duo claimed both authorship and royalties!).

'Are you going to Scarborough Fair
Parsley, sage, rosemary and thyme
Remember me to one who lives there
She once was a true love of mine.'

Scarborough Fair was until the 18th century a major event each August in Yorkshire. This suite of culinary and medicinal herbs that also symbolize emotions might perhaps bring the girl back.

Bob Dylan had earlier borrowed the line 'Remember me to one who lives there' for his own song 'Girl from the North Country', which he most famously sang with Johnny Cash.

'Down by the Salley Gardens'

'It was down by the Salley Gardens, my love and I did meet'...

This beautiful song, sung by a host of Irish singers, feels traditional but was written by the great Irish poet William Butler Yeats (1865–1939), inspired by a few lines (probably 'You Rambling Boys of Pleasure') he'd heard an old lady singing in Co. Sligo.

Salley (Irish, *saileach*) is **Sallow**, a small or shrubby willow tree. Salley gardens were willow plantations established around villages for basket weaving and other uses.

'The Banks of the Sweet Primroses'

'As I walked out on a midsummer's morning
For to view the fields and to take the air
Down by the banks of the sweet primroses ...'

Primroses are one of Britain's best loved wildflowers, heralding the spring in woods and on hedge-banks. This popular folk song, familiar mainly in Sussex, was perhaps most famously recorded by the British folk rock band Fairport Convention. The first line inspired the poet Laurie Lee's memoir '*As I walked out one midsummer morning*'.

'The Nutting Girl'

This bawdy song has been sung all over England, less frequently Scotland, but in recent decades has become associated with Suffolk. Some versions set it in Kent, home of the UK crop of **Kentish Cobnut** or **Hazel** (*Corylus avellana*).

'Now it's of this brisk young damsel, was nutting in the wood,
His voice was so melodious, it charmed her as she stood.
She had no longer power,
In that lone wood to stay,
and what few nuts she had, poor girl,
She threw them all away.'

'Tutti frutti'

A-wop-bop-a-loo-bop-a-lop-bam-boom!

If you ask a cook about Tutti Frutti, they'll talk about desserts, ice cream and cakes based on the tropical fruit **Papaya** or **Pawpaw** (*Carica papaya*), originally native to Central America and usually mixed with other fruits and nuts.

Ask anyone else and they may smile and say, 'Little Richard'. His exuberant 1955 hit has been voted one of '100 records that changed the world'. The Alabama White Citizens' Council entoned, '*Rock 'n' roll is part of a test to undermine the youth of our nation. It is sexualist, unmoralistic and brings people of both races together.'* Quite right! Little Richard, a more powerful force for change than any politician, was crucial to changing attitudes to segregation,

Plants and flowers are so important in our lives and throughout society that it is not surprising their names appear again and again in books, art, poetry, films and music. But that doesn't mean that their influence has gone any further and that they have 'shaped human history and society.' Apart, perhaps, from the monster that the band Genesis immortalized in 'The Return of the Giant Hogweed' (page 68)!

That's why we've had to turn down some other musical gems, however popular they may be:

'Rose of Alendale, Last Rose of Summer, Roses of Picardy, Rose of Tralee, Primrose Polka, Hearts of Oak, Autumn leaves, Daisy, Daisy, Harvest Moon, Poisoned Ivy, Glory, Glory Allelujah, We'll gather Lilacs in the spring, The Bramble and the Rose, A bunch of Thyme, Wild Mountain Thyme, Buttered Peas, Bonny Bunch of Roses, The Yellow Rose of Texas, The Eggplant that ate Chicago, Rockery Rock, Lily the Pink, Strip the Willow, The battle of Epping Forest, Out in the Woods, The Trees, House in the woods, Give my love to Rose, Tiptoe through the Tulips, The biggest Aspidistra in the world, I'm a lonely little Petunia in an onion patch, Kiss from a Rose, Last of the English Roses, Flowers in the rain, Build me up Buttercup' etc.

WHAT OF THE FUTURE?

Plants are the basis of virtually all life on earth and will always be essential to people and will continue to exert their influence on our societies, cultures and everyday lives. A growing awareness of the environment, an expanding interest in plant-based diets and medicines, a burgeoning interest in gardens and indoor plants, and endless media stories about plants – good, bad or just in danger – have at last put them centre stage. Plants will always support life on Earth, so we must therefore continue to help them and their vital function of sustaining animals and indeed our whole civilization. We can all help in small ways.

This book looks at numerous aspects of plants, not least the way in which they have generated immense economic wealth, past and present, and their unfortunate historical role in exploitation, slavery and conflict. In our contemporary world, the emphasis is more the problems that impact on plants and biodiversity, which

should be urgently addressed.

We clearly need to cut down pollution of land, water and air, reducing greenhouse gases to slow global warming, to cherish the seas, to stop deforestation and encourage, restore and plant more woodland, permanent grassland and other vegetation, to plant more trees in cities and suburbs both in streets and parks and, in a rapidly emerging trend, enhancing city blocks with roof gardens and 'vertical planting' of tree balconies, climbers and other plants. To encourage anybody with the smallest yard, garden or plot of land to grow plants and to allow little patches of wildness to remain. To protect and enhance soils on agricultural land and encourage agroforestry and other mixed, sustainable farming so as to encourage biodiversity. And to try, wherever possible, to eat more plant-based, seasonal and locally-sourced foods. In short, to remember that the Earth is 'a common treasury for all'.

But another essential way forward is perhaps less obvious – sustaining animal life. There are countless vital links between plants and Earth's wealth of mammals, birds, fish, other creatures and especially the insects. If we just let them disappear, plants will do the same, and vice versa. Most plants depend for their success, indeed their very future, on pollination and seed dispersal, processes that evolved in intimate tandem with animals. Apart from the loss of insect variety and numbers reported in several countries, the global loss of so many larger mammals, the 'keystone species', has already greatly impacted a range of ecosystems, damage which will be difficult to repair.

But there are reasons to be hopeful.

One of the most gratifying recent trends in conservation has been the integration of plants into public discussion and policy making. For a long time, animals dominated the presentation of conservation issues but the success of ventures such as the Eden Project, the increasing numbers of visitors to botanic gardens and the sheer popularity and commercial success of gardening do indicate

just how important plants are to us.

But now it is the turn of the animals again to have their showcase, and within the plant habitats with which they co-exist. For example, as we note in the previous section of this book, a major new initiative in Southern Africa – the Noah's Ark project – marks a huge capital investment in biodiversity conservation. It is gratifying to see both plant and animal conservation working together. In the years after World War ll, animal conservationists were at first ahead of the botanists, then combining conservation in protected areas in the wild with captive breeding and reintroduction. In the early 1960s, one of the authors, John Akeroyd, remembers seeing Hawaiian geese or *nene* on a school trip to the Wildfowl and Wetlands Trust in Gloucestershire. Just a few years before these wild birds had been reduced to just 30 individuals, but now captive breeding and improvements to their native habitat have ensured that today this state bird of Hawaii, although considered threatened, is no longer endangered.

Wildfowl Trust Founder, Sir Peter Scott (pictured with Prince Philip), was one of a group of eminent naturalists and public figures who in 1961 established the World Wildlife Fund, now the Worldwide Fund for Nature (WWF), with five million supporters the world's largest conservation concern, closely linked to The International Union for the Conservation of Nature (IUCN). Another of WWF's visionary founders was Scott's friend, the late Prince Philip, Duke of Edinburgh, WWF President (1981–96) and long associated with the international conservation work of the Zoological Society of London. His son Prince Charles (above), passionate about plants, has maintained his legacy by promoting links between sustainable agriculture, food security, healthy soils and biodiversity. And now his grandson Prince William (below) too is actively involved in conservation efforts, especially against the illegal trade in wildlife. To borrow a quote from 19th-century poet Francis Thompson, 'All things linked are'.

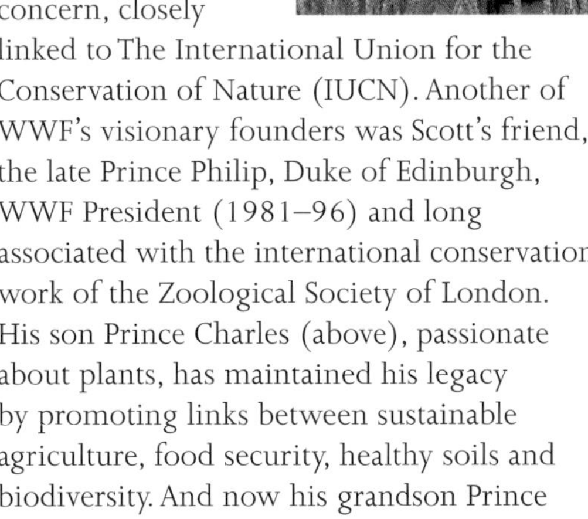

There are so many examples that one could cite of similar projects to the saving of the Hawaiian goose – in both animal and plant conservation. Plant conservationists soon caught up with their animal-studying counterparts, and we would like to mention here the quiet but persuasive influence of our late friend Hugh Synge, who in 1978 with his colleague Gren Lucas, produced a first Plant Red Data Book with information on a selection of globally threatened plants. with their seed banks, targeted cultivation in botanic gardens, plant reintroductions and whole habitat restoration.

The conservation community has been swift to embrace the remarkable advances in modern botany and zoology, combining traditional natural history with powerful data handling, global information networks and technological sophistication. Almost anything may now be possible. Scientists from the US Fish and Wildlife Service in Colorado have recently cloned a black-footed ferret, using genes from the frozen tissues of an animal that died thirty years ago to augment an already successful captive breeding and reintroduction programme – for a species that until 1981 had been thought to be extinct. Many other rare or extinct animals, and plants, may now be re-established or resurrected.

We wish Noah's Ark and all such efforts every success. They will complement the many other practical measures undertaken worldwide and provide the high levels of publicity, interpretation and involvement that need to be maintained for long-term progress. As the disrupted global society and economy emerge from the Covid-19 pandemic, conservation and wise use of our environment and its resources is even more important. Whatever else, many more people have come to realize how much, as well as providing the food and products on which they depend, plants and nature enhance their lives and happiness.

Plants deserve a safe future, as do animals and humans. Now, perhaps more than ever before, our destinies are intertwined. Indeed, many scientists now consider that Earth has moved into a new division of geological time, the 'Anthropocene' epoch, one dominated by massively accelerated human activity.

But, however uncertain the future, plants will always remain vital for life on Earth.

INDEX